D1291627

Frontiers of Science and Philosophy

Volume 1   University of Pittsburgh Series in the Philosophy of Science

Frontiers of Science and

CARL G. HEMPEL

WILFRID SELLARS

MICHAEL SCRIVEN

ERNST CASPARI

ADOLF GRÜNBAUM

P. K. FEYERABEND

Philosophy ▸▸

Editor
ROBERT G. COLODNY

UNIVERSITY OF PITTSBURGH PRESS · 1962

© 1962 University of Pittsburgh Press

Library of Congress Catalog Card Number 61-9401

501
C7188

Preface

In 1960, on the initiative of Vice Chancellor Charles H. Peake, the University of Pittsburgh instituted an annual series of public lectures by noted philosophers of science along with a doctoral program in the philosophy and history of science. By covering various current topics in the philosophy of the physical, biological, and social sciences, these lectures are intended to contribute to the removal of existing barriers to the flow of ideas between diverse fields of knowledge. The philosophy of science draws on the results of major scientific theories and endeavors to interpret, and to contribute to the conceptual innovations wrought by some of the fundamental advances in the sciences. Thus, it promotes the scientific education of students of the humanities no less than the humanistic education of scientists.

The papers delivered in the first annual series during the academic year 1960-1961 are published in this volume with the grateful acknowledgment of assistance from the following sources: the United States Steel Educational Foundation, which provided a grant in support of the lectures, and the National Science Foundation, which awarded a subvention in aid of publication to the University of Pittsburgh Press.

I welcome this opportunity to thank Dr. Charles H. Peake to whose vision and efforts the program in the Philosophy of Science at the University owes its existence, and to Professor Robert G. Colodny for giving unstintingly of his time and assuming editorial responsibility for the volumes in which the annual programs of lectures are published.

ADOLF GRÜNBAUM

Andrew Mellon Professor of Philosophy and Chairman of the Program in the Philosophy of Science
University of Pittsburgh.

184263

Contents

Contents

Introduction

Robert G. Colodny
Associate Professor of History
University of Pittsburgh

Provided as we are with new and basic data on the nature of the universe, we note many reasons why moderns could and should now interpret the world in a way more circumstantial and rational than it could be interpreted by Moses, or Lucretius, or Spinoza, or Locke, or Pascal, whose cosmologies were geocentric or heliocentric and limited. We have deep knowledge and much critical information that was not available to the philosophers of earlier centuries. We have gone far, very far, in the accumulation of verifiable facts. And this we must remember: there will be, if we remain civilized, no return. We must henceforth live with our scientific acquisitions. No amount of skepticism about details, no sweeping denials of observation, no distortion of the recent revelations of science can erase the intellectual progress. Wishing will not revive the dear, dead hypotheses.

HARLOW SHAPLEY, *Of Stars and Men*

Introduction

In an age made magnificent by an ongoing scientific revolution and spectacularly dangerous by the technological by-products thereof, the transitions within philosophy tend to be blurred and overshadowed. Einstein and Bohr, Planck and Oparin, Freud and Pavlov are residents in Everyman's pantheon of the great. Yet all ages of scientific creativity have been ages of philosophical renewal. Despite the post-Enlightenment fragmentization of Western culture, there has always been a wing of philosophers professionally concerned with the conceptual constructs and the empirical content of the sciences. Leibniz and Locke, Kant and D'Alembert have their successors in this modern time. Mach and Poincaré heralded the most recent advance in philosophical inquiry, an activity which derives its penetrating power not from mere contemplation of radical scientific innovations nor from detached criticism, but from direct participation in the clarification of problems and an analysis of tentative answers.

This is not to suggest that all modern philosophy is in fact philosophy of science, nor even that *all* philosophers of science are in intimate intellectual symbiosis with working scientists. Philosophy like other human activities exhibits its atavisms and Don Quixotes; but windmills, even of the metaphysical variety, are now more apt to be recognized as such since the emergence of a rigorous Guild of Philosophers of Science, armed with the tools of contemporary logical and semantic analysis.

In an amazingly short span of time, as measured on the scale of human cultural history, the scientist has developed the puny telescope of Galileo, the microscope of Leeuwenhoek, and the calculator of Pascal into the Palomar Observatory, the electron microscope, and the giant computer systems of the twentieth century. Concurrently, mathematics has expanded from its antique base through the seventeenth century of genius to the supreme instrument of analysis that now sustains knowledge not only of worlds of physics and astronomy, but also of the biological and social sciences. It would be a strange world indeed if philosophy had remained bound by the *Organon* of Aristotle, Gothic additions thereto, the canons of Francis Bacon, the *Methode* of Descartes, and synthetic *a prioris*. Modern symbolic logic, often employed in the pages that follow, has altered many forms of philosophical analysis as dramatically as the infinitesimal calculus changed discussions of dynamics in the age of

Newton. Thus the discourse of philosophers of science tends in some respects to take place at a level as remote from everyday language and experience as the scientific discourse which is its source. Yet it can be argued that the philosophy of science—as an integrated and mature discipline—can provide one of the important bridges between the sciences and the humanities.

This is not to be achieved by simplification or trivialization of scientific theory, nor by popularization of "philosophies of nature." In its critical probing of the scientific process philosophy of science exhibits and analyzes the procedures and spirit of the *community of scientists;* it focuses upon the creative process as well as upon the principles of validation; it illumines science in the moments of transition and crisis before theory tends to ossify into orthodoxy and hieroglyphic formulae. It makes possible a scrutiny of what is universal in active intelligence and valid method, and suggests the applicability of these findings in other domains of intellectual endeavor.

The critical and revolutionizing element embodied in modern philosophy of science makes it a permanent and self-renewing solvent of authority and dogmatism, thus combining features of the Ionian and Socratic traditions. Whether or not philosophy of science comes in fact to be a bridge between the prestige-laden sciences and the humanities is an open question. Few participants in the current debates concerning the state of modern culture will be inclined to deny that the humanities display a fossilized structure and practice as compared to the sciences. Too often the humanities have taken refuge in an assumed venerability and untouchability. Their academic spokesmen have created the myth of the unlettered technician of science and translated their own inability to understand the language of science into a caricature of science, or used this inability as an excuse to wall off their own disciplines from the presumed contamination by inappropriate "scientific method." Philosophers of such diverse viewpoints as M. R. Cohen, Nagel, Whitehead, Reichenbach, Russell, and Dewey *inter alia* have contributed to clearing away some of the debris which has obstructed the free circulation of fruitful ideas and procedures throughout the Republic of Science and Letters.

If one is optimistic and attempts to look beyond the curve of time, extrapolating from the achievements of the last fifty years, it seems probable that a golden age of the biological sciences is directly ahead. Hitherto, philosophy of science has been primarily concerned with the mathematical disciplines such as astronomy, physics, and astrophysics, which have experienced the profound upheavals of relativity theory and quantum mechanics. The problems uncovered by molecular biology, genetics, neurophysiology, and still unimagined results of space exploration promise to pose even more challenging issues than those which have structured the millenial tradition of Western philosophy.

Whether or not the disciplines concerned directly with the study of the human condition will experience a comparable development of insight seems to depend in large measure upon the wide diffusion into all intellectual activities of what has been proven valid during the intellectual pilgrimage which has brought *homo sapiens* from fear-wracked animisms to knowledge of atoms and stars. To this end this volume and its annual successors are dedicated.

Chapter *1* | *Explanation in Science and in History*

Carl G. Hempel
Stuart Professor of Philosophy
Princeton University

For although certain experiments are always necessary to serve as a basis for reasoning, nevertheless, once these experiments are given, we should derive from them everything which anyone at all could possibly derive; and we should even discover what experiments remain to be done for the clarification of all further doubts. That would be an admirable help, even in political science and medicine, to steady and perfect reasoning concerning given symptoms and circumstances. For even while there will not be enough given circumstances to form an infallible judgment, we shall always be able to determine what is most probable on the data given. And that is all that reason can do.

The General Science, LEIBNIZ, 1677

Explanation in Science and in History

1. INTRODUCTION.

Among the divers factors that have encouraged and sustained scientific inquiry through its long history are two pervasive human concerns which provide, I think, the basic motivation for all scientific research. One of these is man's persistent desire to improve his strategic position in the world by means of dependable methods for predicting and, whenever possible, controlling the events that occur in it. The extent to which science has been able to satisfy this urge is reflected impressively in the vast and steadily widening range of its technological applications. But besides this practical concern, there is a second basic motivation for the scientific quest, namely, man's insatiable intellectual curiosity, his deep concern to *know* the world he lives in, and to *explain*, and thus to *understand*, the unending flow of phenomena it presents to him.

In times past questions as to the *what* and the *why* of the empirical world were often answered by myths; and to some extent, this is so even in our time. But gradually, the myths are displaced by the concepts, hypotheses, and theories developed in the various branches of empirical science, including the natural sciences, psychology, and sociological as well as historical inquiry. What is the general character of the understanding attainable by these means, and what is its potential scope? In this paper I will try to shed some light on these questions by examining what seem to me the two basic types of explanation offered by the natural sciences, and then comparing them with some modes of explanation and understanding that are found in historical studies.

First, then, a look at explanation in the natural sciences.

2. TWO BASIC TYPES OF SCIENTIFIC EXPLANATION.

2.1 *Deductive-nomological explanation.* In his book, *How We Think,*[1] John Dewey describes an observation he made one day when, washing dishes, he took some glass tumblers out of the hot soap suds and put them upside down on a plate: he noticed that soap bubbles emerged from under the tumblers' rims, grew for a while, came to a standstill, and finally receded inside the tumblers. Why did this happen? The explanation Dewey outlines comes to this: In transferring a tumbler to the plate, cool air is caught in it; this air is gradually warmed by the glass, which initially has the temperature of the hot suds. The warming of the air is accompanied by an increase in its pressure, which in turn produces an expansion of the soap film between the plate and the rim. Gradually, the glass cools off, and so does the air inside, with the result that the soap bubbles recede.

This explanatory account may be regarded as an argument to the effect that the event to be explained (let me call it the explanandum-event) was to be expected by reason of certain explanatory facts. These may be divided into two groups: (i) particular facts and (ii) uniformities expressed by general laws. The first group includes facts such as these: the tumblers had been immersed, for some time, in soap suds of a temperature considerably higher than that of the surrounding air; they were put, upside down, on a plate on which a puddle of soapy water had formed, providing a connecting soap film, etc. The second group of items presupposed in the argument includes the gas laws and various other laws that have not been explicitly suggested concerning the exchange of heat between bodies of different temperature, the elastic behavior of soap bubbles, etc. If we imagine these various presuppositions explicitly spelled out, the idea suggests itself of construing the explanation as a deductive argument of this form:

(D)

$$\frac{C_1, C_2, \ldots, C_k}{E} \quad L_1, L_2, \ldots, L_r$$

Here, $C_1, C_2, \ldots, C_k$ are statements describing the particular facts invoked; $L_1, L_2, \ldots, L_r$ are general laws: jointly, these statements will be said to form the explanans. The conclusion E is a statement describing the explanandum-event; let me call it the explanandum-statement, and let me use the word "explanandum" to refer to either E or to the event described by it.

The kind of explanation thus characterized I will call *deductive-nomological explanation;* for it amounts to a deductive subsumption of the explanandum under principles which have the character of general laws: it answers the question "*Why* did the explanandum event occur?" by showing that the event resulted from the particular circumstances specified in $C_1, C_2, \ldots, C_k$ in accordance with the laws $L_1, L_2, \ldots, L_r$. This conception of explanation, as exhibited in schema (D), has therefore been referred to as the covering law model, or as the deductive model, of explanation.[2]

A good many scientific explanations can be regarded as deductive-nomological in character. Consider, for example, the explanation of mirror-images, of rainbows, or of the appearance that a spoon handle is bent at the point where it emerges from a glass of water: in all these cases, the explanandum is deductively subsumed under the laws of reflection and refraction. Similarly, certain aspects of free fall and of planetary motion can be accounted for by deductive subsumption under Galileo's or Kepler's laws.

In the illustrations given so far the explanatory laws had, by and large, the character of empirical generalizations connecting different observable aspects of the phenomena under scrutiny: angle of incidence with angle of reflection or refraction, distance covered with falling time, etc. But science raises the question "why?" also with respect to the uniformities expressed by such laws, and often answers it in basically the same manner, namely, by subsuming the uniformities under more inclusive laws, and eventually under comprehensive theories. For example, the question, "Why do Galileo's and Kepler's laws hold?" is answered by showing that these laws are but special consequences of the Newtonian laws of motion and of gravitation; and these, in turn, may be explained by subsumption under the more comprehensive general theory of relativity. Such subsumption under broader laws or theories usually increases both the breadth and the depth of our scientific understanding. There is an increase in breadth, or scope, because the new explanatory principles cover a broader range of phenomena; for example, Newton's principles govern free fall on the earth and on other celestial bodies, as well as the motions of planets, comets, and artificial satellites, the movements of pendulums, tidal changes, and various other phenomena. And the increase thus effected in the depth of our understanding is strikingly reflected in the fact that, in the light of more advanced explanatory principles, the original empirical laws are usually seen to hold only approximately, or within certain limits. For example, Newton's theory implies that the factor g in Galileo's law, $s = \frac{1}{2} gt^2$, is not strictly a constant for free fall near the surface of the earth; and that, since every planet undergoes gravitational attraction not only from the sun, but also from the other planets, the planetary orbits are not strictly ellipses, as stated in Kepler's laws.

One further point deserves brief mention here. An explanation of a particular event is often conceived as specifying its *cause*, or causes. Thus, the account outlined in our first illustration might be held to explain the growth and the recession of the soap bubbles by showing that the phenomenon was *caused* by a rise and a subsequent drop of the temperature of the air trapped in the tumblers. Clearly, however, these temperature changes provide the requisite explanation only in conjunction with certain other conditions, such as the presence of a soap film, practically constant pressure of the air surrounding the glasses, etc. Accordingly, in the context of explanation, a cause must be allowed to consist in a more or less complex set of particular circumstances; these might be described by a set of sentences: $C_1, C_2, \ldots, C_k$. And, as suggested by the principle "Same cause, same effect," the assertion that those circumstances jointly caused a given event — described, let us say, by a sentence E — implies that whenever and wherever circumstances of the kind in question occur, an event of the kind to be explained comes about. Hence, the given causal explanation implicitly claims that there are general laws — such as L_1, $L_2, \ldots, L_r$ in schema (D) — by virtue of which the occurrence of the causal antecedents mentioned in $C_1, C_2, \ldots, C_k$ is a sufficient condition for the occurrence of the event to be explained. Thus, the relation between causal factors and effect is reflected in schema (D): causal explanation is deductive-nomological in character. (However, the customary formulations of causal and other explanations often do not explicitly specify all the relevant laws and particular facts: to this point, we will return later.)

The converse does not hold: there are deductive-nomological explanations which would not normally be counted as causal. For one thing, the subsumption of laws, such as Galileo's or Kepler's laws, under more comprehensive principles is clearly not causal in character: we speak of causes only in reference to *particular* facts or events, and not in reference to *universal facts* as expressed by general laws. But not even all deductive-nomological explanations of particular facts or events will qualify as causal; for in a causal explanation some of the explanatory circumstances will temporally precede the effect to be explained: and there are explanations of type (D) which lack this characteristic. For example, the pressure which a gas of specified mass possesses at a given time might be explained by reference to its temperature and its volume at the same time, in conjunction with the gas law which connects simultaneous values of the three parameters.[3]

In conclusion, let me stress once more the important role of laws in deductive-nomological explanation: the laws connect the explanandum event with the particular conditions cited in the explanans, and this is what confers upon the latter the status of explanatory (and, in some cases, causal) factors in regard to the phenomenon to be explained.

2.2. *Probabilistic explanation.* In deductive-nomological explanation as schematized in (D), the laws and theoretical principles involved are of *strictly universal form*: they assert that in *all* cases in which certain specified conditions are realized an occurrence of such and such a kind will result; the law that any metal, when heated under constant pressure, will increase in volume, is a typical example; Galileo's, Kepler's, Newton's, Boyle's, and Snell's laws, and many others, are of the same character.

Now let me turn next to a second basic type of scientific explanation. This kind of explanation, too, is nomological, i.e., it accounts for a given phenomenon by reference to general laws or theoretical principles; but some or all of these are of *probabilistic-statistical form*, i.e., they are, generally speaking, assertions to the effect that if certain specified conditions are realized, then an occurrence of such and such a kind will come about with such and such a statistical probability.

For example, the subsiding of a violent attack of hay fever in a given case might well be attributed to, and thus explained by reference to, the administration of 8 milligrams of chlor-trimeton. But if we wish to connect this antecedent event with the explanandum, and thus to establish its explanatory significance for the latter, we cannot invoke a universal law to the effect that the administration of 8 milligrams of that antihistamine will invariably terminate a hay fever attack: this simply is not so. What can be asserted is only a generalization to the effect that administration of the drug will be followed by relief with high statistical probability, i.e., roughly speaking, with a high relative frequency in the long run. The resulting explanans will thus be of the following type:

John Doe had a hay fever attack and took 8 milligrams of chlor-trimeton.

The probability for subsidence of a hay fever attack upon administration of 8 milligrams of chlor-trimeton is high.

Clearly, this explanans does not deductively imply the explanandum, "John Doe's hay fever attack subsided"; the truth of the explanans makes the truth of the explanandum not certain (as it does in a deductive-nomological explanation) but only more or less likely or, perhaps "practically" certain.

Reduced to its simplest essentials, a probabilistic explanation thus takes the following form:

$$(P) \quad \left. \begin{array}{c} Fi \\ \hline p(O, F) \text{ is very high} \\ \hline Oi \end{array} \right\} \text{ makes very likely}$$

The explanandum, expressed by the statement "Oi," consists in the fact that in the particular instance under consideration, here called i (e.g., John Doe's allergic attack), an outcome of kind O (subsidence) occurred. This is explained by means of two explanans-statements. The first of these, "Fi," corresponds to C_1, C_2, . . ., C_k in (D); it states that in case i, the factors F (which may be more or less complex) were realized. The second expresses a law of probabilistic form, to the effect that the statistical probability for outcome O to occur in cases where F is realized is very high (close to 1). The double line separating explanandum from explanans is to indicate that, in contrast to the case of deductive-nomological explanation, the explanans does not logically imply the explanandum, but only confers a high likelihood upon it. The concept of likelihood here referred to must be clearly distinguished from that of statistical probability, symbolized by "p" in our schema. A statistical probability is, roughly speaking, the long-run relative frequency with which an occurrence of a given kind (say, F) is accompanied by an "outcome" of a specified kind (say, O). Our likelihood, on the other hand, is a relation (capable of gradations) not between kinds of occurrences, but between statements. The likelihood referred to in (P) may be characterized as the strength of the inductive support, or the degree of rational credibility, which the explanans confers upon the explanandum; or, in Carnap's terminology, as the *logical*, or *inductive*, (in contrast to statistical) *probability* which the explanandum possesses relative to the explanans.

Thus, probabilistic explanation, just like explanation in the manner of schema (D), is nomological in that it presupposes general laws; but because these laws are of statistical rather than of strictly universal form, the resulting explanatory arguments are inductive rather than deductive in character. An inductive argument of this kind *explains* a given phenomenon by showing that, in view of certain particular events and certain statistical laws, its occurrence was to be expected with high logical, or inductive, probability.

By reason of its inductive character, probabilistic explanation differs from its deductive-nomological counterpart in several other important respects; for example, its explanans may confer upon the explanandum a more or less high degree of inductive support; in this sense, probabilistic explanation admits of degrees, whereas deductive-nomological explanation appears as an either-or affair: a given set of universal laws and particular statements either does or does not imply a given explanandum statement. A fuller examination of these differences, however, would lead us far afield and is not required for the purposes of this paper.[4]

One final point: the distinction here suggested between deductive-nomological and probabilistic explanation might be questioned on the ground that, after all, the universal laws invoked in a deductive explanation can have been established only on the basis of a finite body of evidence, which surely affords no exhaustive verification, but only more or less strong probability for it; and that, therefore, all scientific laws have to be regarded as probabilistic. This argument, however, confounds a logical issue with an epistemological one: it fails to distinguish properly between the *claim* made by a given law-statement and the *degree of confirmation,* or *probability,* which it possesses on the available evidence. It is quite true that statements expressing laws of either kind can be only incompletely confirmed by any given finite set—however large—of data about particular facts; but law-statements of the two different types make claims of different kind, which are reflected in their logical forms: roughly, a universal law-statement of the simplest kind asserts that *all* elements of an indefinitely large reference class (e.g., copper objects) have a certain characteristic (e.g., that of being good conductors of electricity); while statistical law-statements assert that in the long run, a specified proportion of the members of the reference class have some specified property. And our distinction of two types of law and, concomitantly, of two types of scientific explanation, is based on this difference in claim as reflected in the difference of form.

The great scientific importance of probabilistic explanation is eloquently attested to by the extensive and highly successful explanatory use that has been made of fundamental laws of statistical form in genetics, statistical mechanics, and quantum theory.

3. ELLIPTIC AND PARTIAL EXPLANATIONS: EXPLANATION SKETCHES.

As I mentioned earlier, the conception of deductive-nomological explanation reflected in our schema (D) is often referred to as the covering law model, or the deductive model, of explanation: similarly, the conception underlying schema (P) might be called the probabilistic or the inductive-statistical, model of explanation. The term "model" can serve as a useful reminder that the two types of explanation as characterized above constitute ideal types or theoretical idealizations and are not intended to reflect the manner in which working scientists actually formulate their explanatory accounts. Rather, they are meant to provide explications, or rational reconstructions, or theoretical models, of certain modes of scientific explanation.

In this respect our models might be compared to the concept of mathe-matical proof (within a given theory) as construed in meta-mathematics. This concept, too, may be regarded as a theoretical model: it is not in-tended to provide a descriptive account of how proofs are formulated in the writings of mathematicians: most of these actual formulations fall short of rigorous and, as it were, ideal, meta-mathematical standards. But the theoretical model has certain other functions: it exhibits the rationale of mathematical proofs by revealing the logical connections underlying the successive steps; it provides standards for a critical appraisal of any proposed proof constructed within the mathematical system to which the model refers; and it affords a basis for a precise and far-reaching theory of proof, provability, decidability, and related concepts. I think the two models of explanation can fulfill the same functions, if only on a much more modest scale. For example, the arguments presented in constructing the models give an indication of the sense in which the models exhibit the rationale and the logical structure of the explanations they are intended to represent.

I now want to add a few words concerning the second of the functions just mentioned; but I will have to forgo a discussion of the third.

When a mathematician proves a theorem, he will often omit mention of certain propositions which he presupposes in his argument and which he is in fact entitled to presuppose because, for example, they follow readily from the postulates of his system or from previously established theorems or perhaps from the hypothesis of his theorem, if the latter is in hypotheti-cal form; he then simply assumes that his readers or listeners will be able to supply the missing items if they so desire. If judged by ideal standards, the given formulation of the proof is elliptic or incomplete; but the de-parture from the ideal is harmless: the gaps can readily be filled in. Simi-larly, explanations put forward in everyday discourse and also in scien-tific contexts are often *elliptically formulated*. When we explain, for ex-ample, that a lump of butter melted because it was put into a hot frying pan, or that a small rainbow appeared in the spray of the lawn sprinkler because the sunlight was reflected and refracted by the water droplets, we may be said to offer elliptic formulations of deductive-nomological ex-planations; an account of this kind omits mention of certain laws or par-ticular facts which it tacitly takes for granted, and whose explicit citation would yield a complete deductive-nomological argument.

In addition to elliptic formulation, there is another, quite important, respect in which many explanatory arguments deviate from the theoreti-cal model. It often happens that the statement actually included in the explanans, together with those which may reasonably be assumed to have been taken for granted in the context at hand, explain the given explanandum only *partially*, in a sense which I will try to indicate by an example. In his *Psychopathology of Everyday Life*, Freud offers the following explanation of a slip of the pen that occurred to him: "On a sheet of paper containing principally short daily notes of business interest, I found, to my surprise, the incorrect date, 'Thursday, October 20th,' bracketed under the correct date of the month of September. It was not difficult to explain this anticipation as the expression of a wish. A few days before I had returned fresh from my vacation and felt ready for any amount of professional work, but as yet there were few patients. On my arrival I had found a letter from a patient announcing her arrival on the 20th of October. As I wrote the same date in September I may certainly have thought 'X. ought to be here already; what a pity about that whole month!,' and with this thought I pushed the current date a month ahead."[5]

Clearly, the formulation of the intended explanation is *at least incomplete* in the sense considered a moment ago. In particular, it fails to mention any laws or theoretical principles in virtue of which the subconscious wish, and the other antecedent circumstances referred to, could be held to explain Freud's slip of the pen. However, the general theoretical considerations Freud presents here and elsewhere in his writings suggests strongly that his explanatory account relies on a hypothesis to the effect that when a person has a strong, though perhaps unconscious, desire, then if he commits a slip of pen, tongue, memory, or the like, the slip will take a form in which it expresses, and perhaps symbolically fulfills, the given desire.

Even this rather vague hypothesis is probably more definite than what Freud would have been willing to assert. But for the sake of the argument let us accept it and include it in the explanans, together with the particular statements that Freud did have the subconscious wish he mentions, and that he was going to commit a slip of the pen. Even then, the resulting explanans permits us to deduce only that the slip made by Freud would, *in some way or other*, express and perhaps symbolically fulfill Freud's subconscious wish. But clearly, such expression and fulfillment might have been achieved by many other kinds of slip of the pen than the one actually committed.

In other words, the explanans does not imply, and thus fully explain, that the particular slip, say s, which Freud committed on this occasion, would fall within the narrow class, say W, of acts which consist in writing the words "Thursday, October 20th"; rather, the explanans implies only that s would fall into a wider class, say F, which includes W as a proper subclass, and which consists of all acts which would express and symbolically fulfill Freud's subconscious wish *in some way or other.*

The argument under consideration might be called a *partial explanation:* it provides complete, or conclusive, grounds for expecting s to be a member of F, and since W is a subclass of F, it thus shows that the explanandum, i.e., s falling within W, accords with, or bears out, what is to be expected in consideration of the explanans. By contrast, a deductive-nomological explanation of the form (D) might then be called *complete* since the explanans here does imply the explanandum.

Clearly, the question whether a given explanatory argument is complete or partial can be significantly raised only if the explanandum sentence is fully specified; only then can we ask whether the explanandum does or does not follow from the explanans. Completeness of explanation, in this sense, is relative to our explanandum sentence. Now, it might seem much more important and interesting to consider instead the notion of a complete explanation of some *concrete event,* such as the destruction of Pompeii, or the death of Adolf Hitler, or the launching of the first artificial satellite: we might want to regard a particular event as completely explained only if an explanatory account of deductive or of inductive form had been provided for all of its aspects. This notion, however, is self-defeating; for any particular event may be regarded as having infinitely many different aspects or characteristics, which cannot all be accounted for by a finite set, however large, of explanatory statements.

In some cases, what is intended as an explanatory account will depart even further from the standards reflected in the model schemata (D) and (P) above. An explanatory account, for example, which is not explicit and specific enough to be reasonably qualified as an elliptically formulated explanation or as a partial one, can often be viewed as an *explanation sketch:* it may suggest, perhaps quite vividly and persuasively, the general outlines of what, it is hoped, can eventually be supplemented so as to yield a more closely reasoned argument based on explanatory hypotheses which are indicated more fully, and which more readily permit of critical appraisal by reference to empirical evidence.

The decision whether a proposed explanatory account is to be qualified as an elliptically formulated deductive or probabilistic explanation, as a partial explanation, as an explanation sketch, or perhaps as none of these is a matter of judicious interpretation; it calls for an appraisal of the intent of the given argument and of the background assumptions that may be assumed to have been tacitly taken for granted, or at least to be available, in the given context. Unequivocal decision rules cannot be set down for this purpose any more than for determining whether a given informally stated inference which is not deductively valid by reasonably strict standards is to count nevertheless as valid but enthymematically formulated, or as fallacious, or as an instance of sound inductive reasoning, or perhaps, for lack of clarity, as none of these.

4. NOMOLOGICAL EXPLANATION IN HISTORY.

So far, we have examined nomological explanation, both deductive and inductive, as found in the natural sciences; and we have considered certain characteristic ways in which actual explanatory accounts often depart from the ideal standards of our two basic models. Now it is time to ask what light the preceding inquiries can shed on the explanatory procedures used in historical research.

In examining this question, we will consider a number of specific explanatory arguments offered by a variety of writers. It should be understood from the beginning that we are here concerned, not to appraise the factual adequacy of these explanations, but only to attempt an explication of the claims they make and of the assumptions they presuppose.

Let us note first, then, that some historical explanations are surely nomological in character: they aim to show that the explanandum phenomenon resulted from certain antecedent, and perhaps, concomitant, conditions; and in arguing these, they rely more or less explicitly on relevant generalizations. These may concern, for example, psychological or sociological tendencies and may best be conceived as broadly probabilistic in character. This point is illustrated by the following argument, which might be called an attempt to explain Parkinson's Law by subsumption under broader psychological principles:

"As the activities of the government are enlarged, more people develop a vested interest in the continuation and expansion of governmental functions. People who have jobs do not like to lose them; those who are habituated to certain skills do not welcome change; those who have become accustomed to the exercise of a certain kind of power do not like to relinquish their control—if anything, they want to develop greater power and correspondingly greater prestige. . . . Thus, government offices and bureaus, once created, in turn institute drives, not only to fortify themselves against assault, but to enlarge the scope of their operations."[6]

The psychological generalizations here explicitly adduced will reasonably have to be understood as expressing, not strict uniformities, but strong *tendencies*, which might be formulated by means of rough probability statements; so that the explanation here suggested is probabilistic in character.

As a rule, however, the generalizations underlying a proposed historical explanation are largely left unspecified; and most concrete explanatory accounts have to be qualified as partial explanations or as explanation sketches. Consider, for example, F. J. Turner's essay "The Significance of the Frontier in American History,"[7] which amplifies and defends the view that "Up to our own day American history has been in a large degree the history of the colonization of the Great West. The existence of an area of free land, its continuous recession, and the advance of American settlement westward explain American development. . . . The peculiarity of American institutions is the fact that they have been compelled to adapt themselves . . . to the changes involved in crossing a continent, in winning a wilderness, and in developing at each area of this progress, out of the primitive economic and political conditions of the frontier, the complexity of city life."[8] One of the phenomena Turner considers in developing his thesis is the rapid westward advance of what he calls the Indian trader's frontier. "Why was it," Turner asks, "that the Indian trader passed so rapidly across the continent?"; and he answers, "The explanation of the rapidity of this advance is bound up with the effects of the trader on the Indian. The trading post left the unarmed tribes at the mercy of those that had purchased firearms—a truth which the Iroquois Indians wrote in blood, and so the remote and unvisited tribes gave eager welcome to the trader. . . . This accounts for the trader's power and the rapidity of his advance."[9] There is no explicit mention here of any laws, but it is clear that this sketch of an explanation presupposes, first of all, various particular facts, such as that the remote and unvisited tribes had heard of the efficacy and availability of firearms, and that there were no culture patterns or institutions precluding their use by those tribes; but in addition, the account clearly rests also on certain assumptions as to how human beings will tend to behave in situations presenting the kinds of danger and of opportunity that Turner refers to.

Similar comments apply to Turner's account of the westward advance of what he calls the farmer's frontier: "Omitting those of the pioneer farmers who move from the love of adventure, the advance of the more steady farmer is easy to understand. Obviously the immigrant was attracted by the cheap lands of the frontier, and even the native farmer felt their influence strongly. Year by year the farmers who lived on soil, whose returns were diminished by unrotated crops, were offered the virgin soil of the frontier at nominal prices. Their growing families demanded more lands, and these were dear. The competition of the unexhausted, cheap, and easily tilled prairie lands compelled the farmer either to go West . . . or to adopt intensive culture."[10] This passage is clearly intended to do more than describe a sequence of particular events: it is meant to afford an understanding of the farmers' westward advance by pointing to their interests and needs and by calling attention to the facts and the opportunities facing them. Again, this explanation takes it for granted that under such conditions normal human beings will tend to seize new opportunities in the manner in which the pioneer farmers did.

Examining the various consequences of this moving-frontier history, Turner states that "the most important effect of the frontier has been in the promotion of democracy here and in Europe,"[11] and he begins his elaboration of this theme with the remark that "the frontier is productive of individualism. . . . The tendency is anti-social. It produces antipathy to control, and particularly to any direct control":[12] and this is, of course, a sociological generalization in a nutshell.

Similarly, any explanation that accounts for a historical phenomenon by reference to economic factors or by means of general principles of social or cultural change are nomological in import, even if not in explicit formulation.

But if this be granted there still remains another question, to which we must now turn, namely, whether, in addition to explanations of a broadly nomological character, the historian also employs certain other distinctly historical ways of explaining and understanding whose import cannot be adequately characterized by means of our two models. The question has often been answered in the affirmative, and several kinds of historical explanation have been adduced in support of this affirmation. I will now consider what seem to me two especially interesting candidates for the role of specifically historical explanation; namely first, genetic explanation, and secondly, explanation of an action in terms of its underlying rationale.

5. Genetic Explanation in History.

In order to make the occurrence of a historical phenomenon intelligible, a historian will frequently offer a "genetic explanation" aimed at exhibiting the principal stages in a sequence of events which led up to the given phenomenon.

Consider, for example, the practice of selling indulgences as it existed in Luther's time. H. Boehmer, in his work, *Luther and the Reformation*, points out that until about the end of the 19th century, "the indulgence was in fact still a great unknown quantity, at sight of which the scholar would ask himself with a sigh: 'Where did it come from?' "[13] An answer was provided by Adolf Gottlob,[14] who tackled the problem by asking himself what led the Popes and Bishops to offer indulgences. As a result, ". . . origin and development of the unknown quantity appeared clearly in the light, and doubts as to its original meaning came to an end. It revealed itself as a true descendant of the time of the great struggle between Christianity and Islam, and at the same time a highly characteristic product of Germanic Christianity."[15]

In brief outline,[16] the origins of the indulgence appear to go back to the 9th century, when the popes were strongly concerned with the fight against Islam. The Mohammedan fighter was assured by the teachings of his religion that if he were to be killed in battle his soul would immediately go to heaven; but the defender of the Christian faith had to fear that he might still be lost if he had not done the regular penance for his sins. To allay these doubts, John VII, in 877, promised absolution for their sins to crusaders who should be killed in battle. "Once the crusade was so highly thought of, it was an easy transition to regard participation in a crusade as equivalent to the performance of atonement . . . and to promise remission of these penances in return for expeditions against the Church's enemies."[17] Thus, there was introduced the indulgence of the Cross, which granted complete remission of the penitential punishment to all those who participated in a religious war. "If it is remembered what inconveniences, what ecclesiastical and civil disadvantages the ecclesiastical penances entailed, it is easy to understand that the penitents flocked to obtain this indulgence."[18] A further strong incentive came from the belief that whoever obtained an indulgence secured liberation not only from the ecclesiastical penances, but also from the corresponding suffering in purgatory after death. The benefits of these indulgences were next extended to those who, being physically unfit to participate in a religious war, contributed the funds required to send a soldier on a crusade: in 1199, Pope Innocent III recognized the payment of money as adequate qualification for the benefits of a crusading indulgence.

When the crusades were on the decline, new ways were explored of raising funds through indulgences. Thus, there was instituted a "jubilee indulgence," to be celebrated every hundred years, for the benefit of pilgrims coming to Rome on that occasion. The first of these indulgences, in 1300, brought in huge sums of money; and the time interval between successive jubilee indulgences was therefore reduced to 50, 33 and even 25 years. And from 1393 on the jubilee indulgence was made available, not only in Rome, for the benefit of pilgrims, but everywhere in Europe, through special agents who were empowered to absolve the penitent of their sins upon payment of an appropriate amount. The development went even further: in 1477, a dogmatic declaration by Sixtus IV attributed to the indulgence the power of delivering even the dead from purgatory.

Undeniably, a genetic account of this kind can enhance our understanding of a historical phenomenon. But its explanatory role, far from being *sui generis*, seems to me basically nomological in character. For the successive stages singled out for consideration surely must be qualified for their function by more than the fact that they form a temporal sequence and that they all precede the final stage, which is to be explained: the mere enumeration in a yearbook of "the year's important events" in the order of their occurrence clearly is not a genetic explanation of the final event or of anything else. In a genetic explanation each stage must be shown to "lead to" the next, and thus to be linked to its successor by virtue of some general principle which makes the occurrence of the latter at least reasonably probable, given the former. But in this sense, even successive stages in a physical phenomenon such as the free fall of a stone may be regarded as forming a genetic sequence whose different stages— characterized, let us say, by the position and the velocity of the stone at different times—are interconnected by strictly universal laws; and the successive stages in the movement of a steel ball bouncing its zigzaggy way down a Galton pegboard may be regarded as forming a genetic sequence with probabilistic connections.

The genetic accounts given by historians are not, of course, of the purely nomological kind suggested by these examples from physics. Rather, they combine a certain measure of nomological interconnecting with more or less large amounts of straight description. For consider an intermediate stage mentioned in a genetic account: some aspects of it will be presented as having evolved from the preceding stages (in virtue of connecting laws, which often will be no more than hinted at); while other aspects, which are not accounted for by information about the preceding development, will be descriptively added because they are relevant to an understanding of subsequent stages in the genetic sequence. Thus, schematically speaking, a genetic explanation will begin with a pure description of an initial stage; thence, it will proceed to an account of a second stage, part of which is nomologically linked to, and explained by, the characteristic features of the initial stage; while the balance is simply described as relevant for a nomological account of some aspects of the third stage; and so forth.[19]

In our illustration the connecting laws are hinted at in the mention made of motivating factors: the explanatory claims made for the interest of the popes in securing a fighting force and in amassing ever larger funds clearly presuppose suitable psychological generalizations as to the manner in which an intelligent individual will act, in the light of his factual beliefs, when he seeks to attain a certain objective. Similarly, general assumptions underly the reference to the fear of purgatory in explaining the eagerness with which indulgences were bought. And when, referring to the huge financial returns of the first jubilee indulgence, Schwiebert says "This success only whetted the insatiable appetite of the popes. The intervening period of time was variously reduced from 100 to 50, to 33, to 25 years . . . ,"[20] the explanatory force here implied might be said to rest on some principle of reinforcement by rewards. As need hardly be added, even if such a principle were explicitly introduced, the resulting account would provide at most a partial explanation; it could not be expected to show, for example, why the intervening intervals should have the particular lengths here mentioned.

In the genetic account of the indulgences, those factors which are simply described (or tacitly presupposed) rather than explained include, for example, the doctrines, the organization, and the power of the Church; the occurrence of the crusades and their eventual decline; and innumerable other factors which are not even explicitly mentioned, but which have to be understood as background conditions if the genetic survey is to serve its explanatory purpose.

The general conception here outlined of the logic of genetic explanation could also be illustrated by reference to Turner's studies of the American frontier; this will be clear even from the brief remarks made earlier on Turner's ideas.

Some analysts of historical development put special emphasis on the importance of the laws underlying a historical explanation; thus, e.g., A. Gerschenkron maintains, "Historical research consists essentially in application to empirical material of various sets of empirically derived hypothetical generalizations and in testing the closeness of the resulting fit, in the hope that in this way certain uniformities, certain typical situations, and certain typical relationships among individual factors in these situations can be ascertained,"[21] and his subsequent substantive observations include a brief genetic survey of patterns of industrial development in 19th century Europe, in which some of the presumably relevant uniformities are made reasonably explicit.

6. EXPLANATION BY MOTIVATING REASONS.

Let us now turn to another kind of historical explanation that is often considered as *sui generis,* namely, the explanation of an action in terms of the underlying *rationale,* which will include, in particular, the ends the agent sought to attain, and the alternative courses of action he believed to be open to him. The following passage explaining the transition from the indulgence of the Cross to the institution of the jubilee indulgence illustrates this procedure: ". . . in the course of the thirteenth century the idea of a crusade more and more lost its power over men's spirits. If the Popes would keep open the important source of income which the indulgence represented, they must invent new motives to attract people to the purchase of indulgences. It is the merit of Boniface VIII to have recognized this clearly. By creating the jubilee indulgence in 1300 he assured the species a further long development most welcome to the Papal finances."[22] This passage clearly seeks to explain the establishment of the first jubilee indulgence by suggesting the reasons for which Boniface VIII took this step. If properly spelled out, these reasons would include not only Boniface's objective of ensuring a continuation of the income so far derived from the indulgence of the Cross, but also his estimate of the relevant empirical circumstances, including the different courses of action open to him, and their probable efficacy as well as potential difficulties in pursuing them and adverse consequences to which they might lead.

The kind of explanation achieved by specifying the rationale underlying a given action is widely held to be fundamentally different from nomological explanation as found in the natural sciences. Various reasons have been adduced in support of this view; but I will limit my discussion largely to the stimulating ideas on the subjects that have been set forth by Dray.[23] According to Dray, there is an important type of historical explanation whose features "make the covering law model peculiarly inept"; he calls it "rational explanation," i.e., "explanation which displays the *rationale* of what was done," or, more fully, "a reconstruction of the agent's *calculation* of means to be adopted toward his chosen end in the light of the circumstances in which he found himself." The object of rational explanation is not to subsume the explanandum under general laws, but "to show that what was done was the thing to have done for the reasons given, rather than merely the thing that is done on such occasions, perhaps in accordance with certain laws." Hence, a rational explanation has "an element of *appraisal*" in it: it "must exhibit what was done as appropriate or justified." Accordingly, Dray conceives a rational explanation as being based on a standard of appropriateness or of rationality of a special kind which he calls a *"principle of action,"* i.e., "a judgment of the form 'When in a situation of type C_1, C_2, . . . C_n the thing to do is X.' "

Dray does not give a full account of the kind of "situation" here referred to; but to do justice to his intentions, these situations must evidently be taken to include, at least, items of the following three types: (i) the end the agent was seeking to attain; (ii) the empirical circumstances, as seen by the agent, in which he had to act; (iii) the moral standards or principles of conduct to which the agent was committed. For while this brief list requires considerable further scrutiny and elaboration, it seems clear that only if at least these items are specified does it make sense to raise the question of the appropriateness of what the agent did in the given "situation."

It seems fair to say, then, that according to Dray's conception a rational explanation answers a question of the form "Why did agent A do X?" by offering an explanans of the following type (our formulation replaces the notation "C_1, C_2 . . . C_n" by the simpler "C", without, of course, precluding that the kind of situation thus referred to may be extremely complex.):

(R)

A was in a situation of type C

In a situation of type C, the appropriate thing to do is X

But can an explanans of this type possibly serve to explain A's having in fact done X? It seems to me beyond dispute that in any adequate explanation of an empirical phenomenon the explanans must provide good grounds for believing or asserting that the explanandum phenomenon did in fact occur. Yet this requirement, which is necessary though not sufficient[24] for an adequate explanation, is not met by a rational explanation as conceived by Dray. For the two statements included in the contemplated explanans (R) provide good reasons for believing that the appropriate thing for A to do was X, but not for believing that A did in fact do X. Thus, a rational explanation in the sense in which Dray appears to understand it does not explain what it is meant to explain. Indeed, the expression "the thing to do" in the standard formulation of a principle of action, "functions as a value term," as Dray himself points out:

but then, it is unclear, on purely logical grounds, how the valuational principle expressed by the second sentence in (R), in conjunction with the plainly empirical, non-valuational first sentence, should permit any inferences concerning empirical matters such as A's action, which could not be drawn from the first sentence alone.

To explain, in the general vein here under discussion, why A did in fact do X, we have to refer to the underlying rationale not by means of a normative principle of action, but by descriptive statements to the effect that, at the time in question A was a rational agent, or had the disposition to act rationally; and that a rational agent, when in circumstances of kind C, will always (or: with high probability) do X. Thus construed, the explanans takes on the following form:

(R')

   (a) A was in a situation of type C

   (b) A was disposed to act rationally

   (c) Any person who is disposed to act rationally will, when in a situation of type C, invariably (with high probability) do X

But by this explanans A's having done X is accounted for in the manner of a deductive or of a probabilistic nomological explanation. Thus, in so far as reference to the rationale of an agent does explain his action, the explanation conforms to one of our nomological models.

An analagous diagnosis applies, incidentally, also to explanations which attribute an agent's behavior in a given situation not to rationality and more or less explicit deliberation on his part, but to other dispositional features, such as his character and emotional make-up. The following comment on Luther illustrates this point: "Even stranger to him than the sense of anxiety was the allied sense of fear. In 1527 and 1535, when the plague broke out in Wittenberg, he was the only professor besides Bugenhagen who remained calmly at his post to comfort and care for the sick and dying. . . . He had, indeed, so little sense as to take victims of the plague into his house and touch them with his own hand. Death, martyrdom, dishonor, contempt . . . he feared just as little as infectious disease."[25] It may well be said that these observations give more than a description: that they shed some explanatory light on the particular occurrences mentioned. But in so far as they explain, they do so by presenting Luther's actions as manifestations of certain personality traits, such as fearlessness; thus, the particular acts are again subsumed under generalizations as to how a fearless person is likely to behave under certain circumstances.

It might seem that both in this case and in rational explanation as construed in (R'), the statements which we took to express general laws —namely, (c) in (R'), and the statement about the probable behavior of a fearless person in our last illustration—do not have the character of empirical laws at all, but rather that of analytic statements which simply express part of what is *meant* by a rational agent, a fearless person, or the like. Thus, in contrast to nomological explanations, these accounts in terms of certain dispositional characteristics of the agent appear to presuppose no general laws at all. Now, the idea of analyticity gives rise to considerable philosophical difficulties; but let us disregard these here and take the division of statements into analytic and synthetic to be reasonably clear. Even then, the objection just outlined cannot be upheld. For dispositional concepts of the kind invoked in our explanations have to be regarded as governed by entire clusters of general statements—we might call them symptom statements—which connect the given disposition with various specific manifestations, or symptoms, of its presence (each symptom will be a particular mode of "responding," or acting, under specified "stimulus" conditions); and the whole cluster of these symptom statements for a given disposition will have implications which are plainly not analytic (in the intuitive sense here assumed). Under these circumstances it would be arbitrary to attribute to some of the symptom statements the analytic character of partial definitions.

The logic of this situation has a precise representation in Carnap's theory of reduction sentences.[26] Here, the connections between a given disposition and its various manifest symptoms are assumed to be expressed by a set of so-called reduction sentences (these are characterized by their logical form). Some of these state, in terms of manifest characteristics, sufficient conditions for the presence of the given disposition; others similarly state necessary conditions. The reduction sentences for a given dispositional concept cannot, as a rule, all be qualified as analytic; for jointly they imply certain non-analytic consequences which have the status of general laws connecting exclusively the manifest characteristics; the strongest of the laws so implied is the so-called representative sentence, which "represents, so to speak, the factual content of the set" of all the reduction sentences for the given disposition concept. This representative sentence asserts, in effect, that whenever at least one of the sufficient conditions specified by the given reduction sentences is satisfied, then so are all the necessary conditions laid down by the reduction sentences. And when A is one of the manifest criteria sufficient for the presence of a given disposition, and B is a necessary one, then the statement that whenever A is present so is B will normally turn out to be synthetic.

So far then, I have argued that Dray's construal of explanation by motivating reasons is untenable; that the normative principles of action envisaged by him have to be replaced by statements of a dispositional kind; and that, when this is done, explanations in terms of a motivating rationale, as well as those referring to other psychological factors, are seen to be basically nomological.

Let me add a few further remarks on the idea of rational explanation. First: in many cases of so-called purposive action, there is no conscious deliberation, no rational calculation that leads the agent to his decision. Dray is quite aware of this; but he holds that a rational explanation in his sense is still possible; for "in so far as we say an action is purposive at all, no matter at what level of conscious deliberation, there is a calculation which could be constructed for it: the one the agent would have gone through if he had had time, if he had not seen what to do in a flash, if he had been called upon to account for what he did after the event, etc. And it is by eliciting some such calculation that we explain the action."[27] But the explanatory significance of reasons or "calculations" which are "reconstructed" in this manner is certainly puzzling. If, to take Dray's example, an agent arrives at his decision "in a flash" rather than by deliberation, then it would seem to be simply false to say that the decision can be accounted for by some argument which the agent might have gone through under more propitious circumstances, or which he might produce later if called upon to account for his action; for, by hypothesis, no such argument was in fact gone through by the agent at the crucial time; considerations of appropriateness or rationality played no part in shaping his decision; the rationale that Dray assumes to be adduced and appraised in the corresponding rational explanation is simply fictitious.

But, in fairness to Dray, these remarks call for a qualifying observation: in at least some of the cases Dray has in mind it might not be fictitious to ascribe the action under study to a disposition which the agent acquired through a learning process whose initial stages did involve conscious ratiocination. Consider, for example, the various complex maneuvers of accelerating, braking, signalling, dodging jaywalkers and animals, swerving into and out of traffic lanes, estimating the changes of traffic lights, etc., which are involved in driving a car through city traffic. A beginning driver will often perform these only upon some sort of conscious deliberation or even calculation; but gradually, he learns to do the appropriate thing automatically, "in a flash," without giving them any conscious thought. The habit pattern he has thus acquired may be viewed as consisting in a set of dispositions to react in certain appropriate ways in various situations; and a particular performance of such an appropriate action would then be explained, not by a "constructed" calculation which actually the agent did not perform but by reference to the disposition just mentioned and thus, again, in a nomological fashion.

The method of explaining a given action by "constructing," in Dray's sense, the agent's calculation of means faces yet another, though less fundamental, difficulty: it will frequently yield a rationalization rather than an explanation, especially when the reconstruction relies on the reasons the agent might produce when called upon to account for his action. As G. Watson remarks, "Motivation, as presented in the perspective of history, is often too simple and straightforward, reflecting the psychology of the Age of Reason. . . . Psychology has come . . . to recognize the enormous weight of irrational and intimately personal impulses in conduct. In history, biography, and in autobiography, especially of public characters, the tendency is strong to present 'good' reasons instead of 'real' reasons."[28] Accordingly, as Watson goes on to point out, it is important, in examining the motivation of historical figures, to take into account the significance of such psychological mechanisms as reaction formation, "the dialectic dynamic by which stinginess cloaks itself in generosity, or rabid pacifism arises from the attempt to repress strong aggressive impulses."[29]

These remarks have a bearing also on an idea set forth by P. Gardiner in his illuminating book on historical explanation.[30] Commenting on the notion of the "real reason" for a man's action, Gardiner says: "In general, it appears safe to say that by a man's 'real reasons' we mean those reasons he would be prepared to give under circumstances where his confession would not entail adverse consequences to himself." And he adds "An exception to this is the psychoanalyst's usage of the expression where different criteria are adopted."[31] This observation might be taken to imply that the explanation of human actions in terms of underlying motives is properly aimed at exhibiting the agent's "real reasons" in the ordinary sense of the phrase, as just described; and that, by implication, reasons in the psychoanalyst's sense require less or no consideration. But such a construal of explanation would give undue importance to considerations of ordinary language. Gardiner is entirely right when he reminds us that the "language in which history is written is for the most part the language of ordinary speech"[32]; but the historian in search of reasons that will correctly explain human actions will obviously have to give up his reliance on the everyday conception of "real reasons" if psychological or other investigations show that real reasons, thus understood, do not yield as adequate an account of human actions as an analysis in terms of less familiar conceptions such as, perhaps, the idea of motivating factors which are kept out of the agent's normal awareness by processes of repression and reaction formation.

I would say, then, first of all, that historical explanation cannot be bound by conceptions that might be implicit in the way in which ordinary language deals with motivating reasons. But secondly, I would doubt that Gardiner's expressly tentative characterization does justice even to what we ordinarily mean when we speak of a man's "real reasons." For considerations of the kind that support the idea of subconscious motives are quite familiar in our time, and we are therefore prepared to say in ordinary, non-technical discourse that the reasons given by an agent may not be the "real reasons" behind his action, even if his statement was subjectively honest, and he had no grounds to expect that it would lead to any adverse consequences for him. For no matter whether an explanation of human actions is attempted in the language of ordinary speech or in the technical terms of some theory, the overriding criterion for what-if-anything should count as a "real," and thus explanatory, reason for a given action is surely not to be found by examining the way in which the term "real reason" has thus far been used, but by investigating what conception of real reason would yield the most satisfactory explanation of human conduct; and ordinary usage gradually changes accordingly.

7. Concluding Remarks.

We have surveyed some of the most prominent candidates for the role of characteristically historical mode of explanation; and we have found that they conform essentially to one or the other of our two basic types of scientific explanation.

This result and the arguments that led to it do not in any way imply a mechanistic view of man, of society, and of historical processes; nor, of course, do they deny the importance of ideas and ideals for human decision and action. What the preceding considerations do suggest is, rather, that the nature of understanding, in the sense in which explanation is meant to give us an understanding of empirical phenomena, is basically the same in all areas of scientific inquiry; and that the deductive and the probabilistic model of nomological explanation accommodate vastly more than just the explanatory arguments of, say, classical mechanics: in particular, they accord well also with the character of explanations that deal with the influence of rational deliberation, of conscious and subconscious motives, and of ideas and ideals on the shaping of historical events. In so doing, our schemata exhibit, I think, one important aspect of the methodological unity of all empirical science.

NOTES

1. See Dewey, John. *How We Think*. Boston, New York, Chicago, 1910; Chapter VI.

2. For a fuller presentation of the model and for further references, see, for example, Hempel, C. G. and P. Oppenheim, "Studies in the Logic of Explanation," *Philosophy of Science* 15: 135-175 (1948). (Secs. 1-7 of this article, which contain all the fundamentals of the presentation, are reprinted in Feigl, H. and M. Brodbeck (eds.), *Readings in the Philosophy of Science*. New York, 1953.)—The suggestive term "covering law model" is W. Dray's; cf. his *Laws and Explanation in History*. Oxford, 1957; Chapter I. Dray characterizes this type of explanation as "subsuming what is to be explained under a general law" (*loc. cit.*, p. 1), and then rightly urges, in the name of methodological realism, that "the requirement of a *single* law be dropped" (*loc. cit.*, p. 24; italics, the author's): it should be noted, however, that, like the schema (D) above, several earlier publications on the subject (among them the article mentioned at the beginning of this note) make explicit provision for the inclusion of more laws than one in the explanans.

3. The relevance of the covering-law model to causal explanation is examined more fully in sec. 4 of Hempel, C. G., "Deductive-Nomological *vs.* Statistical Explanation." In Feigl, H., et al. (eds.), *Minnesota Studies in the Philosophy of Science*, vol. III. Minneapolis, 1962.

4. The concept of probabilistic explanation, and some of the peculiar logical and methodological problems engendered by it, are examined in some detail in Part II of the essay cited in note 3.

5. Freud, S. *Psychopathology of Everyday Life*. Translated by A. A. Brill. New York (Mentor Books) 1951; p. 64.

6. McConnell, D. W., *et al., Economic Behavior*. New York, 1939; pp. 894-95.

7. First published in 1893, and reprinted in several publications, among them: Edwards, Everett E. (ed.), *The Early Writings of Frederick Jackson Turner*. Madison, Wisconsin, 1938. Page references given in the present article pertain to this book.

8. *loc. cit.*, pp. 185-86.

9. *loc. cit.*, pp. 200-201.

10. *loc. cit.*, p. 210.

11. *loc. cit.*, p. 219.

12. *loc. cit.,* p. 220.

13. Boehmer, H., *Luther and the Reformation.* Translated by E. S. G. Potter. London, 1930; p. 91.

14. Gottlob's study, *Kreuzablass und Almosenablass,* was published in 1906; cf. the references to the work of Gottlob and other investigators in Schwiebert, E. G., *Luther and His Times.* St. Louis, Missouri, 1950, notes to Chapter 10.

15. Boehmer, *loc. cit.,* p. 91.

16. This outline follows the accounts given by Boehmer, *loc. cit.,* Chapter III and by Schwiebert, *loc. cit.,* Chapter 10.

17. Boehmer, *loc. cit.,* p. 92.

18. Boehmer, *loc. cit.,* p. 93.

19. The logic of genetic explanations in history is examined in some detail in E. Nagel's recent book, *The Structure of Science.* New York, 1961; pp. 564-568. The conception outlined in the present paper, though arrived at without any knowledge of Nagel's work on this subject, accords well with the latter's results.

20. Schwiebert, *loc. cit.,* p. 304.

21. Gerschenkron, A. "Economic Backwardness in Historical Perspective," in Hoselitz, B. F. (ed.), *The Progress of Underdeveloped Areas.* Chicago, 1952; pp. 3-29.

22. Boehmer, *loc. cit.,* pp. 93-94.

23. Dray, W. *Laws and Explanation in History.* Oxford, 1957; Chapter V. All quotations are from this chapter; italics in the quoted passages are Dray's.

24. Empirical evidence supporting a given hypothesis may afford strong grounds for believing the latter without providing an explanation for it.

25. Boehmer, *loc. cit.,* p. 234.

26. See especially Carnap's classical essay, "Testability and Meaning," *Philosophy of Science* 3, 419-71 (1936) and 4, 1-40 (1937); reprinted, with some omissions, in Feigl and Brodbeck, *loc. cit.* On the point here under discussion, see sec. 9 and particularly sec. 10 of the original essay or sec. 7 of the reprinted version.

27. Dray, *loc. cit.,* p. 123.

28. Watson, G. "Clio and Psyche: Some Interrelations of Psychology and History." In Ware, C. F. (ed.), *The Cultural Approach to History.* New York, 1940, pp. 34-47; quotation from p. 36.

29. Watson, *ibid.*

30. Gardiner, P. *The Nature of Historical Explanation.* Oxford, 1952.

31. Gardiner, *loc. cit.,* p. 136.

32. Gardiner, *loc. cit.,* p. 63.

Chapter 2 | *Philosophy and the Scientific Image of Man*

Wilfrid Sellars
Professor of Philosophy
Yale University

The initial steps toward man's intellectual and cultural life may be described as acts which involve a sort of mental adjustment to the immediate environment. But as human culture progresses we very soon meet with an opposite tendency to human life. From the earliest glimmering of human consciousness we find an introvert view of life accompanying and complementing this extrovert view. The farther we trace the development of human culture from these beginnings the more this introvert view seems to come to the fore. Man's natural curiosity begins slowly to change its direction. We can study this growth in almost all the forms of the cultural life of man. In the first mythological explanations of the universe we always find a primitive anthropology side by side with a primitive cosmology. The question of the origin of the world is inextricably interwoven with the question of the origin of man.

ERNST CASSIRER, *An Essay on Man.*

Philosophy and the Scientific Image of Man

I. The Philosophical Quest.

The aim of philosophy, abstractly formulated, is to understand how things in the broadest possible sense of the term hang together in the broadest possible sense of the term. Under "things in the broadest possible sense" I include such radically different items as not only "cabbages and kings," but numbers and duties, possibilities and finger snaps, aesthetic experience and death. To achieve success in philosophy would be, to use a contemporary turn of phrase, to "know one's way around" with respect to all these things, not in that unreflective way in which the centipede of the story knew its way around before it faced the question, "how do I walk?" but in that reflective way which means that no intellectual holds are barred.

Knowing one's way around is, to use a current distinction, a form of "knowing *how*" as contrasted with "knowing *that*." There is all the difference in the world between knowing *how* to ride a bicycle and knowing *that* a steady pressure by the legs of a balanced person on the pedals would result in forward motion. Again, to use an example somewhat closer to our subject, there is all the difference in the world between knowing *that* each step of a given proof in mathematics follows from the preceding steps, and knowing *how* to find a proof. Sometimes being able to find a proof is a matter of being able to follow a set procedure; more often it is not. It can be argued that anything which can be properly called "knowing how to do something" presupposes a body of knowledge *that*; or, to put it differently, knowledge of truth or facts. If this were so, then the statement that "ducks know *how* to swim" would be as metaphorical as the statement that they know *that* water supports them. However this may be, knowing how to do something at the level of characteristically human activity presupposes a great deal of knowledge *that*, and it is obvious that the reflective knowing one's way around in the scheme of things, which is the aim of philosophy, presupposes a great deal of reflective knowledge of truths.

Now the subject-matter of this knowledge of truths which is presupposed by philosophical "know-how," falls, in a sense, completely within the scope of the special disciplines. Philosophy in an important sense has no special subject matter which stands to it as other subject matters stand to other special disciplines. If philosophers did have such a special subject matter, they could turn it over to a new group of specialists, as they have turned other special subject matters to nonphilosophers over the past 2,500 years, first mathematics, more recently psychology and sociology, and, currently, certain aspects of theoretical linguistics. What is characteristic of philosophy is not a special subject matter, but the aim of knowing one's way around with respect to the subject matters of all the special disciplines.

Now the special disciplines know their way around their subject matters, and each learns to do so in the process of discovering truths about its own subject matter. But each special discipline must also have a sense of how its bailiwick fits into the countryside as a whole. This sense, in many cases, amounts to a little more than the unreflective "knowing one's way around," which is a common possession of us all. Again, the specialist must have a sense of how not only his subject matter but also the methods and principles of his thinking about it fit into the intellectual landscape. Thus, the historian reflects not only on historical events themselves, but on what it is to think historically. It is part of his business to reflect on his own thinking—its aims, its criteria, its pitfalls. In dealing with historical questions he must face and answer questions which are not, themselves, in a primary sense historical questions. But he deals with these questions as they arise in the attempt to answer specifically historical questions.

Reflection on any special discipline can soon lead one to the conclusion that the *ideal* practitioner of that discipline would see his special subject matter and his thinking about it in the light of a reflective insight into the intellectual landscape as a whole. There is much truth in the platonic conception that the special disciplines are perfected by philosophy, but the companion conception that the philosopher must know his way around in each discipline, as does the specialist, has been an evermore elusive ideal since the scientific revolution began. But if the philosopher cannot hope to know his way around in each discipline as does the specialist, there is a sense in which he can know his way around with respect to the subject matter of that discipline, and must do so if he is to approximate to the philosophic aim.

The multiplication of sciences and disciplines is a familiar feature of the intellectual scene. Scarcely less familiar is the unification of this manifold which is taking place by the building of scientific bridges between them. I shall have something to say about this unification below. What is not so obvious to the layman is that the task of "seeing all things together" has itself been (paradoxically) broken down into specialities. And there *is* a place for specialization in philosophy. For just as one cannot come to know one's way around in the highway system as a whole without knowing one's way around in the parts, so one can't hope to know one's way around in "things in general," without knowing one's way around in the major groupings of things.

It is, therefore, the "eye on the whole" which distinguishes the philosophical enterprise. Otherwise, there is little to distinguish the philosopher from the persistently reflective specialist; the philosopher of history from the persistently reflective historian. To the extent that a specialist is more concerned to reflect on how his work as a specialist joins up with other intellectual pursuits, than in asking and answering questions within his specialty, he is said, properly, to be philosophically-minded. And, indeed, one can "have one's eye on the whole" without staring at it all the time. The latter would be a fruitless enterprise. Furthermore, like other specialists, the philosopher who specializes may derive much of his sense of the whole from the prereflective orientation which is our common heritage. On the other hand, a philosopher could scarcely be said to have his eye on the whole in the relevant sense, unless he has reflected on the nature of philosophical thinking. It is this reflection on the place of philosophy itself in the scheme of things which is the distinctive trait of the philosopher as contrasted with the reflective specialist; and in the absence of this critical reflection on the philosophical enterprise, one is at best but a potential philosopher.

It has often been said in recent years that the aim of the philosopher is not to discover new truths, but to "analyze" what we already know. But while the term "analysis" was helpful in its implication that philosophy as such makes no *substantive* contribution to what we know, and is concerned in some way to improve the *manner* in which we know it, it is most misleading by its contrast to "synthesis." For by virtue of this contrast, these statements suggest that philosophy is evermore myopic, tracing parts within parts, losing each in turn from sight as new parts come into view. One is tempted, therefore, to contrast the analytic conception of philosophy as myopia with the synoptic vision of true philosophy. And it must be admitted that if the contrast between "analysis" and "synthesis" were the operative connotation in the metaphor, then a purely analytic philosophy would be a contradiction in terms. Even if we construe "analysis" on the analogy of making ever smaller scale maps of the same overall terrain, which does more justice to the synoptic element, the analogy disturbs because we would have to compare philosophy to the making of small scale maps from an original large scale map; and a smaller scale map in this sense is a triviality.

Even if the analogy is changed to that of bringing a picture into focus, which preserves the synoptic element and the theme of working within the framework of what is already known while adding a dimension of gain, the analogy is disturbing in two respects:

(a) It suggests that the special disciplines are confused; as though the scientist had to wait for the philosopher to clarify his subject matter, bring it into focus. To account for the creative role of philosophy it is not necessary to say that the scientist doesn't know his way around in his own area. What we must rather say is that the specialist knows his way around in his own neighborhood, as his neighborhood, but doesn't know his way around in it in the same way *as a part of the landscape as a whole.*

(b) It implies that the essential change brought about by philosophy is the standing out of detail within a picture which is grasped as a whole from the start. But, of course, to the extent that there is *one* picture to be grasped reflectively as a whole, the unity of the reflective vision is a task rather than an initial datum.

The search for this unity at the reflective level is therefore more appropriately compared to the contemplation of a large and complex painting which is not seen as a unity without a prior exploration of its parts. The analogy, however, is not complete until we take into account a *second* way in which unity is lacking in the original datum of the contemporary philosopher. For he is confronted not by one picture, but, *in principle*, by *two* and, in fact, by *many*. The plurality I have in mind is not that which concerns the distinction between the fact-finding, the ethical, the aesthetic, the logical, the religious, and other aspects of experience, for these are but aspects of one complex picture which is to be grasped reflectively as a whole. As such, it constitutes one term of a crucial duality which confronts the contemporary philosopher at the very beginning of his enterprise. Here the most appropriate analogy is stereoscopic vision, where two differing perspectives on a landscape are fused into one coherent experience.

For the philosopher is confronted not by one complex many dimensional picture, the unity of which, such as it is, he must come to appreciate; but by *two* pictures of essentially the same order of complexity, each of which purports to be a complete picture of man-in-the-world, and which, after separate scrutiny, he must fuse into one vision. Let me refer to these two perspectives, respectively, as the *manifest* and the *scientific* images of man-in-the-world. And let me explain my terms. First, by calling them images I do not mean to deny to either or both of them the status of "reality." I am, to use Husserl's term, "bracketing" them, transforming them from ways of experiencing the world into objects of philosophical reflection and evaluation. The term "image" is usefully ambiguous; on the one hand it suggests the contrast between an object, e.g., a tree, and a projection of the object on a plane, or its shadow on a wall. In this sense, an image is as much an existent as the object imaged, though, of course, it has a dependent status.

In the other sense, an "image" is something imagined, and that which is imagined may well not exist, although the imagining of it does—in which case we can speak of the image as *merely* imaginary or unreal. But the imagined *can* exist; as when one imagines that someone is dancing in the next room, and someone is. This ambiguity enables me to imply that the philosopher is confronted by two projections of man-in-the-world on the human understanding. One of these projections I will call the manifest image, the other the scientific image. These images exist and are as much a part and parcel of the world as this platform or the Constitution of the United States. But in addition to being confronted by these images as existents, he is confronted by them as images in the sense of "things imagined"—or, as I had better say at once, *conceived;* for I am using "image" in this sense as a metaphor for conception, and it is familiar fact that not everything that can be conceived, in the ordinary sense, can be imagined. The philosopher, then, is confronted by two conceptions, equally public, equally nonarbitrary, of man-in-the-world, and he cannot shirk the attempt to see how they fall together in one stereoscopic view.

Before I begin to explain the contrast between "manifest" and "scientific," as I shall use these terms, let me make it clear that they are both "idealizations" in something like the sense in which a frictionless body or an ideal gas is an idealization. They are designed to illuminate the inner dynamics of the development of philosophical ideas, as scientific idealizations illuminate the development of physical systems. From a somewhat different point of view they can be compared to the "ideal types" of Max Weber's sociology. The story is complicated by the fact that each image has a history, and while the main outlines of what I shall call the manifest image took shape in the mists of prehistory, the scientific image, promissory notes apart, has taken shape before our very eyes.

II. THE MANIFEST IMAGE.

The "manifest" image of man-in-the-world can be characterized in two ways, which are supplementary rather than alternative. It is, first, the framework in terms of which man came to be aware of himself as man-in-the-world. It is the framework in terms of which, to use an existentialist turn of phrase, man first encountered himself—which is, of course, when he came to be man. For it is no merely incidental feature of man that he has a conception of himself as man-in-the-world, just as it is obvious, on reflection, that if man had a radically different conception of himself he would be a radically different kind of man.

I have given this quasi-historical dimension of our construct pride of place, because I want to highlight from the very beginning what might be called the paradox of man's encounter with himself, the paradox consisting of the fact that man couldn't be man until he encountered himself. It is this paradox which supports the last stand of Special Creation. Its central theme is the idea that anything which can properly be called conceptual thinking can occur only within a framework of conceptual thinking in terms of which it can be criticized, supported, refuted, in short, evaluated. To be able to think is to be able to measure one's thoughts by standards of correctness, of relevance, of evidence. In this sense a diversified conceptual framework is a whole which, however sketchy, is prior to its parts, and cannot be construed as a coming together of parts which are already conceptual in character. The conclusion is difficult to avoid that the transition from preconceptual patterns of behavior to conceptual thinking was a holistic one, a jump to a level of awareness which is irreducibly new, a jump which was the coming into being of man.

There is a profound truth in this conception of a radical difference in level between man and his precursors. The attempt to understand this difference turns out to be part and parcel of the attempt to encompass in one view the two images of man-in-the-world which I have set out to describe. For, as we shall see, this difference in level appears as an irreducible discontinuity in the *manifest* image, but as, in a sense requiring careful analysis, a reducible difference in the *scientific* image.

I have characterized the manifest image of man-in-the-world as the framework in terms of which man encountered himself. And this, I believe, is a useful way of characterizing it. But it is also misleading, for it suggests that the contrast I am drawing between the manifest and the scientific images is that between a prescientific, uncritical, naïve conception of man-in-the-world, and a reflected, disciplined, critical—in short a scientific conception. This is not at all what I have in mind. For what I mean by the manifest image is a refinement or sophistication of what might be called the "original" image; a refinement to a degree which makes it relevant to the contemporary intellectual scene. This refinement or sophistication can be construed under two headings: (a) empirical; (b) categorial.

By empirical refinement I mean the sort of refinement which operates within the broad framework of the image and, by approaching the world in terms of something like the canons of inductive inference defined by John Stuart Mill, supplemented by canons of statistical inference, adds to and subtracts from the contents of the world as experienced in terms of this framework and the correlations which are believed to obtain between them. Thus, the conceptual framework which I am calling the manifest image is, in an appropriate sense, itself a scientific image. It is not only disciplined and critical; it also makes use of those aspects of scientific method which might be lumped together under the heading "correlational induction." There is, however, one type of scientific reasoning which it by stipulation does *not* include, namely, that which involves the postulation of imperceptible entities, and principles pertaining to them, to explain the behavior of perceptible things.

This makes it clear that the concept of the manifest image of man-in-the-world is not that of an historical and bygone stage in the development of man's conception of the world and his place in it. For it is a familiar fact that correlational and postulational methods have gone hand in hand in the evolution of science, and, indeed, have been dialectically related; postulational hypotheses, presupposing correlations to be explained and suggesting possible correlations to be investigated. The notion of a purely correlational scientific view of things is both a historical and a methodological fiction. It involves abstracting correlational fruits from the conditions of their discovery, and the theories in terms of which they are explained. Yet it is a useful fiction (and hence no *mere* fiction), for it will enable us to define a way of looking at the world, which, though disciplined and, in a limited sense, scientific, contrasts sharply with an image of man-in-the-world which is implicit in and can be constructed from the postulational aspects of contemporary scientific theory. And, indeed, what I have referred to as the "scientific" image of man-in-the-world and contrasted with the "manifest" image, might better be called the "postulational" or "theoretical" image. But, I believe, it will not be too misleading if I continue, for the most part, to use the former term.

Now, the manifest image is important for our purposes, because it defines one of the poles to which philosophical reflection has been drawn. It is not only the great speculative systems of ancient and medieval philosophy which are built around the manifest image, but also many systems and quasi-systems in recent and contemporary thought, some of which seem at first sight to have little if anything in common with the great classical systems. That I include the major schools of contemporary Continental thought might be expected. That I lump in with these the trends of contemporary British and American philosophy which emphasize the analysis of "common sense" and "ordinary usage" may be somewhat more surprising. Yet this kinship is becoming increasingly apparent in recent years, and I believe that the distinctions I am drawing in these lectures will make possible an understanding and interpretation of this kinship. For all these philosophies can, I believe, be fruitfully construed as more or less adequate accounts of the manifest image of man-in-the-world, which accounts are then taken to be an adequate and full description in general terms of what man and the world really are.

Let me elaborate on this theme by introducing another construct which I shall call borrowing a term with a not unrelated meaning—the perennial philosophy of man-in-the-world. This construct, which is the "ideal type" around which philosophies in what might be called in a suitably broad sense the platonic tradition cluster, is simply the manifest image endorsed as real, and its outline taken to be the large scale map of reality to which science brings a needlepoint of detail and elaborate technique of map-reading.

It will probably have occurred to you by now that there are negative over-tones to both constructs: the "manifest image" and the "perennial philosophy." And, in a certain sense, this is indeed the case. I *am* implying that the perennial philosophy is analogous to what one gets when one looks through a stereoscope with one eye dominating. The manifest image dominates and mislocates the scientific image. But if the perennial philosophy of man-in-the-world is in this sense distorted, an important consequence lurks in the offing. For I have also implied that man is *essentially* that being which conceives of itself *in terms of the image which the perennial philosophy refines and endorses*. I seem, therefore, to be saying that man's conception of himself in the world does not easily accommodate the scientific image; that there is a genuine tension between them; that man is not the sort of thing he conceives himself to be; that his existence is in some measure built around error. If this were what I wished to say, I would be in distinguished company. One thinks, for example, of

Spinoza, who contrasted man as he falsely conceives himself to be with man as he discovers himself to be in the scientific enterprise. It might well be said that Spinoza drew a distinction between a "manifest" and a "scientific" image of man, rejecting the former as false and accepting the latter as true.

But if in Spinoza's account the scientific image, as he interprets it, dominates the stereoscopic view (the manifest image appearing as a tracery of explainable error), the very fact that I use the analogy of stereoscopic vision implies that as I see it the manifest image is not overwhelmed in the synthesis.

But before there can be any point to these comparisons, I must characterize these images in more detail, adding flesh and blood to the bare bones I have laid before you. I shall devote the remainder of this section to developing the manifest image. In the concluding section I shall characterize the scientific image, and attempt to describe certain key features of how the two images blend together in a true stereoscopic view.

I distinguished above between two dimensions of the refinement which turned the "original" image into the "manifest" image: the empirical and the categorial. Nothing has been said so far about the categorial. Yet it is here that the most important things are to be said. It is in this connection that I will be able to describe the general structure of the manifest image.

A fundamental question with respect to any conceptual framework is, "Of what sort are the basic objects of the framework?" This question involves, on the one hand, the contrast between an object and what can be true of it in the way of properties, relations, and activities; and, on the other, a contrast between the basic objects of the framework and the various kinds of groups they can compose. The basic objects of a framework need not be things in the restricted sense of perceptible physical objects. Thus, the basic objects of current theoretical physics are notoriously imperceptible and unimaginable. Their "basic-ness" consists in the fact that they are not properties or groupings of anything more basic (at least until further notice). The questions, "Are the basic objects of the framework of physical theory *thing-like?* and if so, to what extent?" are meaningful ones.

Now to ask, "What are the basic objects of a (given) framework?" is to ask not for a *list*, but a *classification*. And the classification will be more or less "abstract" depending on what the purpose of the inquiry is. The philosopher is interested in a classification which is abstract enough to provide a synoptic view of the contents of the framework, but which falls short of simply referring to them as objects or entities. Thus we are approaching an answer to the question, "what are the basic objects of the manifest image?" when we say that it includes persons, animals, lower forms of life, and "merely material" things, like rivers and stones. The list is not intended to be complete, although it is intended to echo the lower stages of the "great chain of being" of the platonic tradition.

The first point I wish to make is that there is an important sense in which the primary objects of the manifest image are *persons*. And to understand how this is so, is to understand central, and indeed, crucial themes in the history of philosophy. Perhaps the best way to make the point is to refer back to the construct which we called the "original" image of man-in-the-world, and characterize it as a framework in which *all* the "objects" are persons. From this point of view, the refinement of the "original" image into the manifest image, is the gradual "de-personalization" of objects other than persons. That something like this has occurred with the advance of civilization is a familiar fact. Even persons, it is said (mistakenly, I believe), are being "de-personalized" by the advance of the scientific point of view.

The point I now wish to make is that although this gradual de-personalization of the original image is a familiar idea, it is radically misunderstood, if it is assimilated to the gradual abandonment of a superstitious belief. A primitive man did not *believe* that the tree in front of him was a person, in the sense that he thought of it both as a tree *and* as a person, as I might think that this brick in front of me is a doorstop. If this were so, then when he abandoned the idea that trees were persons, his concept of a tree could remain unchanged, although his beliefs about trees would be changed. The truth is, rather, that *originally* to be a tree was *a way of being a person*, as, to use a close analogy, to be a woman is a way of being a person, or to be a triangle is a way of being a plane figure. That a woman is a person is not something that one can be said to *believe;* though there is enough historical bounce to this example to make it worthwhile to use the different example, that one cannot be said to believe that a triangle is a plane figure. When primitive man ceased to think of what we called trees as persons, the change was more radical than a change in belief; it was a change in category.

Now, the human mind is not limited in its categories to what it has been able to refine out of the world view of primitive man, anymore than the limits of what we can conceive are set by what we can imagine. The categories of theoretical physics are not essences distilled from the framework of perceptive experience, yet, if the human mind can conceive of *new* categories, it can also refine the old; and it is just as important not to over-estimate the rule of creativity in the development of the framework in terms of which you and I experience the world, as it is not to underestimate its role in the scientific enterprise.

I indicated above that in the construct which I have called, the "original" image of man-in-the-world, all "objects" are persons, and all kinds of objects, ways of being persons. This means that the sort of things that are said of objects in this framework are the sort of things that are said of persons. And let me make it clear that by "person" I do not mean "spirit" or "mind." The idea that a man is a team of two things, a mind *and* a body, is one for which many reasons of different kinds and weights have been given in the course of human intellectual development. But it is obvious, on reflection, that whatever philosophers have made of the idea of a *mind*, the pre-philosophical conception of a *spirit*, where it is found, is that of a ghostly *person*, something closely analogous to flesh and blood persons which "inhabits" them, or is otherwise intimately connected with them. It is, therefore, a development *within the framework of persons*, and it would be incorrect to construe the manifest image in such a way that persons are composite objects. On the other hand, if it is to do its work, the manifest framework must be such as to make meaningful the assertion that what we ordinarily call persons are composites of a person proper and a body—and, by doing so, make meaningful the contrary view that although man has many different types of ability, ranging from those he has in common with the lowest of things, to his ability to engage in scientific and philosophical reflections, he nevertheless is one object and not a team. For we shall see that the essential dualism in the manifest image is not that between mind and body as substances, but between two radically different ways in which the human individual is related to the world. Yet it must be admitted that most of the philosophical theories which are dominated by the manifest image are dualistic in the substantive sense. There are many factors which account for this, most of which fall outside the scope of this essay. Of the factors which concern us, one is a matter of the influence of the developing scientific image of man, and will be discussed in the following section. The other arises in the attempt to make sense of the manifest image in its own terms.

Now to understand the manifest image as a refinement or de-personalization of the "original" image, we must remind ourselves of the range of activities which are characteristic of persons. For when I say that the objects of the manifest image are primarily persons, I am implying that what the objects of this framework, primarily *are* and *do*, is what persons are and do. Thus persons are "impetuous" or "set in their ways." They apply old policies or adopt new ones. They do things from habit or ponder alternatives. They are immature or have an established character. For my present purposes the most important contrasts are those between actions which are expressions of character and actions which are *not* expressions of character, on the one hand, and between habitual actions and deliberate actions, on the other. The first point that I want to make is that only a being capable of deliberation can properly be said to act, either impulsively or from habit. For in the full and non-metaphorical sense an action is the sort of thing that can be done deliberately. We speak of actions as *becoming* habitual, and this is no accident. It is important to realize that the use of the term "habit," in speaking of an earthworm as acquiring the habit of turning to the right in a T-maze, is a metaphorical extension of the term. There is nothing dangerous in the metaphor until the mistake is made of assuming that the habits of persons are the same sort of thing as the (metaphorical) "habits" of earthworms and white rats.

Again, when we say that something a person did was an expression of his character, we mean that it is "in character"—that it was to be expected. We do not mean that it was a matter of *habit*. To be *habitual* is to be "in character," but the converse is not true. To say of an action that it is "in character," that it was to be expected, is to say that it was predictable —*not*, however, predictable "no holds barred," but predictable with respect to evidence pertaining to what the person in question has done in the past, and the circumstances as he saw them in which he did it. Thus, a person can not, *logically* can not, *begin* by acting "in character," anymore than he can *begin* by acting from habit.

It is particularly important to see that while to be "in character" is to be predictable, the converse is not true. It does not follow from the fact that a piece of human behavior is predictable, that it is an expression of character. Thus the behavior of a burnt child with respect to the fire is predictable, but not an expression of character. If we use the phrase, "the nature of a person" to sum up the predictabilities *no holds barred* pertaining to that person, then we must be careful not to equate the *nature* of a person with his *character*, although his character will be a "part" of his nature in the broad sense. Thus, if everything a person did were predictable (in principle), given sufficient knowledge about the person and the circumstances in which he was placed, and was, therefore, an "expression of his nature," it would not follow that everything the person did was an expression of his *character*. Obviously, to say of a person that everything that he does is an expression of his character is to say that his life is simply a carrying out of formed habits and policies. Such a person is a type only approximated in real life. Not even a mature person always acts in character. And as we have seen, it cannot possibly be true that he has always acted in character. Yet, if determinism is true, everything he has done has been an expression of his "nature."

I am now in a position to explain what I mean when I say that the primary objects of the manifest image are persons. I mean that it is the modification of an image in which *all* the objects are capable of *the full range* of personal activity, the modification consisting of a gradual pruning of the implications of saying with respect to what *we* would call an inanimate object, that it *did* something. Thus, in the original image to say of the wind that it blew down one's house would imply that the wind *either* decided to do so with an end in view, and might, perhaps, have been persuaded not to do it, *or* that it acted thoughtlessly (either from habit or impulse) or, perhaps, inadvertently, in which case other appropriate action on one's part might have awakened it to the enormity of what it was about to do.

In the early stages of the development of the manifest image the wind was no longer conceived as acting deliberately, with an end in view; but rather from habit or impulse. Nature became the locus of "truncated persons"; that which things could be expected to do, its habits; that which exhibits no order, its impulses. Inanimate things no longer "did" things in the sense in which persons do them—not, however, because a *new* category of impersonal things and impersonal processes has been achieved, but because the category of *person* is now applied to these things in a pruned or truncated form. It is a striking exaggeration to say of a person that he is a "mere creature of habit and impulse," but in the early stages of the development of manifest image, the world includes truncated persons which *are* mere creatures of habit, acting out routines, broken by impulses, in a life which never rises above what ours is like in our most unreflective moments. Finally, the sense in which the wind "did" things was pruned, save for poetic and expressive purposes—and, one is tempted to add, for philosophical purposes—of implications pertaining to "knowing what one is doing" and "knowing what the circumstances are."

Just as it is important not to confuse between the "character" and the "nature" of a person (that is to say, between an action's being predictable with respect to evidence pertaining to prior action, and its being predictable no holds barred) so it is important not to confuse between an action's being *predictable* and its being *caused*. These terms are often treated as synonyms, but only confusion can arise from doing so. Thus, in the "original" image one person causes another person to do something he otherwise would not have done. But most of the things people do are not things they are *caused* to do, even if what they do is highly predictable. For example: when a person has well-established habits, what he does in certain circumstances is highly predictable, but it is not for that reason *caused*. Thus, the category of causation (as contrasted with the more inclusive category of predictability) betrays its origin in the "original" image. When all things were persons it was certainly not a framework conception that everything a person did was caused; nor, of course, was it a framework principle that everything a person did was predictable. To the extent that relationships between the truncated "persons" of the manifest framework were analogous to the causal relationships between persons, the category itself continued to be used, although pruned of its implications with respect to plans, purposes, and policies. The most obvious analogue at the inanimate level of causation in the original sense is one billiard ball causing another to change its course, but it is important to note that no one who distinguishes between causation and predictability would ask, "What *caused* the billiard ball on a smooth table to continue in a straight line?" The distinctive trait of the scientific revolution was the conviction that all events are *predictable* from relevant information about the context in which they occur, not that they are all, in any ordinary sense, *caused*.

III. CLASSICAL PHILOSOPHY AND THE MANIFEST IMAGE.

I have characterized the concept of the manifest image as one of the poles toward which philosophical thinking is drawn. This commits me, of course, to the idea that the manifest image is not a mere external standard, by relation to which one interested in the development of philosophy classifies philosophical positions, but has in its own way an objective existence in philosophical thinking itself, and, indeed, in human thought generally. And it can influence philosophical thinking only by having an existence which transcends in some way the individual thought of individual thinkers. I shall be picking up this theme shortly, and shall ask how an image of the world, which, after all, is a way of thinking *can* transcend the individual thinker which it influences. (The general lines of the answer must be obvious, but it has implications which have not always been drawn.) The point I wish to make now is that since this image has a being which transcends the individual thinker, *there is truth and error with respect to it, even though the image itself might have to be rejected in the last analysis as false.*

Thus, whether or not the world as we encounter it in perception and self-awareness is ultimately real, it is surely incorrect, for example, to say as some philosophers have said that the physical objects of the encountered world are "complexes of sensations" or, equally, to say that apples "aren't *really* colored," or that mental states are "behavioral dispositions," or that one cannot intend to do something without knowing that one intends to do it, or that to say that something is good is to say that one likes it, etc. For there is a correct and an incorrect way to describe this objective image which we have of the world in which we live, and it is possible to evaluate the correctness or incorrectness of such a description. I have already claimed that much of academic philosophy can be interpreted as an attempt by individual thinkers to delineate the manifest image (not recognized, needless to say, as such), an image which is both immanent in and transcendent of their thinking. In this respect, a philosophy can be evaluated as perceptive or imperceptive, mistaken or correct, even though one is prepared to say that the image they delineate is but one way in which reality appears to the human mind. And it is, indeed, a task of the first importance to delineate this image, particularly in so far as it concerns man himself. For, as was pointed out before, man is what he is because he thinks of himself in terms of this image, and the latter must be understood before it is proper to ask, "To what extent does manifest man survive in the synoptic view which does equal justice to the scientific image which now confronts us?"

I think it correct to say that the so-called "analytic" tradition in recent British and American philosophy, particularly under the influence of the later Wittgenstein, has done increasing justice to the manifest image, and has increasingly succeeded in isolating it in something like its pure form, and has made clear the folly of attempting to replace it *piecemeal* by fragments of the scientific image. By doing so it has made apparent and has come to realize its continuity with the perennial tradition.

Now one of the most interesting features of the perennial philosophy is its attempt to understand the status in the individual thinker of the framework of ideas in terms of which he grasps himself as a person in the world. How do individuals come to be able to think in terms of this complex conceptual framework? How do they come to have this image? Two things are to be noticed here: (1) The manifest image does not present conceptual thinking as a complex of items which, considered in themselves

184363

and apart from these relations, are not conceptual in character. (The most plausible candidates are images, but all attempts to construe thoughts as complex patterns of images have failed, and, as we now know, were bound to fail.) (2) Whatever the ultimate constituents of conceptual thinking, the process itself as it occurs in the individual mind must echo, more or less adequately, the intelligible structure of the world.

There was, of course, a strong temptation not only to think of the constituents of thinking as qualitatively similar to the constituents of the world, but also to think of the world as causing these constituents to occur in patterns which echo the patterns of events. The attempt by precursors of scientific psychology to understand the genesis of conceptual thinking in the individual in terms of an "association" of elemental processes which were not themselves conceptual, by a direct action of the physical environment on the individual—the paradigm case being the burnt child fearing the fire—was a premature attempt to construct a scientific image of man.

The perennial tradition had no sympathy with such attempts. It recognized (a) that association of *thoughts* is not association of images, and, as presupposing a framework of conceptual thinking cannot account for it; (b) that the direct action of perceptible nature, *as perceptible*, on the *individual* can account for associative connection, *but not the rational connections of conceptual thinking*.

Yet, somehow the world *is* the cause of the individual's image of the world, and, as is well-known, for centuries the dominant conception of the perennial tradition was that of a direct causal influence of the world as intelligible on the individual mind. This theme, initiated by Plato, can be traced through Western thought to the present day. In the Platonic tradition this mode of causation is attributed to a being which is analogous, to a greater or lesser degree, to a person. Even the Aristotelian distinguishes between the way in which sensations make available the intelligible structure of things to man, from the way in which contingencies of perceptual experience establish expectations and permit a nonrational accommodation of animals to their environment. And there is, as we know today, a sound score to the idea that while reality is the "cause" of the human conceptual thinking which represents it, this causal role cannot be equated with a conditioning of the individual by his environment in a way which could in principle occur without the mediation of the family and the community. The Robinson Crusoe conception of the world as generating conceptual thinking directly in the individual is too simple a model. The perennial tradition long limited itself to accounting for the presence in the individual of the framework of conceptual thinking in terms of a unique kind of action of reality as intelligible on the individual mind. The accounts differed in interesting respects, but the main burden remained the same. It was not until the time of Hegel that the essential role of the group as a mediating factor in this causation was recognized, and while it is easy for us to see that the immanence and transcendence of conceptual frameworks with respect to the individual thinker is a social phenomenon, and to find a recognition of this fact implicit in the very form of our image of man-in-the-world, it was not until the 19th Century that this feature of the manifest image was, however inadequately, taken into account.

The Platonic theory of conceptual abilities as the result of the "illumination" of the mind by intelligible essences limited the role of the group, and in particular the family, to that of calling these abilities into play— a role which could, in principle, be performed by perceptual experience— and to that of teaching the means of giving verbal expression to these abilities. Yet the essentially social character of conceptual thinking comes clearly to mind when we recognize that there is no thinking apart from common standards of correctness and relevance, which relate what *I do* think to what *anyone ought to* think. The contrast between "I" and "anyone" is essential to rational thought.

It is current practice to compare the intersubjective standards without which there would be no thinking to the intersubjective standards without which there would be no such a thing as a game, and with the acquisition of a conceptual framework to learning to play a game. It is worth noting, however, that conceptual thinking is a unique game in two respects: (a) one cannot learn to play it by being told the rules; (b) whatever else conceptual thinking makes possible—and without it there is nothing characteristically human—it does so by virtue of containing a way of representing the world.

When I said that the individual as a conceptual thinker is essentially a member of a group, this does not mean, of course, that the individual cannot exist apart from the group, for example as sole survivor of an atomic catastrophe, any more than the fact that chess is a game played by two people means that one can not play chess with oneself. A group is not a group in the relevant sense unless it consists of a number of individuals, each of which thinks of himself as "I" in contrast to "others." Thus a group exists in the way in which members of the group represent themselves. Conceptual thinking is not by accident that which is *communicated* to others, any more than the decision to move a chess piece is by accident that which finds an expression in a move on a board between two people.

The manifest image must, therefore, be construed as containing a conception of itself as a group phenomenon, the group mediating between the individual and the intelligent order. But any attempt to *explain* this mediation within the framework of the manifest image was bound to fail, for the manifest image contains the resources for such an attempt only in the sense that it provides the foundation on which scientific theory can build an explanatory framework; and while conceptual structures of this framework are *built on* the manifest image, they are not definable within it. Thus, the Hegelian, like the Platonist of whom he is the heir, was limited to the attempt to understand the relation between intelligible order and individual minds in analogical terms.

It is in the *scientific* image of man-in-the-world that we begin to see the main outlines of the way in which man came to have an image of himself-in-the-world. For we begin to see this a matter of evolutionary development as a group phenomenon, a process which is illustrated at a simpler level by the evolutionary development which explains the correspondence between the dancing of a worker bee and the location, relative to the sun, of the flower from which he comes. This correspondence, like the relation between man's "original" image and the world, is incapable of explanation in terms of a direct conditioning impact of the environment on the individual as such.

I have called attention to the fact that the manifest image involves two types of causal impact of the world on the individual. It is, I have pointed out, this duality of causation, and the related irreducibility, within the manifest image, of conceptual thinking in all its forms to more elementary processes, which is the primary and essential dualism of the perennial philosophy. The dualistic conception of mind and body characteristic of, but by no means an invariable feature of, *philosophia perennis*, is in part an inference from this dualism of causation and of process. In part, however, as we shall see, it is a result of the impact of certain themes present in even the earliest stages of the developing scientific image.

My primary concern in this discussion is with the question, "In what sense, and to what extent, does the manifest image of man-in-the-world survive the attempt to unite this image in one field of intellectual vision with man as conceived in terms of the postulated object of scientific theory?" The bite to this question lies, we have seen, in the fact that man is that being which conceives of itself in terms of the manifest image. To the extent that the manifest does not survive in the synoptic view, to that extent man himself would not survive. Whether the adoption of the synoptic view would transform man in bondage into man free, as Spinoza believed, or man free into man in bondage, as many fear, is a question that does not properly arise until the claims of the scientific image have been examined.

IV. THE SCIENTIFIC IMAGE.

I devoted my attention in the previous sections to defining what I called the "manifest" image of man-in-the-world. I argued that this image is to be construed as a sophistication and refinement of the image in terms of which man first came to be aware of himself as man-in-the-world; in short, came to be man. I pointed out that in any sense in which this image, in so far as it pertains to man, is a "false" image. This falsity threatens man himself, inasmuch as he, is in an important sense, the being which has this image of himself. I argued that what has been called the perennial tradition in philosophy—*philosophia perennis*—can be construed as the attempt to understand the structure of this image, to know one's way around in it reflectively with no intellectual holds barred. I analyzed some of the main features of the image and showed how the categories in terms of which it approaches the world can be construed as progressive prunings of categories pertaining to the person and his relation to other persons and the group. I argued that the perennial tradition must be construed to include not only the Platonic tradition in its broadest sense, but philosophies of "common sense" and "ordinary usage." I argued what is common to all these philosophies is an acceptance of the manifest image as the *real*. They attempt to understand the achievements of theoretical science in terms of this framework, subordinating the categories of theoretical science to its categories. I suggested that the most fruitful way of approaching the problem of integrating theoretical science with the framework of sophisticated common sense into one comprehensive synoptic vision is to view it not as a piecemeal task—e.g., first a fitting together of the common sense conception of physical objects with that of theoretical physics, and then, as a separate venture, a fitting together of the common sense conception of man with that of theoretical psychology—but rather as a matter of articulating two whole ways of seeing the sum of things, two images of man-in-the-world and attempting to bring them together in a "stereoscopic" view.

My present purpose is to add to the account I have given of the manifest image, a comparable sketch of what I have called the scientific image, and to conclude this essay with some comments on the respective contributions of these two to the unified vision of man-in-the-world which is the aim of philosophy.

The scientific image of man-in-the-world is, of course, as much an idealization as the manifest image—even more so, as it is still in the process of coming to be. It will be remembered that the contrast I have in mind is not that between an *unscientific* conception of man-in-the-world and a *scientific* one, but between that conception which limits itself to what correlational techniques can tell us about perceptible and introspectible events and that which postulates imperceptible objects and events for the purpose of explaining correlations among perceptibles. It was granted, of course, that in point of historical fact many of the latter correlations were suggested by theories introduced to explain previously established correlations, so that there has been a dialectical interplay between correlational and postulational procedures. (Thus we might not have noticed that litmus paper turns red in acid, until this hypothesis had been suggested by a complex theory relating the absorption and emission of electromagnetic radiation by objects to their chemical composition; yet in principle this familiar correlation could have been, and, indeed, was discovered before any such theory was developed.) Our contrast, then, is between two ideal constructs: (a) the correlational and categorial refinement of the "original image," which refinement I am calling the manifest image; (b) the image derived from the fruits of postulational theory construction which I am calling the scientific image.

It may be objected at this point that there is no such thing as *the* image of man built from postulated entities and processes, but rather as many images as there are sciences which touch on aspects of human behavior. And, of course, in a sense this is true. There *are* as many scientific images of man as there are sciences which have something to say about man. Thus, there is man as he appears to the theoretical physicist—a swirl of physical particles, forces, and fields. There is man as he appears to the biochemist, to the physiologist, to the behaviorist, to the social scientist; and all of these images are to be contrasted with man as he appears to himself in sophisticated common sense, the manifest image which even today contains most of what he knows about himself at the properly human level. Thus the conception of *the* scientific or postulational image is an idealization in the sense that it is a conception of an integration of a manifold of images, each of which is the application to man of a framework of concepts which have a certain autonomy. For each scientific theory, from the standpoint of methodology, is a structure which is built at a different "place" and by different procedures within the intersubjectively accessible world of perceptible things. Thus *the* scientific image is a construct from a number of images, each of which is *supported by* the manifest world.

The fact that each theoretical image is a construction on a foundation provided by the manifest image, and *in this methodological sense* presupposes the manifest image, makes it tempting to suppose that the manifest image is prior in a *substantive* sense; that the categories of a theoretical science are logically dependent on categories pertaining to its methodological foundation in the manifest world of sophisticated common sense in such a way that there would be an absurdity in the notion of a world which illustrated its theoretical principles *without also illustrating the categories and principles of the manifest world.* Yet, when we turn our attention to *the* scientific image which emerges from the several images proper to the several sciences, we note that although the image is *methodologically* dependent on the world of sophisticated common sense, and in this sense does not stand on its own feet, yet it purports to be a *complete* image, i.e., to define a framework which could be the *whole truth* about that which belongs to the image. Thus although methodologically a development *within* the manifest image, the scientific image presents itself as a *rival* image. From its point of view the manifest image on which it rests is an "inadequate" but pragmatically useful likeness of a reality which first finds its adequate (in principle) likeness in the scientific image. I say, "in principle," because the scientific image is still in the process of coming into being—a point to which I shall return at the conclusion of this essay.

To all of which, of course, the manifest image or, more accurately, the perennial philosophy which endorses its claims, replies that the scientific image cannot replace the manifest without rejecting its own foundation.

But before attempting to throw some light on the conflicting claims of these two world perspectives, more must be said about the constitution of *the* scientific image from the several scientific images of which it is the supposed integration. There is relatively little difficulty about telescoping *some* of the "partial" images into one image. Thus, with due precaution, we can unify the biochemical and the physical images; for to do this requires only an appreciation of the sense in which the objects of biochemical discourse can be equated with complex patterns of the objects of theoretical physics. To make this equation, of course, is not to equate the sciences, for as sciences they have different procedures and connect their theoretical entities via different instruments to intersubjectively accessible features of the manifest world. But diversity of this kind is compatible with intrinsic "identity" of the theoretical entities themselves, that is, with saying that biochemical compounds are "identical" with patterns of subatomic particles. For to make this "identification" is simply to say that the *two* theoretical structures, each with its own connection to the perceptible world, could be replaced by *one* theoretical framework connected *at two levels of complexity* via different instruments and procedures to the world as perceived.

I distinguished above between the unification of the postulated *entities* of two sciences and the unification of the *sciences*. It is also necessary to distinguish between the unification of the theoretical *entities* of two sciences and the unification of the theoretical *principles* of the two sciences. For while to say that biochemical substances are complexes of physical particles is in an important sense to imply that the laws obeyed by biochemical substances are "special cases" of the laws obeyed by physical particles, there is a real danger that the sense in which this is so may be misunderstood. Obviously a specific pattern of physical particles cannot obey different laws in biochemistry from those it obeys in physics. It may, however, be that the behavior of very complex patterns of physical particles is related in no simple way to the behavior of less complex patterns. Thus it may well be that the only way in which the laws pertaining to those complex systems of particles which are biochemical compounds could be *discovered*, might be through the techniques and procedures of biochemistry, i.e., techniques and procedures appropriate to dealing with biochemical substances.

There is, consequently, an ambiguity in the statement: The laws of biochemistry are "special cases" of the laws of physics. It may mean: (a) Biochemistry needs no variables which cannot be defined in terms of the variables of atomic physics; (b) The laws relating to certain complex patterns of subatomic particles, the counterparts of biochemical compounds, are related in a simple way to laws pertaining to less complex patterns. The former, of course, is the only proposition to which one is committed by the identification of the theoretical objects of the two sciences in the sense described above.

Similar considerations apply, *mutatis mutandis*, to the physiological and biochemical images of man. To weld them into one image would be to show that physiological (particularly neurophysiological) entities can be equated with complex biochemical systems, and therefore, that in the weaker sense, at least, the theoretical principles which pertain to the former can be interpreted as "special cases" of principles pertaining to the latter.

More interesting problems arise when we consider the putative place in *the* scientific image of man as conceived in behavioristics. In the first place, the term "behavioristic psychology" has more than one meaning, and it is important for our purpose to see that in at least one sense of the term, its place is not in the scientific image (in the sense in which I am using the term) but rather in the continuing correlational sophistication of the manifest image. A psychology is behavioristic in the broad sense, if, although it permits itself the use of the full range of psychological concepts belonging to the manifest framework, it always confirms hypotheses about psychological events in terms of behavioral criteria. It has no anxieties about the concepts of sensation, image, feeling, conscious or unconscious thought, all of which belongs to the manifest framework; but requires that the occurrence of a feeling of pain, for example, be asserted only on behavioral grounds. Behaviorism, thus construed, is simply good sense. It is not necessary to redefine the language of mental events in terms of behavior criteria for it to be true that observable behavior provides evidence for mental events. And, of course, even in the common-sense world, even in the manifest image, perceptible behavior is the only *intersubjective* evidence for mental events.

Clearly "behaviorism" in this sense does not preclude us from paying attention to what people say about themselves. For *using autobiographical statements as evidence for* what a person is thinking and feeling is different from simply *agreeing with* these statements. It is part of the force of autobiographical statements in ordinary discourse—not unrelated to the way in which children learn to make them—that, other things being equal, if a person says, "I am in state Ψ," it is reasonable to believe that he is in state Ψ, the probability ranging from almost certainty in the case of, "I have a toothache," to considerably less than certainty in the case of, "I don't hate my brother." The discounting of verbal and nonverbal behavior as evidence is not limited to professional psychologists.

Thus, behaviorism in the first sense is simply a sophistication within the manifest framework which relies on pre-existent evidential connections between publicly observable verbal and nonverbal behavior on the one hand and mental states and processes on the other, and should, therefore, be considered as belonging to the manifest, rather than the scientific image as I have defined these terms. Behaviorism in a second sense not only restricts its evidential base to publicly observable behavior, but conceives of its task as that of finding correlations between constructs which it introduces and defines in terms of publicly accessible features of the organism and its environment. The interesting question in this connection is: "Is there reason to think that a framework of correlation between constructs of this type could constitute a scientific understanding of human behavior?" The answer to this question depends in part on how it is interpreted, and it is important to see why this is so.

Consider first the case of animal behavior. Obviously, we know that animals are complex physiological systems and, from the standpoint of a finer-grained approach, biochemical systems. Does this mean that a science of animal behavior has to be formulated in neurophysiological or biochemical terms? In one sense the answer is "obviously no." We bring to our study of animal behavior a background knowledge of some of the relevant large-scale variables for describing and predicting the behavior of animals in relation to their environments. The fact that these large-scale variables (the sort of thing that is grouped under such headings as "stimulus," "response," "goal behavior," "deprivation") are such that we can understand the behavior of the animal in terms of them is something which is not only suggested by our background knowledge, but is, indeed, *explained* by evolutionary theory. But the correlations themselves can be discovered by statistical procedures; and, of course, it *is* important to establish these correlations. Their discovery and confirmation by the procedures of behavioristics must, of course, be distinguished from their *explanation* in terms of the postulated entities and processes of neurophysiology. And, indeed, while physiological considerations may *suggest* correlations to be tested, the correlations themselves must be establishable independently of physiological consideration, if, and this is a "definitional" point, they are to belong to a distinguishable science of behavior.

Thus, if we mean by "earthworm behavioristics" the establishing of correlation in large-scale terms in respect to the earthworm and its environments, there may not be much to it, for a correlation does not belong to "earthworm behavioristics" unless it is a correlation in these large-scale terms. On the other hand, it is obvious that not every scientific truth about earthworms is a part of earthworm behavioristics, unless the latter term is so stretched as to be deprived of its distinctive sense. It follows that one cannot explain everything an earthworm does in terms of earthworm behavioristics *thus defined*. Earthworm behavioristics works within a background knowledge of "standard conditions"—conditions in which correlations in terms of earthworm behavior categories *are* sufficient to explain and predict what earthworms do in so far as it can be described in these categories. This background knowledge is obviously an essential part of the scientific understanding of what earthworms do, but it is not a part of earthworm behavioristics, but rather the application to earthworms of physics, chemistry, parasitology, medicine, and neurophysiology.

We must also take into consideration the fact that most of the interesting constructs of correlational behavioristics will be "iffy" properties of organisms, properties to the effect that *if* at that time a certain stimulus *were* to occur, a certain response *would be made*. Thus, to use an example from another field, we are able to correlate the fact that a current has been run through a helix in which a piece of iron has been placed, with the "iffy" property of being such that *if* an iron filing *were* placed near it, the latter *would be* attracted.

Now it may or may not be helpful, at a given stage of scientific development, to suppose that "iffy" properties of organisms are connected with states of a postulated system of entities operating according to certain postulated principles. It is helpful, if the postulated entities are sufficiently specific and can be connected to a sufficient diversity of large-scale behavioral variables to enable the prediction of new correlations. The methodological utility of postulational procedures for the behavioristics of lower organisms has, perhaps, been exaggerated, primarily because until recently little was known in neurophysiology which was suited to throw much light on correlations at the large-scale level of behavioristics. In human behavioristics, however, the situation has been somewhat different from the start, for an important feature of characteristically human behavior is that any two successive pieces of observable behavior *essentially* involve complex, very complex, "iffy" facts about what the person *would have said or done* at each intervening moment, *if he had been asked certain questions;* and it happens that our background knowledge makes reasonable the supposition that these "iffy" facts obtain *because an inner process is going on which is, in important respects, analogous to overt verbal behavior, and each stage of which would find a natural expression in overt speech*. This is a point to which I shall return later on.

Thus it *does* prove helpful in human behavioristics to postulate an inner sequence of events in order to interpret what could *in principle* be austerely formulated as correlations between behavioral states and properties, including the *very* important and, indeed, *essential* "iffy" ones. But, and this is an important point, the postulated episodes are not postulated on neurophysiological grounds—at least this was not true until very recently, but because of our background knowledge that something analogous to speech goes on while people are sitting "like bumps on a log."

For our present purposes it does not make too much difference whether we say that human behavioristics *as such* postulates inner speechlike processes, or that whatever their contribution to explanation or discovery, they fall by definition outside behavioristics proper. Whether or not human behavioristics, as a distinctive science, includes any statements about postulated entities, the correlations it establishes must find their counterparts in the postulational image, as was seen to be true in the case of the correlations established by earthworm behavioristics. Thus, the scientific explanation of human behavior must take account of those cases where the correlations characteristic of the organism in "normal" circumstances breaks down. And, indeed, no behaviorist would deny that the correlations he seeks and establishes are in some sense the counterparts of neurophysiological and, consequently, biochemical connections, nor that the latter are special cases within a spectrum of biochemical connections (pertaining to human organisms), many of which are reflected in observable phenomena which, *from the standpoint of behavioristics*, represent breakdowns in explanation. I shall, therefore, provisionally assume that although behavioristics and neurophysiology remain distinctive sciences, the correlational content of behavioristics points to a structure of postulated processes and principles which telescope together with those of neurophysiological theory, with all the consequences which this entails. On this assumption, if we trace out these consequences, the scientific image of man turns out to be that of a complex physical system.

V. The Clash of the Images.

How, then, are we to evaluate the conflicting claims of the manifest image and the scientific image thus provisionally interpreted to constitute *the true* and, in principle, *complete* account of man-in-the-world? What are the alternatives? It will be helpful to examine the impact of the earlier stages of postulational science on philosophy. Some reflections on the Cartesian attempt at a synthesis are in order, for they bring out the major stresses and strains involved in any attempt at a synoptic view. Obviously, at the time of Descartes theoretical science had not yet reached the neurophysiological level, save in the fashion of a clumsy promissory note. The initial challenge of the scientific image was directed at the manifest image of inanimate nature. It proposed to construe physical things, in a manner already adumbrated by Greek atomism, as systems of imperceptible particles, lacking the perceptible qualities of manifest nature. Three lines of thought seemed to be open: (1) Manifest objects are identical with systems of imperceptible particles in that simple sense in which a forest is identical with a number of trees. (2) Manifest objects are what really exist, systems of imperceptible particles being "abstract" or "symbolic" ways of representing them. (3) Manifest objects are "appearances" to human minds of a reality which is constituted by systems of imperceptible particles. Although (2) merits serious consideration, and has been defended by able philosophers, it is (1) and (3), particularly the latter, which I shall be primarily concerned to explore.

First, some brief remarks about (1). There is nothing immediately paradoxical about the view that an object can be both a perceptible object with perceptible qualities *and* a system of imperceptible objects, none of which has perceptible qualities. Cannot systems have properties which their parts do not have? Now the answer to this question is "yes," if it is taken in a sense of which a paradigm example would be the fact that a system of pieces of wood can be a ladder, although none of its parts is a ladder. Here one might say that for the system as a whole to be a ladder is for its parts to be of such and such shapes and sizes and to be related to one another in certain ways. Thus, there is no trouble about systems having properties which its parts do not have *if these properties are a matter of the parts having such and such qualities and being related in such and such ways.* But the case of a pink ice cube, it would seem clear, cannot be treated in this way. It does not seem plausible to say that for a system of particles to be a pink ice cube is for them to have such and such imperceptible qualities, and to be so related to one another as to make up an approximate cube. *Pink* does not seem to be made up of imperceptible qualities in the way in which being a ladder is made up of being cylindrical (the rungs), rectangular (the frame), wooden, etc. The manifest ice cube presents itself to us as something which is pink through and through, as a pink continuum, all the regions of which, however small, are pink. It presents itself to us as *ultimately homogeneous;* and an ice cube variegated in color is, though not homogeneous in its specific color, "ultimately homogeneous," in the sense to which I am calling attention, with respect to the generic trait of being colored.

Now reflection on this example suggests a principle which can be formulated approximately as follows:

> If an object is *in a strict sense* a system of objects, then every property of the object must consist in the fact that its constituents have such and such qualities and stand in such and such relations or, roughly,
>
> every property of a system of objects consists of properties of, and relations between, its constituents.

With something like this principle in mind, it was argued that if a physical object is *in a strict sense* a system of imperceptible particles, then it cannot as a whole have the perceptible qualities characteristic of physical objects in the manifest image. It was concluded that manifest physical objects are "appearances" *to human perceivers of* systems of imperceptible particles, which is alternative (3) above.

This alternative, (3), however, is open to an objection which is ordinarily directed not against the alternative itself, but against an imperceptive formulation of it as the thesis that the perceptible things around us "really have no color." Against *this* formulation the objection has the merit of calling attention to the fact that in the manifest framework it is as absurd to say that a visible object has no color, as it is to say of a triangle that it has no shape. However, against the above formulation of alternative (3), namely, that *the very objects themselves* are appearances to perceivers of systems of imperceptible particles, the objection turns out on examination to have no weight. The objection, for which the British "common sense" philosopher G. E. Moore is directly or indirectly responsible, runs:

> Chairs, tables, etc., as we ordinarily think them to be, can't be 'appearances' of systems of particles lacking perceptible qualities, because we *know* that there are chairs, tables, etc., and it is a framework feature of chairs, tables, etc., that they have perceptible qualities.

It simply *disappears* once it is recognized that, properly understood, the claim that physical objects do not really have perceptible qualities is not analogous to the claim that something generally believed to be true about a certain kind of thing is actually false. It is not the denial of a belief *within a framework*, but a challenge to the framework. It is the claim that although the framework of perceptible objects, the manifest framework of everyday life, is adequate for the everyday purposes of life, it is ultimately inadequate and should not be accepted as an account of what there is *all things considered*. Once we see this, we see that the argument from "knowledge" cuts no ice, for the reasoning

> We know that there are chairs, pink ice cubes, etc. (physical objects); chairs, pink ice cubes are colored; are perceptible objects with perceptible qualities. Therefore, perceptible physical objects with perceptible qualities exist.

operates *within* the framework of the manifest image and cannot *support* it. It fails to provide a point of view outside the manifest image from which the latter can be evaluated.

A more sophisticated argument would be to the effect that we successfully find our way around in life by using the conceptual framework of colored physical objects in space and time, therefore, this framework represents things as they really are. This argument has force, but is vulnerable to the reply that the success of living, thinking and acting in terms of the manifest framework can be accounted for by the framework which proposes to replace it; by showing that there are sufficient structural similarities between manifest objects and their scientific counterparts to account for this success.*

One is reminded of a standard move designed to defend the reality of the manifest image against *logically* rather than *scientifically* motivated considerations. Thus it has been objected that the framework of physical objects in space and time is incoherent, involving antinomies or contradictions, and that therefore this framework is unreal. The counter to this objection has often been, *not* a painstaking refutation of the arguments claiming to show that the framework is incoherent, but rather something along the following lines:

> *We know* that this collision occurred at a different place and time than that collision.
>
> Therefore, the statement that the first collision occurred at a different place and time from the other collision *is true.*
>
> Therefore, the statement that the two collisions occurred at different times and places *is consistent.*
>
> Therefore, statements about events happening at various times and places are, as such, consistent.

This argument, like the one we have already considered, does not prove what is sets out to prove, because it operates within the framework to be evaluated and does not provide an external point of view from which to defend it. It makes the tacit assumption that if a framework is inconsistent, its incoherence must be such as to lead to retail and immediate inconsistencies, as though it would force people using it to contradict themselves on every occasion. This is surely false. The framework of space and time could be internally inconsistent and yet be a successful conceptual

---

*It might seem that the manifest framework accounts for the success of the scientific framework, so that the situation is symmetrical. But I believe that a more penetrative account of the order of theories than I have been able to sketch in this essay would show that this claim is illusory. I have discussed this topic at some length in "The Language of Theories" in *Current Issues in the Philosophy of Science*, edited by Herbert Feigl and Grover Maxwell (New York, 1961).

tool at the retail level. We have examples of this in mathematical theory, where inconsistencies can be present which do not reveal themselves in routine usage.

I am not, however, concerned to argue that the manifest image is unreal because ultimately incoherent in a narrowly conceived logical sense. Philosophers who have taken this line have either (a) left it at that (Hume; scepticism), or (b) attempted to locate the source of the inconsistency in features of the framework, and interpreted reality as an inadequately known structure *analogous* to the manifest image, but lacking just those features which are responsible for the inconsistency. In contrast to this, the critique of the manifest image in which we are engaged is based on logical considerations in a broader and more constructive sense, one which compares it unfavorably with a *more* intelligible account of what there is.

It is familiar fact that those features of the manifest world which play no role in mechanical explanation were relegated by Descartes and other interpreters of the new physics to the mind of the perceiver. Color, for example, was said to exist only in sensation; its *esse* to be *percipi*. It was argued, in effect, that what scientifically motivated reflection recognizes to be states of the perceiver are conceptualized in ordinary experience as traits of independent physical things, indeed that these supposed independent colored things are actually conceptual constructions which ape the mechanical systems of the real world.

The same considerations which led philosophers to deny the reality of perceptible things led them to a dualistic theory of man. For if the human body is a system of particles, the body cannot be the subject of thinking and feeling, *unless thinking and feeling are capable of interpretation as complex interactions of physical particles;* unless, that is to say, the manifest framework of man as *one* being, a *person,* capable of doing radically different kinds of things can be replaced without loss of descriptive and explanatory power by a postulational image in which he is a complex of physical particles, and all his activities a matter of the particles changing in state and relationship.

Dualism, of course, denied that either sensation or feeling or conceptual thinking could in this sense be construed as complex interactions of physical particles, or man as a complex physical system. Dualists were prepared to say that a *chair* is really a system of imperceptible particles which "appears" in the manifest framework as a "color solid" (cf. our example of the ice cube), but they were not prepared to say that man himself was a complex physical system which "appears" to itself to be the sort of thing man is in the manifest image.

Let us consider in more detail the Cartesian attempt to integrate the manifest and the scientific images. Here the interesting thing to note is that Descartes took for granted (in a promissory-note-ish kind of way) that the scientific image would include items which would be the counterparts of the sensations, images, and feelings of the manifest framework. These counterparts would be complex states of the brain which, obeying purely physical laws, would resemble and differ from one another in a way which corresponded to the resemblances and differences between the conscious states with which they were correlated. Yet, as is well-known, he denied that there were brain states which were, in the same sense, the cerebral counterparts of conceptual thinking.

Now if we were to ask Descartes, "Why can't we say that sensations 'really are' complex cerebral processes as, according to you, we *can* say that physical objects 'really are' complex systems of imperceptible particles?" he would have a number of things to reply, some of which were a consequence of his conviction that sensation, images, and feelings belong to the same family as believing, choosing, wondering, in short are low-grade examples of conceptual thinking and share its supposed irreducibility to cerebral states. But when the chips are down there would remain the following argument:

> We have pulled perceptible qualities out of the physical environment and put them into sensations. If we now say that all there really is to sensation is a complex interaction of cerebral particles, then we have taken them out of our world picture altogether. We will have made it unintelligible how things could even *appear* to be colored.

As for conceptual thinking, Descartes not only refused to identify it with neurophysiological process, he did not see this as a live option, because it seemed obvious to him that no complex neurophysiological process could be sufficiently analogous to conceptual thinking to be a serious candidate for being what conceptual thinking "really is." It is not as though Descartes granted that there might well be neurophysiological processes which are strikingly analogous to conceptual thinking, but which it would be philosophically incorrect to *identify* with conceptual thinking (as he had identified physical objects of the manifest world with systems of imperceptible particles). He did not take seriously the idea that there *are* such neurophysiological processes.

67

Even if he had, however, it is clear that he would have rejected this identification on the ground that we had a "clear and distinct," well-defined idea of what conceptual thinking is before we even suspected that the brain had anything to do with thinking. Roughly: we know what thinking is without conceiving of it as a complex neurophysiological process, therefore, it can't *be* a complex physiological process.

Now, of course, the same is true of physical objects. We knew what a physical object was long before we knew that there were imperceptible physical particles. By parity of reasoning we should conclude that a physical object can not *be* a complex of imperceptible particles. Thus, if Descartes had had reason to think that neurophysiological processes strikingly analogous to conceptual thinking exist, it would seem that he should *either* have changed his tune with respect to physical objects *or* said that conceptual thinking *really* is neurophysiological process.

Now in the light of recent developments in neurophysiology, philosophers have come to see that there is no reason to suppose there cannot be neurophysiological processes which stand to conceptual thinking as sensory states of the brain stand to conscious sensations. And, indeed, there have not been wanting philosophers (of whom Hobbes was, perhaps, the first) who have argued that the analogy should be viewed philosophically as an *identity*, i.e., that a world picture which includes *both* thoughts *and* the neurophysiological counterparts of thoughts would contain a redundancy; just as a world picture which included *both* the physical objects of the manifest image *and* complex patterns of physical particles would contain a redundancy. But to this proposal the obvious objection occurs, that just as the claim that "physical objects are complexes of imperceptible particles" left us with the problem of accounting for the status of the perceptible qualities of manifest objects, so the claim that "thoughts, etc., are complex neurophysiological processes" leaves us with the problems of accounting for the status of the *introspectable qualities* of thoughts. And it would seem obvious that there is a vicious regress in the claim that these qualities exist in introspective awareness of the thoughts which seem to have them, but not in the thoughts themselves. For, the argument would run, surely introspection is itself a form of thinking. Thus one thought (Peter) would be robbed of its quality only to pay it to another (Paul).

We can, therefore, understand the temptation to say that even if there are cerebral processes which are strikingly analogous to conceptual thinking, they are processes which *run parallel* to conceptual thinking (and cannot be identified with it) as the sensory states of the brain *run parallel* to conscious sensation. And we can, therefore, understand the temptation to say that all these puzzles arise from taking seriously the claim of *any* part of the scientific image to be *what really is*, and to retreat into the position that reality is the world of the manifest image, and that all the postulated entities of the scientific image are "symbolic tools" which function (something like the distance-measuring devices which are rolled around on maps) to help us find our way around in the world, but do not themselves describe actual objects and processes. On this view, the theoretical counterparts of *all* features of the manifest image would be *equally* unreal, and that philosophical conception of man-in-the-world would be correct which endorsed the manifest image and located the scientific image within it as a conceptual tool used by manifest man in his capacity as a scientist.

VI. The Primacy of the Scientific Image: A Prolegomenon.

Is this the truth of the matter? Is the manifest image, subject, of course, to continual empirical and categorial refinement, the measure of what there really is? I do not think so. I have already indicated that of the three alternatives we are considering with respect to the comparative claims of the manifest and scientific images, the first, which, like a child, says "both," is ruled out by a principle which I am not defending in this essay, although it does stand in need of defense. The second alternative is the one I have just reformulated and rejected. I propose, therefore, to re-examine the case against the third alternative, the primacy of the scientific image. My strategy will be to argue that the difficulty, raised above, which seems to stand in the way of the identification of thought with cerebral processes, arises from the mistake of supposing that in self-awareness conceptual thinking presents itself to us in a qualitative guise. Sensations and images *do*, we shall see, present themselves to us in a qualitative character, a fact which accounts for the fact that they are stumbling blocks in the attempt to accept the scientific image as real. *But* one scarcely needs to point out these days that however intimately conceptual thinking is related to sensations and images, it cannot be equated with them, nor with complexes consisting of them.

It is no accident that when a novelist wishes to represent what is going on in the mind of a person, he does so by "quoting" the person's thoughts as he might quote what a person says. For thoughts not only are the sort of thing that finds overt expression in language, we conceive of them as analogous to overt discourse. Thus, *thoughts* in the manifest image are conceived not in terms of their "quality," but rather as inner "goings-on" which are analogous to speech, and find their overt expression in speech—though they can go on, of course, in the absence of this overt expression. It is no accident that one learns to think in the very process of learning to speak.

From this point of view one can appreciate the danger of misunderstanding which is contained in the term "introspection." For while there is, indeed, an analogy between the direct knowledge we have of our own thoughts and the perceptual knowledge we have of what is going on in the world around us, the analogy holds only inasmuch as both self-awareness and perceptual observation are basic forms of noninferential knowledge. They differ, however, in that whereas in perceptual observation we know objects as being of a certain quality, in the direct knowledge we have of what we are thinking (e.g. I am thinking that it is cold outside) what we know noninferentially is that *something analogous to and properly expressed by the sentence, "It is cold outside," is going on in me.*

The point is an important one, for if the concept of a thought is the concept of an inner state analogous to speech, this leaves open the possibility that the inner state conceived in terms of this analogy is *in its qualitative character* a neurophysiological process. To draw a parallel: if I begin by thinking of the cause of a disease as a substance (to be called "germs") which is analogous to a colony of rabbits, in that it is able to reproduce itself in geometrical proportion, but, unlike rabbits, imperceptible and, when present in sufficient number in the human body, able to cause the symptoms of disease, and to cause epidemics by spreading from person to person, there is no logical barrier to a subsequent identification of "germs" thus conceived with the bacilli which microscopic investigation subsequently discovers.

But to point to the analogy between conceptual thinking and overt speech is only part of the story, for of equally decisive importance is the analogy between speech and what sophisticated computers can do, and, finally, between computer circuits and conceivable patterns of neurophysiological organization. All of this is more or less speculative, less so now than even a few years ago. What interests the philosopher is the matter of principle; and here the first stage is decisive—the recognition that the concept of a thought is a concept by analogy. Over and above this, all we need is to recognize the force of Spinoza's statement: "No one has thus far determined what the body can do, or no one has yet been taught by experience what the body can do merely by the laws of nature, insofar as nature is considered merely as corporeal and extended." (*Ethics*, Third Part, Prop. II (note)).

Another analogy which may be even more helpful is the following: Suppose we are watching the telegraphic report of a chess game in a foreign country.

White	Black
White	*Black*
P-K3	P-Q3

And suppose that we are sophisticated enough to know that chess pieces can be made of all shapes and sizes, that chess boards can be horizontal or vertical, indeed, distorted in all kinds of ways provided that they preserve certain topological features of the familiar board. Then it is clear that while we will think of the players in the foreign country as moving kings, pawns, etc., castling and checkmating, our concepts of the pieces they are moving and the moving of them will be simply the concept of items and changes which play a role analogous to the pieces and moves which take place when *we* play chess. We know that the items must have some intrinsic quality (shape, size, etc.), but we think of these qualities as "those which make possible a sequence of changes which are structurally similar to the changes which take place on our own chess boards."

Thus our concept of "what thoughts are" might, like our concept of what a castling is in chess, be abstract in the sense that it does not concern itself with the *intrinsic* character of thoughts, *save as items which can occur in patterns of relationships which are analogous to the way in which sentences are related to one another and to the contexts in which they are used.*

Now, if thoughts are items which are conceived in terms of the roles they play, then there is no barrier *in principle* to the identification of conceptual thinking with neurophysiological process. There would be no "qualitative" remainder to be accounted for. The identification, curiously enough, would be even more straightforward than the identification of the physical things in the manifest image with complex systems of physical particles. And in this key, if not decisive, respect, the respect in which they are concerned with conceptual thinking (which is the distinctive trait of man), *the manifest and scientific images could merge without clash in the synoptic view.*

How does the situation stand in respect to sensation and feeling? Any attempt at identification of these items with neurophysiological process runs into a difficulty to which reference has already been made, and which we are now in a position to make more precise. This difficulty accounts for the fact that, with few exceptions, philosophers who have been prepared to identify conceptual thinking with neurophysiological process have *not* been prepared to make a similar identification in the case of sensation.

Before restating the problem let us note that curiously enough there is more similarity between the two cases than is commonly recognized. For it turns out on reflection that just as conceptual thinking is construed in the manifest image by analogy with overt speech, so sensation is construed by analogy with its external cause, sensations being the states of persons which correspond, in their similarities and differences, to the similarities and differences of the objects which, in standard conditions, bring them about. Let me assume that this is so. But if it *is* so, why not suppose that the inner-states which *as sensations* are conceived by analogy with their standard causes, are *in propria persona*, complex neurophysiological episodes in the cerebral cortex? This would parallel the conclusion we were prepared to draw in the case of conceptual thinking.

Why do we feel that there would be something extremely odd, even absurd, about such a supposition? The key to the answer lies in noticing an important difference between identifying thoughts with neurophysiological states and identifying sensations with neurophysiological states. Whereas both thoughts and sensations are conceived by analogy with publicly observable items, in the former case the analogy concerns the *role* and hence leaves open the possibility that thoughts are radically different *in their intrinsic character* from the verbal behavior by analogy with which they are conceived. But in the case of sensations, the analogy concerns the *quality* itself. Thus a "blue and triangular sensation" is conceived by analogy with the blue and triangular (facing) surface of a physical object which, when looked at in daylight, is its cause. The crucial issue then is this: Can we define, in the framework of neurophysiology, states which are sufficiently analogous in their *intrinsic* character to sensations to make identification plausible?

The answer seems clearly to be "no." This is not to say that neurophysiological states cannot be defined (in principle) which have a high degree of analogy to the sensations of the manifest image. That this can be done is an elementary fact in psychophysics. The trouble is, rather, that the feature which we referred to as "ultimate homogeneity," and which characterizes the perceptible qualities of things, e.g., their color, seems to be essentially lacking in the domain of the definable states of nerves and their interactions. Putting it crudely, color expanses in the manifest world consist of regions which are themselves color expanses, and consist in their turn of regions which are color expanses; and so on;

whereas the state of a group of neurons, though it has regions which are also states of groups of neurons, has ultimate regions which are *not* states of groups of neurons but rather states of single neurons. And the same is true if we move to the finer-grained level of biochemical process.

Nor do we wish to say that the ultimate homogeneity of the sensation of a red rectangle is a matter of each physical particle in the appropriate region of the cortex *having* a color; for whatever other difficulties such a view would involve, it does not make sense to say of the particles of physical theory that they are colored. And the principle of reducibility, which we have accepted without argument, makes impossible the view that groups of particles can have properties which are not "reducible to" the properties and relations of the members of the group.

It is worth noting that we have here a recurrence of the essential features of Eddington's "two tables" problem—the two tables being, in our terminology, the table of the manifest image and the table of the scientific image. There the problem was to "fit together" the manifest table with the scientific table. Here the problem is to fit together the manifest sensation with its neurophysiological counterpart. And, interestingly enough, the problem in both cases is essentially the same: *how to reconcile the ultimate homogeneity of the manifest image with the ultimate nonhomogeneity of the system of scientific objects.*

Now we are rejecting the view that the scientific image is a mere "symbolic tool" for finding our way around in the manifest image; and we are accepting the view that the scientific account of the world is (in principle) the adequate image. Having, therefore, given the perceptible qualities of manifest objects their real locus in sensation, we were confronted with the problem of choosing between dualism or identity with respect to the relation of conscious sensations to their analogues in the visual cortex, and the above argument seems to point clearly in the dualistic direction. The "ultimate homogeneity" of perceptible qualities, which, among other things, prevented *identifying* the perceptible qualities of physical objects with complex properties of systems of physical particles, stands equally in the way of *identifying*, rather than *correlating*, conscious sensations with the complex neural processes with which they are obviously connected.

But such dualism is an unsatisfactory solution, because, *ex hypothesi*, sensations are essential to the explanation of how we come to construct the "appearance" which is the manifest world. They are essential to the explanation of how there even *seem* to be colored objects. But the scientific image presents itself as a closed system of explanation, and *if the scientific image is interpreted as we have interpreted it up to this point the explanation will be in terms of the constructs of neurophysiology,* which, according to the argument, *do not involve the ultimate homogeneity, the appearance of which in the manifest image is to be explained.*

We are confronted, therefore, by an antimony, *either,* (a) the neurophysiological image is *incomplete,* i.e., and must be supplemented by new objects ("sense fields") which do have ultimate homogeneity, and which somehow make their presence felt in the activity of the visual cortex as a system of physical particles; *or,* (b) the neurophysiological image is complete and the ultimate homogeneity of the sense qualities (and, hence, the sense qualities, themselves) is *mere appearance* in the very radical sense of not existing in the spatiotemporal world at all.

Is the situation irremediable? Does the assumption of the reality of the scientific image lead us to a dualism of particles and sense fields? of matter and "consciousness?" If so, then, in view of the obviously intimate relation between sensation and conceptual thinking (for example, in perception), we must surely regress and take back the identification of conceptual thinking with neurophysiological process which seemed so plausible a moment ago. We could then argue that although in the absence of other considerations it would be plausible to equate conceptual thinking with neurophysiological process, when the chips are *all* down, we must rather say that although conceptual thinking and neurophysiological process are each analogous to verbal behavior as a public social phenomenon (the one by virtue of the very way in which the very notion of "thinking" is formed; the other as a scientifically ascertained matter of fact), they are also *merely* analogous to one another and cannot be identified. If so, the manifest and the scientific conception of *both* sensations *and* conceptual thinking would fit into the synoptic view as parallel processes, a dualism which could only be avoided by interpreting the scientific image *as a whole* as a "symbolic device" for coping with the world as it presents itself to us in the manifest image.

Is there any alternative? As long as the ultimate constitutents of the scientific image are particles forming ever more complex systems of particles, we are inevitably confronted by the above choice. But the scientific image is not yet complete; we have not yet penetrated all the secrets of nature. And if it should turn out that particles instead of being the primitive entities of the scientific image could be treated as singularities in a space-time continuum which could be conceptually "cut up" without significant loss—*in inorganic contexts, at least*—into interacting particles, then we would not be confronted at the level of neurophysiology with the problem of understanding the relation of *sensory consciousness* (with its ultimate homogeneity) to *systems of particles*. Rather, we would have the alternative of saying that although for many purposes the central nervous system can be construed without loss as a complex system of physical particles, *when it comes to an adequate understanding of the relation of sensory consciousness to neurophysiological process*, we must penetrate to the nonparticulate foundation of the particulate image, and recognize that in this nonparticulate image the qualities of sense are a dimension of natural process which occurs only in connection with those complex physical processes which, when "cut up" into particles in terms of those features which are the least common denominators of physical process—present in inorganic as well as organic processes alike—become the complex system of particles which, in the current scientific image, *is* the central nervous system.

VII. Putting Man into the Scientific Image.

Even if the constructive suggestion of the preceding section were capable of being elaborated into an adequate account of the way in which the scientific image could recreate in its own terms the sensations, images, and feelings of the manifest image, the thesis of the primacy of the scientific image would scarcely be off the ground. There would remain the task of showing that categories pertaining to man as a *person* who finds himself confronted by standards (ethical, logical, etc.) which often conflict with his desires and impulses, and to which he may or may not conform, can be reconciled with the idea that man is what science says he is.

At first sight there would seem to be only one way of recapturing the specifically human within the framework of the scientific image. The categories of the person might be reconstructed without loss in terms of the fundamental concepts of the scientific image in a way analogous to that in which the concepts of biochemistry are (in principle) reconstructed in terms of subatomic physics. To this suggestion there is, in the first place, the familiar objection that persons as responsible agents who make genuine choices between genuine alternatives, and who could on many occasions have done what in point of fact they did not do, simply *can not* be construed as physical systems (even broadly interpreted to include sensations and feelings) which evolve in accordance with laws of nature (statistical or nonstatistical). Those who make the above move can be expected to reply (drawing on distinctions developed in section II) that the concepts in terms of which we think of a person's "character," or the fact that "he could have done otherwise," or that "his actions are predictable" would appear in the reconstruction as extraordinarily complex defined concepts not to be confused with the concepts in terms of which we think of the "nature" of NaCl, or the fact that "system X could have failed to be in state S given the same initial conditions," or that "it is predictable that system X will assume state S given these initial conditions." And I think that a reply along these lines could be elaborated which would answer *this* objection to the proposed reconstruction of categories pertaining to persons.

But even if the proposed reconstruction could meet what might be called the "free will" objection, it fails decisively on another count. For it can, I believe, be conclusively shown that such a reconstruction is *in principle* impossible, the impossibility in question being a strictly logical one. (I shall not argue the point explicitly, but the following remarks contain the essential clues). If so, that would seem to be the end of the matter. Must we not return to a choice between (a) a dualism in which men as scientific objects are contrasted with the "minds" which are the source and principle of their existence as persons; (b) abandoning the reality of persons as well as manifest physical objects in favor of the exclusive reality of scientific objects; (c) returning once and for all to the thesis of the merely "calculational" or "auxiliary" status of theoretical frameworks and to the affirmation of the primacy of the manifest image?

Assuming, in accordance with the drift of the argument of this essay, that none of these alternatives is satisfactory, is there a way out? I believe there is, and that while a proper exposition and defense would require at least the space of this whole volume, the gist can be stated in short compass. To say that a certain person desired to do A, thought it his duty to do B but was forced to do C is not to *describe* him as one might describe a scientific specimen. One does, indeed, describe him, but one does something more. And it is this something more which is the irreducible core of the framework of persons.

In what does this something more consist? First, a relatively superficial point which will guide the way. To think of a featherless biped as a person is to think of it as a being with which one is bound up in a network of rights and duties. From this point of view, the irreducibility of the personal is the irreducibility of the "ought" to the "is." But even more basic than this (though ultimately, as we shall see, the two points coincide) is the fact that to think of a featherless biped as a person is to construe its behavior in terms of actual or potential membership in an embracing group each member of which thinks itself as a member of the group. Let us call such a group a "community." Once the primitive tribe, it is currently (almost) the "brotherhood" of man, and is potentially the "republic" of rational beings (cf. Kant's "Kingdom of Ends"). An individual may belong to many communities, some of which overlap, some of which are arranged like Chinese boxes. The most embracing community to which he belongs consists of those with whom he can enter into meaningful discourse. The scope of the embracing community is the scope of "we" in its most embracing nonmetaphorical use. "We," in this fundamental sense (in which it is equivalent to the French "*on*" or English "one") is no less basic than the other "persons" in which verbs are conjugated. Thus, to recognize a featherless biped or dolphin or Martian as a person is to think of oneself and it as belonging to a community.

Now, the fundamental principles of a community, which define what is "correct" or "incorrect," "right" or "wrong," "done" or "not done" are the most general common *intentions* of that community with respect to the behavior of members of the group. It follows that to recognize a featherless biped or dolphin or Martian as a person requires that one think thoughts of the form "We (one) shall do (or abstain from doing) actions of kind A in circumstances of kind C." To think thoughts of this kind is not to *classify* or *explain*, but to *rehearse an intention.*

(Community intentions ("One shall . . .") are not just private intentions ("I shall . . .") which everybody has. (This is another way of putting the above-mentioned irreducibility of "we"). There is, however, a logical connection between community and private intentions. For one does not really share a community intention unless, however often one may rehearse it, it is not reflected, where relevant, in the corresponding private intention.)

Thus, the conceptual framework of persons is the framework in which we think of one another as sharing the community intentions which provide the ambience of principles and standards (above all, those which make meaningful discourse and rationality itself possible), within which we live our individual lives. A person can almost be defined as a being that has intentions. Thus, the conceptual framework of persons is not something that needs to be *reconciled with* the scientific image, but rather something to be *joined to* it. Thus, to complete the scientific image we need to enrich it *not* with more ways of saying what is the case, but with the language of community and individual intentions, so that by construing the actions we intend to do and the circumstances in which we intend to do them in scientific terms we *directly* relate the world as conceived by scientific theory to our purposes, and make it *our* world and no longer an alien appendage to the world in which we do our living. We can, of course, as matters now stand, realize this direct incorporation of the scientific image into our way of life only in imagination. But to do so is, if only in imagination, to transcend the dualism of the manifest and scientific images of man-in-the-world.

Chapter **3** | *The Frontiers of Psychology:*
Psychoanalysis and Parapsychology

Michael Scriven
Professor, Logic and History of Science
Indiana University

Sometimes we suspect the existence of senses other than those we recognize in ourselves, among animal and plant form on this planet—not merely extended ranges of hearing or of vision or smell, but entirely different responses. The bees and ants respond, as we do not, to polarized light; the birds in migration—to what? And there are those among us who dream of vestigial or embryonic senses hovering about the human psyche.

HARLOW SHAPLEY, *Of Stars and Men*

The Frontiers of Psychology: Psychoanalysis and Parapsychology

It seems to me (as it does to most of the participants in this program) of the greatest importance that a philosopher of science should be able to make some substantial contribution to the work of practising scientists, either empiricists or theoreticians.

Here, I shall be discussing in some detail, at a level which is very close to that at which subjects are discussed in the relevant technical journals, two topics which are very close to what I have called the "Frontiers of Psychology." In Part II of this Essay I shall be taking up topics which are of a much more philosophical nature; and I want to begin here by giving you some idea of how I intend to relate these analyses.

I. KINDS OF FRONTIERS.

There are, it seems to me, three kinds of scientific frontiers; and it will be helpful for us to consider a geographical analogy. At the moment there are three different kinds of geographical frontiers. Let us take as examples the following three places: first, Antarctica; second, the Moon, and third, the Andromeda Nebula. If we were speaking in the middle of the past century instead of the middle of this century, the first item could be the West, the second Antarctica, and the third the Moon. Now the distinction that I have in mind is this. When we refer to the coastal areas of Antarctica today or to the West as it was in the 1840's as "frontiers," we think of them as the boundary of current civilization, everything this side of such a point being more or less within the orbit of regular commerce, and everything beyond it being beyond that orbit, while the place itself is—with hardship—inhabited.

The moon, on the other hand, represents for us, at this stage, the boundary of current technical possibility. We have no permanent installations on the Moon, though there are a number of small metal tags up there with the Hammer and Sickle or Red Star on them, but it is nevertheless clear that, given the sociological and financial incentives, we can place man on the Moon; and it is only a matter of time before we do that, and so expand to new frontiers. Nevertheless, in a very important sense, it is a problem of a kind quite different from that of placing men in Antarctica, where we can go and live uncomfortably tomorrow by simply chartering a plane or boat today.

The third of my examples, the Andromeda Nebula, raises quite different questions and only in a very different sense can it be called a "frontier." It is a frontier in the sense that I shall be talking about in Part II, a last frontier, perhaps, because in connection with the settlement of the planets of other stars in other galaxies there arise extremely serious questions of technical possibility, so serious, indeed, that there are plenty of people today who are willing to argue that it is not physically possible we shall ever succeed in doing this. And they say this not because it is obviously a long way, but for much more interesting reasons, such as the upper limit on the possible velocity of travel, and the length of time it would take to get there, traveling at that rate, relative to our own earth time, of course; and the problems that would arise in passing through clouds of cosmic dust traveling at *that* kind of velocity, and so on. These difficulties are not as simple as those which face us in putting men on the Moon. It is by no means certain that money will solve these difficulties at any stage.

Now in terms of the field of scientific investigation, and in particular in the field of psychology, it seems to me that a reasonable analogy can be drawn in the following way: a frontier in psychology, in the sense in which Antarctica is today a frontier for us geographically, is the area studied by any current research problem in recognized fields of psychology. For example: the study of the effects of beliefs on perception; of drugs on performance and on feelings, and so on. Now we need something that stands in the same relationship to intellectual exploration as the Moon does to geographical exploration, that is, at the point where the limits of our current technical capacity are strained but there seems to be in principle no impossibility about the investigation. Here we have a series of topics in psychology and related fields, such as psychoanalysis (about which I shall talk first); the nature of hypnosis (where there arise questions about, for example, the possibility of the self-induction of hypnotic states, which, of course, is of great practical importance in introducing anaesthesia after a serious wound); infant learning of complex languages (the work which has been going on at Yale, attempting to get the normal three-year-old to speak, write, and explain himself in English, and do arithmetic); psychosomatic effects of various kinds (that is, the area where we are studying not the therapeutic effect of drugs operating through physiological mechanisms, but the effects of, for example, the laying on of hands—or the "laying on of drugs," where, in fact, we think there is no physiological mechanism at work). The placebo studies, for example, supply an excellent example of the beginning of this. These are all areas which do not fit into the regular run of current psychological investigations, but they are not so far beyond us that we would want to deny they are appropriate subjects for scientific study today.

I have so far said nothing about parapsychology. Let us first look at the third category of frontier, the ultimate boundaries for psychology, the "last frontiers" beyond which there will, in fact, so it is alleged, never be scientific progress. Here we are concerned with such a barrier to the possibility of total prediction of human behavior as is supposedly provided by the existence of free will in man, and such barriers to the total description of human behavior as are provided by the existence in men's conceptual schemes of *values*, which are in certain respects impractical subjects for scientific investigation and description. Other supposedly insurmountable difficulties are provided by man's possession of a soul, his life after death, and the uniqueness of the individual. All these are hoary puzzles, long discussed amongst psychologists and philosophers; all of them recognizable as candidates for a "last frontier," candidates for an ultimate limit to psychology.

Parapsychology has been thought by some to lie in this third category, to be a discussion of something which it is essentially impossible or improper for science to handle. It has been thought by others to lie within the realm of proper, though very little practiced investigation, that is, the second category. Those who think there is nothing to the phenomena will think it entirely proper that there is relatively little active research in the area. Others will think it a sign of the excessive conservatism of a newly-independent and insecure discipline. I shall leave the decision as to the category until after I have said something about the subject. One category or another, however, it qualifies as a frontier area.

In Part II of this essay I shall discuss some of the philosophically more puzzling and interesting claims that are associated with the phrase, "the last frontiers," by an analogy. I shall not be taking the position that they are "last frontiers" in the way in which they have sometimes been held, but I shall not, on the other hand, be taking the position that they can be dismissed as insignificant in an assessment of the potentialities of psychology.

Returning to the specific topics of Part I, I shall begin by attempting to relate the fields of parapsychology and psychoanalysis. First of all, we must ask, "What are the claims of these fields?" and in particular, "What claim can we take as representative of these fields in order to discuss the question of whether, in fact, these subjects have or could be scientifically investigated?" In the case of parapsychology I shall take the basic claim to be the assertion that some people can acquire information about states of affairs which they are not able to perceive by means of the normal senses, nor able to infer from any data that is available to their senses. The claim then is the claim that *some* people have the power that is sometimes popularly referred to as "extrasensory perception." Notice that I am not considering the claim that everybody can, nor the claim that there are some people who can *always* do this. There are in fact *many* claims I am not considering which have on occasion been made by parapsychologists. It is unnecessary to stick out one's neck any farther than with the more modest claim. I wish to confine our attention precisely to this claim.

Now the nature of this claim deserves a moment of prior consideration. Suppose that it is disputed; what kind of objection is likely to be raised? There are two importantly distinct objections.

It might be argued in the first place that the conditions referred to in the definition do not apply; that, in fact, it is possible in the experimental situations for ordinary sensory information to be received by the subjects in the study. That would be an attack upon the question of whether the conditions have been met. Now, what are the conditions? It is stipulated that the subjects are not able to gather the information they acquire by means of the normal senses, nor able to infer it from any data that is available to their senses. You cannot perceive that it is going to rain tomorrow, but you may be perfectly able to infer this from available meteorological data, and we wouldn't, of course, call that "extrasensory perception." Now the trouble with this statement of conditions is that it is negative. It says that a certain procedure or normal perception is ruled out, is not possible in the conditions mentioned. It is not easy to establish a negative condition, and it is because of that logical feature of the claim that some of the difficulties arise. The claim is, in fact, a negative causal claim; it is the claim that the transfer of information, if it occurs, is not due to ordinary sensory perception. And that is always much harder to establish than a straightforward positive causal claim, such as that caffeine induces insomnia.

The second kind of objection that may be raised in a particular case of alleged extrasensory perception is a doubt whether the effect actually does occur. The first is whether the conditions are met, for the alleged transfer of information; the second is whether or not there is a transfer of information. This matter is not as easily settled as you might think because, in almost all cases, the transfer is statistical in nature, and not absolute in nature. It is not like the case where I transferred to you a second ace of spades from the bottom of the pack, a fact that we can very readily disclose by a suitable examination; it is much more like the case where you are unable and I am able to give the correct description of certain objects at some distance through a slight fog. I do not always get them right, but I get them right a little more often than you, and that suggests that I have in that particular case, better fog sight than you, or else that I have been making lucky guesses. In the extrasensory case, success suggests the same; it might be skill or it might be luck. So we have a special kind of difficulty in handling the extrasensory work, that of demonstrating the improbability of coincidence. These are the two features of the claim that lead into certain difficulties for the experimenters.

Now, what about psychoanalysis? The term is used to refer to many things, including a particular kind of psychotherapy, and theories about the development of man in his own lifetime and in the course of history. These involve at least two very distinct kinds of claim, customarily referred to as "process hypotheses" and "outcome hypotheses." A process hypothesis in psychoanalysis is a hypothesis about what goes on "within" people: for example, the hypothesis that someone who had a certain dream was representing his father by the masked figure in the dream, or the hypothesis that successful therapy involves countertransference, i.e. a stage involving a reversal of the affectual attachment to the analyst of the patient. Any hypothesis about what happens during the going-on of psychoanalytic therapy, or during the going-on of any normal living situation which is subjected to psychoanalysis, is said to be a "process hypothesis." I am particularly interested in those that refer to therapy.

The second kind of hypothesis is an "outcome hypothesis," and here we have a relatively simple and distinct kind of hypothesis, the hypothesis that people are "better" after having psychoanalytic therapy. In particular, people of a certain kind that is not too easy to specify, the so-called neurotic.

Now I cannot discuss, in the space at my disposal, both kinds of claim. I shall therefore make the following comment on them and then concentrate on an "outcome" study. The comment is this, that essentially similar features must be involved in both types of study. This is generally disputed by analysts. It is often said that hypotheses about what goes on in the patient's mind, his unconscious mind, during the course of therapy can really only be studied by the words that are produced and the affectual indications that are available to the analyst. They cannot be studied by the use of control groups, by the use of any kind of objective "test" which involves verbal responses to some test by the patient, which could be scored by any judge. They cannot, in fact—it is said—be done in any way except by the use of free association and the standard techniques of psychoanalysis.

I am not going to concern myself much with the question of how to meet these comments, these complaints. They are relatively easy to meet and involve both plain confusions and more complicated question begging. I make the claim then that both types of study—although importantly different, since one is about the efficiency of therapy, the other is about what happens psychologically inside a person—are, from the methodological point of view, very similar.

I shall now concentrate on the second. I do that rather than concentrating on the first because it seems to me that this is the fundamental claim in the moral and social sense the psychoanalyst has to make. It seems to me of the very greatest importance, in fact, of the first importance, that we get to work on the question of whether we can help those people who are seriously ill, psychologically speaking, and who fall into the category which an analyst claims he can help. This is, very roughly speaking, the wide-ranging category of neuroses, a certain range of psychosomatic disorders, and a certain range of character disorders. There is great disagreement about what this exact range is; but there are certainly some cases which are clearly claimed by analysts to be such that their techniques will be a help.

I remind you, then, that I am here concerned with dynamic or process hypotheses, and I am here not talking about the question of whether other medical disciplines are superior to or worse than psychoanalytic theory in therapeutic efficiency. I certainly do not wish to imply this last in what follows, which will involve some pretty solid criticisms of psychoanalysis and psychoanalytic therapy. I do mean to imply that it is not at all clear that psychoanalytic therapy is much good, that this is a pretty serious complaint and that it should be met as immediately as possible by bringing to bear a great deal of research, interest, and backing. I intend to outline in some brisk detail how to do that.

Let us look at the logical features of this particular claim, the claim that a substantial portion of people with certain kinds of psychological malady can be significantly improved by psychoanalytic therapy. The conditions are vague, that is, the exact specifications of the people we are intending to study is not too clear; that is not a serious drawback, since we can usually agree on some of them and we can study the effect on these. The important issue is then two-fold. "Does the improvement take place, (however improvement may be defined)?" and, secondly, "What is it that produces this improvement?" So this is a *direct* causal claim. The extrasensory claim is a claim that something happens under certain conditions which exclude certain causes. The psychoanalytic claim is the claim that: (a) something happens, and (b) something specific causes it, namely, the psychoanalytic therapy.

I am going to begin by looking at psychoanalysis because the contrast is better drawn in this way for reasons that you will see in the course of the description.

The basic phenomenon that we are investigating is this: "At a certain time the patient is in a certain condition C_1; from that time till a certain second time he undergoes a treatment called "T", and he is then in condition C_2. C_1 may or may not be the same as C_2."

In these terms there are two claims to investigate. The first is the claim that C_2 is a "better" state than C_1, whatever that is going to turn out to mean; that is, the claim that the patient is somehow improved. It is not the claim at all that the patient is cured. Analysts are extremely cautious and sensible about that claim—and so are doctors in general about claims with that kind of strength. If there is not any improvement at all, then, of course, it is very difficult to see how one would justify psychotherapy. There is, however, a possible exception to that conclusion. Supposing that you could prove that the patient would have gotten worse if he had not had analysis, then the fact that C_2 is no better than C_1 does not show that psychoanalysis did not help. It shows that it prevented things from getting worse and that is always a gain in this world! So the first claim is that C_2 is better than C_1. The second part of the claim, the tricky part, is the claim that the change is due to a particular feature of the patient's environment, viz. "T."

I am going to discuss the claim by raising a series of questions that a skeptic might raise about psychoanalytical therapy and then produce the kind of response that scientists trying to support the claim or, at any rate, trying to find out the truth about it, could give in reply. These questions may bear on one or the other of the two elements in the "outcome" claim.

Suppose that we begin with the remark which one often hears from people whose friends have been analyzed, "There really isn't any difference at all about him afterwards." That is a plain denial that C_2 is any different from C_1. A number of comments have to be made about that. The first one is—it is totally improbable, since the individual is two or five years older; and if he has not changed at all, then he is very unlike a normal human being. Therefore, it is extremely likely that there was something of a change in him. When the critics say there was really no change, they are not denying that he has lost some more hair, they are, of course, referring to a change in the relevant neurotic symptoms. For us that raises the difficulty, a very serious one, of identifying the neurotic symptoms, as distinct from the symptoms of aging, incidental illnesses and accidents, emotional traumas due to death of spouse or relatives, etc. There are other changes that indisputably occur in many, though perhaps not all individuals, who have completed analysis. In the first place, they are almost certain to have a different vocabulary for describing their difficulties. It is very rare that one cannot make some reasonable estimate of the likelihood that somebody has had analysis, or has not had analysis, from their vocabulary when they are talking about mental stress of various kinds. It is not infallible, but there is at least likely to be a difference in their vocabulary; and we have no hesitation in saying that the analyst is responsible for that. There will be occasions when he is not; but it is very rare and we can reasonably give him credit for that. But it is not *this* kind of change we care about. The question we have to ask ourselves is whether, and to what extent, differences in the appropriate and interesting dimension, the dimension of neurotic symptomatology, are due to the analyst. A third kind of reported difference that will be noticed is the subjective account given by the ex-patient. It is often the case that the patient, or the ex-patient, will describe himself as very much better. This is obviously more relevant than the changes discussed earlier. But the skeptic may still have some comments. He may say that even though the patient *thinks* he is better, in fact there is no difference. To that we reply, "There certainly is a series of differences of a fairly readily identifiable kind, including a difference in how he feels about himself." Now then, he makes his complaint a little more interesting. The second comment is, "All right, so there are these differences, but they are not really improvements. Sure he can talk about his troubles now, and now he knows that he is arrested in a pregenital phase and this makes him feel better about being a homosexual (or perhaps it doesn't) but the fundamental fact remains that he still is a homosexual, (or impotent, or claustrophobic, or etc.)."

Thus we are unavoidably brought to the problem of defining improvement. It is very interesting to read through the psychoanalytic literature, looking for a discussion of what is called the "Goal of Therapy." These begin at one extreme with something produced not long ago by Szasz. In an extremely sophisticated article, he announced that, so far as he could see, the proper goal of therapy was teaching the scientific method. Now it seems to me that this is an admirable aim; but it is not clear to me that the patient is, in fact, expecting this; nor whether, in fact, for $25.00 an hour he might not be able to get it a little more quickly. At any rate, I first wish to distinguish the people who explicitly reject any claim to producing improvement, of which he is one.

Then you get views of a slightly different kind, e.g., "The goal of therapy is better self-understanding." Now immediately one asks this question, "How do you know that it is really better self-understanding and not simply a new vocabulary for talking about his problem?" For I can easily give you an astrological jargon with which to talk about your problems and the question will then still arise as to whether you understand your problems any better. Now the same problem arises about psychoanalysis, and I answer it perfectly straightforwardly, saying it has to be *shown* that the patient's hypotheses about his own behavior are correct, and that means substantiating process hypotheses, so you would immediately have to do both studies to handle an assessment of therapy, if we took this as the goal.

There is, on the other hand, the possibility which I think most therapists are interested in, that the increased "self-understanding," real or not, actually leads to a real improvement in the ordinary sense; for example, to the reduction of anxiety in the patient. Perhaps he feels less shocked by his behavior pattern; he feels that he can now fit it into the story of the things that have happened to him over which he had no control, and he therefore sees this as something which is in a way a justification for him, and he feels less uneasy. There are various ways in which that might occur, but if there is any such improvement, we ought to be able to detect that directly. So I then move on to the straightforward claim that there is a genuine gain of the ordinary kind in the patient.

Now, what enters into the ordinary claim that there is an improvement? There are a number of factors: First, and often thought to be the only matter of concern, is the question of the patient's objective report about himself. It is certainly important in assessing improvement that we take account of that kind of improvement. On the other hand, there are many situations well known to therapists where the subject reports that he is much better, whereas the study of his family relationship shows that this subjective gain has been obtained by transferring his aggression from himself, where its impact made him feel bad, to his kids, which makes *them* feel bad, but makes him feel good. It would then hardly be appropriate for us to regard the subject's feeling of improvement as equivalent to improvement in all cases. The analyst is, of course, often in a difficult situation about evaluating the impact of this particular kind of a point because he is not always (though he is sometimes, and increasingly so in recent years) discussing matters with others in the family, concurrently with the patient. To make an assessment of improvement, therefore, we must take account of social relations and social behavior, as well as the subject's report. We shall have to do this with the aid of field investigators interviewing those in social contact with the patient.

Next, there are the psychosomatic symptoms. Regardless of whether there are any social gains, regardless of whether the patient reports feeling better or does not, there is the question of whether paralysis has vanished; whether a particular kind of tic stopped; whether other sorts of behavioral peculiarities supposedly due to the psychological conditions of the patient have diminished, vanished, or begun.

Next, there is the question of whether his objective judgment, his rational capacity for insight into material affairs and personal relationships has improved. This is quite separate from the previous things and will, of course, need an independent kind of assessment.

Possibly, in addition to these, there is the problem of whether his moral judgment and his moral forms of behavior have changed. This raises a lot of interesting and difficult problems. I want to make it perfectly clear that I am not ruling it out in the way the definition has been given. Suppose we found a man who was feeling worse, behaving worse to his family; his judgment of the attitudes of his neighbors had become almost paranoid, but he was now able to stand up in the cause of integration in a Southern community where previously he could not, and as a result, feels that he is doing the right thing and is rewarded by that fact; then it would be possible to argue that he has not improved in any respect, if we only take account of the things I have mentioned so far. Thus, it seems not to be possible to rule out consideration of the morality of his behavior, when you are assessing improvement. Whatever you do, however, you cannot rule out the preceding four considerations. Those are difficult things to evaluate, as difficult as anything there is to evaluate about a person, but I do not introduce them as a kind of nasty burden to place on the shoulders of the analyst; I introduce them as necessary parts of what must be meant by someone who claims that psychoanalysis does improve the people whom it treats. If this could not be said, if that claim could not be made to stick in terms of the definition given, then the analyst's therapeutic claim is in doubt and, of course, it would require a very substantial investigation to determine whether these things do apply.

Having given an account of improvement, which I have been obliged to construct since no explicit account of this kind is available in the literature, we pass to the third complaint which is: "All right, so now there is a *difference*, and we have an idea of what *improvement* means, but how are we ever going to judge those differences as improvements?" The judgment of improvement is hopelessly subjective, it is suggested; it is hopelessly subjective for a reason which provides the experimenter with an unsolvable dilemma. Either he asks the analyst himself whether the patient is better, in which case, of course, the judgment is hopelessly biased, or he does not ask the analyst. In the latter case, you apply these tests for improvement quite independently of the analyst's judgment of improvement, in which case it could be said it is a hopelessly unsatisfactory judgment and could be said to be a judgment by some ignorance, rather than anything else. It would be argued that the most important material of all is revealed only in the analyst's sessions, and without his insights we are without the best based judgment of all.

There are a number of replies to this. I will only mention them. The first is the use of what is called "uncontaminated judges," a nice phrase, which means judges who do not know whether the person they are judging for improvement has actually undergone psychoanalytic therapy or not. That is, they do not know whether he is a member of the control group, or whether he is a member of the experimental group, the group that received the treatment. There are extremely difficult problems that have to be met here. There is the problem of whether the vocabulary he uses provides an index to which group he was in, so that the judges' prejudices in favor of or against psychoanalysis would be able to operate. There are ways of handling this that are not *completely* satisfactory, but, using this panel, and the analyst's own report, and studying further cases of discrepancy between them, we have a study which is well worth doing, since until we have done it we do not know whether even a possibly—slightly— biased judgment of improvement exists. We, of course, know that the analyst, who simply sees the analysis of his patient, very often says that there was some improvement as a result of the therapy, but we do not know whether it is true, nor can he. We, therefore, have got to have some attack on the problem of objective evaluation, before and after, of the patients who go through. Remember, that if the difference in the patient is not detectable to other people, then it is not going to be the kind of improvement we primarily desire. It would not be very much good if the analyst always said, "Yes, he is better," but nobody else could see any improvement at all and neither could the patient.

Now the fourth point: Supposing all this is said and done, the above points are all met, the suggestion might still be made that the improvement is only *temporary*. It might even be suggested that the termination of the therapy will actually lead to a collapse on the part of the patient who has become dependent on the analyst. Of course, a standard part of psychoanalytic therapy is that this possibility be meticulously investigated and carefully avoided. However, an unfortunate feature of the standard arrangement is that there is no good way of telling whether it *was* avoided, because if the patient, having been through five years of analysis, terminating with a judgment of improvement by the analyst, then finds himself falling in the same neurotic depression that he was previously subject to, he is rather less than likely to go back to the same individual. We therefore require what is known as a follow-up, i.e., a repetition of the evaluation tests some time after the conclusion of therapy, and we have got to apply this again at various intervals after the conclusion of therapy in order to see whether the improvement, whatever it may be, is relatively permanent.

Supposing now that we are satisfied that there has been a change for the better, and that it is a relatively permanent one; the fifth question arises, whether the patient would not have improved anyway.

Five years is a long time in the life of a neurosis, and the evidence that we have, inadequate as it is, suggests that there is a tendency for neuroses to get better in the course of time, without therapy, in approximately two-thirds of the cases accepted. Now the question is, "Just how much more than two-thirds of his patients is the analyst helping?" To discover whether the figure is two-thirds, *and* whether the analyst is doing better than the great healer time, we need a control group. Suppose he judges that out of a number of people that come to him for help, and perhaps after a number of diagnostic interviews, he could help a certain group of them, we then take that group, split it in half randomly, and give him half. Now then, what are we comparing? We are comparing the control group, the people he thought he could help, though we do not allow him to help them, with the people he thought he could help, whom we do allow him to try to help. If there is no significant difference between these groups at the end of therapy with the group he does treat, it is going to be very difficult to support the claim that he really did help them.

Might it not be that he gets all the really hard cases in his group? If we use a very large number of individuals in these groups, we can take care of such a possibility. Moreover, supposing it is said, for example, that obviously when there is a difference of sex, there must be a completely different method of treatment, perhaps owing to the special role of the

Oedipus relationship in male development. Then it must be replied that we can match perfectly well for sex, that is, we can arrange that there will be exactly the same number of women in the control group as in the experimental, and so on. Any feature that is said to be relevant to the method of treatment can immediately be matched. Now, supposing that there turned out to be an indefinite number of these. It might be said that every respect in which a patient had childhood experiences of a particular kind is relevant to therapy and, therefore, we must, in fact, match with this. Obviously we would be getting an experimental group running several thousand people. However, this line of attack on an experimental study only raises a problem for the analyst, who often suggests it. The problem is this: if there are that many relevant variables, how did the therapist ever learn which ones to treat, since he has never had that many patients? Hence, there is a point at which we can turn the proliferation of relevant features into a complaint about the therapist's own claims.

We now turn to the last three questions, which provide many difficulties. It might be argued that, although the analyst's group should show a substantial gain over the control group, it was not the psychoanalysis that cured the patients, but the experience of discussing their problems with somebody who is not going to rattle off to them a lot of complaints about immoral behavior. There are a number of other factors that have been suggested as being the truly curative element in psychoanalysis. True or false, the loophole must be closed. It immediately introduces the necessity for *several* control groups. We have got to have other control groups in which an attempt is made to match for these things which might be curative. For example: We could have one group which is referred to a "naïve" (of Freud) graduate student who interviews the patients (naïve means graduate student in geology, for example). We take great care that he knows nothing about psychoanalysis, or as near as can be to nothing, and we give him a free hand to discuss the problems which the patient has. We prefer him with a beard and so on. We match with as many of these factors (which the analyst says are *not* the crucial therapeutic elements in his treatment) as we can, and we then see whether there is still a significant difference.

Suppose that there is a significant difference, we then come to the last two difficulties. Suppose that it is still the case that the analyst, in fact, is doing better than the other groups. The difficulty still remains that the analyst has, in the contacts with the patients that come to him, a tremendous advantage over the bearded Greek graduate students, and that is that they are talking Freudian talk, and that the patient came to you for Freudian analysis (or some other kind). It is, therefore, perfectly clear to the patient that he is in one case getting and in the other not getting what he came for, and since he most likely believes in the therapeutic power of what he came for, or he would not have come for it, the analyst still has up his sleeve a trick which has nothing to do with psychoanalytic theory as such, but has a great deal to do with the prestige of psychoanalytic theory.

Finally, there is the possibility that the analysts select from the applicant group just those people with whom they personally interact well and then success is due entirely to a personality interaction, the psychoanalytic terminology and rituals being essentially or largely irrelevant. Again it is possible to match, in order to eliminate these possibilities, and without matching we shall simply never be able to answer the question whether psychoanalysis helps neurotics. There is no substitution for a study that involves all of those features; without them, other highly probable interpretations will still be possible. And they may not be exhaustive. What is absolutely certain is that no study has ever been done which takes account of half of these points. It would be expensive to answer this question about psychoanalysis, but important: less expensive and more important than one B-58 bomber.

An interesting moral problem that arises in the course of all this is the question of whether one should say these things to people who might need to get analyzed, namely the readers of this Essay. However, I will leave that to one side and try and stick to the question—whether you should.

Now remember these points in closing on that subject; it does not follow from the fact that no study that remotely meets the conditions I've mentioned has been done, that a psychoanalyst has no therapeutic effect. Of course, he may well have a therapeutic effect; he is a person with prestige, listening to your problems, willing to discuss them with you, willing to help you with them. It is quite likely that he does for many reasons. But we have been raising the question about whether psychoanalysis as such has any therapeutic efficacy and that is, in the long run, the important question; because if the other factors are doing it we can easily produce the other factors. It will then be a relatively inexpensive kind of therapy, and it will not mean that people will have to put in 17 years' training to do it. So I am not arguing that going to an analyst is silly. I am arguing that it is impossible to claim that it is the psychoanalytic part of what he says that is responsible for the improvement, if any, and we do not *know* whether there is any. There may be some; and it is quite clear that if you feel sick (psychologically sick) you can afford it;

you dislike burdening friends with your troubles; you are an atheist, (and, therefore, do not want to go to a priest) and you believe in Freud; then you should go to an analyst. Why? Because there is nothing else you can go to and there is no good reason for supposing this will not help. But do not make the claim that psychoanalysis as such cured you, unless you have got something a little better up your sleeve than the sequence of events, neurosis, psychoanalysis, no neurosis.

I am usually asked at this stage, or shortly after such discussion, whether I have been analyzed or whether I have been run over by an analyst or whether my father was an analyst. Well, those considerations are irrelevant to the truth of my comments and so we will leave them open. If you can meet these objections logically, that is fine—if you cannot, it will not help you to know what I was or was not.

Now let us turn to parapsychology. We are here considering a different claim, a negative claim. We are considering a claim that a particular thing is happening and it *is not* due to this, this, and this—the normal sensory processes. We need to set out a situation in which no sensory communication or inference is possible. Now the standard situation in extrasensory perception experiments is a very simple one. An individual in one room, supervised by an experimenter in that room, and called the "agent," looks at a pack of cards that have been randomly shuffled and have on them certain very simple designs, perhaps numbers, perhaps letters, perhaps colored pictures, animals—a number of items have been used. In another room or another house at the other end of the street or in another country, depending on the study, somebody else—the subject supervised by another experimenter—attempts to write down on a list the order of cards that the first individual is looking at. You can see that the elimination of sensory communication is pretty direct.

Let us take one of the standard cases in which one of the best subjects that has worked in this area was used. This was Mrs. Stewart, who kept going for a number of years, producing scores at a very even level, as high as forty or fifty per cent better than chance expectations, depending on the agent. In one series she was set up in Belgium; watches of the two experimenters were synchronized; and the "agent" (Mrs. Holding) was set up and supervised in London. It is very difficult to explain how they would have communicated using the ordinary senses. They did not communicate using the telephone, which would of course be physically possible, nor radio. We have a number of supervisory reports about this. All that happened was that on the BBC 7:00 o'clock time signal they started, and every three seconds the agent would turn over a card and look at it, while at the other end, every three seconds, the subject would write down another response. The results were then sealed by the separate experimenters and given to another investigator for tabulation, and it turned out that Mrs. Stewart was able to score, as I said, about forty or fifty per cent above chance on this. There was an expectation that she would get five right by just guessing, and in fact most people do—many studies have been done to see whether they, in fact, do. She was getting seven, better than half right, and in financial terms, of course, that is a very profitable arrangement and would rapidly accumulate for her a disproportionate amount of money in a betting game. It seems reasonable to conclude that extrasensory perception is hereby demonstrated.

That is a standard kind of experiment that has been done by a number of people with a good many subjects and it is substantially similar in each of them, Now, let us use the same procedure we used with the psychoanalysis study: let us consider some possible objections. First: it is done with secret signals. I have explicitly described the experiment in such a way that it is very difficult to see how that could be. On some of the other ESP experiments it is possible to see how it *could* be done, but we have people there watching for it to be done who cannot detect it being done. One very interesting maneuver came out of a recent series involving two boys as subjects. The possibility arose that they were using a hypersonic whistle, to which, of course, their ears are sensitive, whereas the ears of the older experimenters would not be sensitive. It is an interesting hypothesis, and the experimental design was such that it is not possible to rule it out, and the experiments must therefore be completely disregarded. It is a rare occasion in the recent history of this type of investigation, because most of these traps have been thought out so thoroughly now that it is very unusual for anybody even to bother with an experimental design that does not rule them out. Ordinary suggestions about whispered messages and subvocal remarks and so on are quite easily met by separating the subject from the agent by greater distance and more closed doors.

Now, the second possibility: recording errors made unconsciously due to motivation to produce exciting results. The man who compares the subject's results with the original card order is presumably anxious to see success or he would not be in the business of investigating this, and it is relatively easy when you are checking off these long columns of paired symbols to make errors. This point is readily met by using photographic recording techniques or keeping the record for independent check, which has been done with all the major series. They are available for inspection, and the study of them shows an occasional recording error, but they work out very nearly equal in both directions: sometimes a "hit" is actually scored as a "miss" and sometimes the other way around. But this does not turn out to be a very significant fact and it is always open to subsequent inspection.

Third objection: these studies are not repeatable. Telepathy is not a truly scientific effect, according to this suggestion, because these results cannot be reliably produced by anybody that sets up this kind of an experiment. This complaint is based on a simple misunderstanding of the requirements of scientific experiments. We cannot repeat the study of the eclipse that was made three years ago and there are important respects in which each eclipse is different—for example, the solar flares that occur on these occasions are unique—and these are respects in which we are quite clear significant scientific information resides.

Repeatability is not a requirement unless the claim made is of a very strong kind. If I make the claim that a certain kind of drug will cure diabetes, administered in a specific way, then I expect when I administer it in this way to find this result. That is not the kind of claim that is being made here. The claim that is being made here is that *some* people have a certain *capacity*. The appropriate comparison is with claims about individuals who are alleged to be calculating prodigies or eidetic imagers. The calculating prodigy is a very good case for comparison.

The prodigy is often a poor shepherd boy or peasant child who has had no formal education but can perform miraculous calculating feats using a kind of mental imagery that they find very difficult to explain. Such children often are taken in hand, after having been exhibited publicly for some years, by some kind patron who then gives them a formal education. Towards the end of this they frequently lose their capacity for lightning calculations. There have been some important exceptions to this, of course, some of the great mathematicians amongst them, but there are on record a considerable number of cases of the sort that I have described. These are cases which have been very thoroughly investigated; there is no possibility of straight-forward fraud here. But when one makes the claim that such skills exist, one does not thereby guarantee that they will be discovered in every child, nor indeed in children selected by any particular method of selection except direct test on the kind of task which the prodigy performs. The only repeatability to which one is committed extends over the active life span of the calculating skill in a particular individual; that is, one makes a claim about him very like the claim one might make about a child to the effect that he can hear notes of a frequency of 20,000 cycles per second. For a certain span of his life this will be true, and he will repeatedly perform tasks which are dependent upon this skill. Exactly the same kind of repeatability is both required of and constantly evidenced in the ESP work.

The next sceptical move about ESP consists in the suggestion that it is nothing more than a kind of mental radio—simply another electromagnetic phenomenon. Now it is important to notice that even if this were true, it would hardly result in a serious weakening of most of the ESP claims because it would demonstrate a hitherto completely unrecognized sensitivity by means of which information is indeed passed from individual to individual other than by means of the usual senses. In point of fact, however, several studies have been made where the subjects were separated from the agents by a substantial thickness of lead, without noticeable diminution in the ESP performance. Moreover, on independent grounds, the estimates we have of the extent of the electrical activity in the brain make it clear that telepathy across the English Channel from London to Belgium would be incompatible with our current electromagnetic theory, if for no other reasons than from considerations of the impossibility of exhibiting the degree of sensitivity and selectivity required. In general, we have no evidence which would enable us to say that there is a falling off in ESP performance with distance, though this is by no means decisive in attempting to determine whether it is a signal propagation procedure which obeys an inverse square law.

We now come to some more fundamental suggestions. Surely, it has been said, you will get this kind of effect sometimes, if you look long enough. Indeed, it is true that if you were to make a very large number of investigations into the success with which people guess, say, the outcome of horse races, you would expect to find a number of individuals whose performance was substantially better than average. And the longer you looked, the more likely it would be that you would find some really remarkably successful guesses. In fact, unlike previous considerations, this criticism does not rest on some kind of intrinsically fallacious hypothesis. Its only defect, albeit a fatal one, is that it is quantitatively hopeless. That is, the odds against a chance explanation of the results that were obtained in Soal's basic series of experiments are about 10^{70} to one, and there is no significant chance at all that we would come across scoring of this degree of success, however long we or other people looked. To back this up, imagine that the entire series of his experiments, which ran for a period of some years and involved 37,000 separate trials, had been performed every minute throughout the entire history of the earth back to the days when it was a cloud of gas, i.e., for about three thousand million years. In the course of all *that* searching, what would be the chance that we would come across someone who performed so well? It would be about one chance in 10^{54}, i.e., still completely negligible. So the argument that the ESP results are based upon counting the positive instances and ignoring the negative ones is hopeless because even the most absurd assumptions about the number of negative ones still leaves us with a staggering preponderance of successes in this area—far too large to be accounted for by chance alone. When the roulette wheel keeps coming up on the number three, time after time, no matter how we spin it, we must eventually take seriously the hypothesis that it has jammed, or that someone is jamming it. The same applies when we find someone who can guess at a rate 50 per cent better than chance, and keep it up for years.

Having considered an attempt to dismiss the results as insignificant, it is now appropriate for us to look at the suggestion that the results were imaginary.

It has been suggested on a number of occasions that the ESP work is a gigantic fraud, involving deliberate deception by a considerable number of people of great professional eminence in several countries. There is absolutely no doubt that this is possible, and there is absolutely no way to calculate the odds of it being true. Hence we cannot demonstrate, as we did in connection with the last difficulty, that there is a gross divergence between the suggested hypothesis and the actual quantitative evidence. One can only make an attempt to weigh the imponderables, such as the tremendous risk to a professional career that results from getting involved in parapsychological work. These considerations by no means rule out the possibility, of course, and the sceptic who takes this line must follow it up making a serious attempt to attend the sessions of the experimentalists whose honesty he is impugning, by examining their records for the kind of slip that fraudulent manipulation would undoubtedly reveal sooner or later, and by attempting to perform experiments of a similar kind himself. This is not an issue which can be settled by any *a priori* considerations. It is not only pointless but immoral for critics to suggest dishonesty amongst their colleagues unless they are prepared to substantiate this or apply it to other scientists producing wholly novel claims, as a result of which large sections of earlier physics or chemistry are overthrown.

The scientific attitude indeed requires that we remain perpetually aware of and seriously prepared to consider claims of dishonesty just as we should have this attitude towards claims of startling discoveries. Neither claim should be accepted without supporting evidence, and until very recently, in the present dispute the evidence was all on one side. A forthcoming book by C. E. M. Hansel will contain the most serious attempt—indeed one might say, the only really serious attempt—so far. Judging its contents from points made in correspondence and earlier papers by Hansel, one can only say that he has made the possibility of a rather complicated deception much more significant, though in my judgment still not as probable as the alternative.

It is commonly argued in discussions of the fraud hypothesis that no matter how unlikely fraud may be, it is still far *more* likely than the alleged extrasensory phenomena. George Price put this as a form of Hume's argument against miracles; miracles (or extrasensory phenomena) are incompatible with the laws of nature as we now understand them; the latter are supported by a gigantic body of evidence, hence this same evidence counts against the possibility of miracles (or ESP) and far outweighs the probability of an alternative explanation of the effects. In short, if we have to choose between the evidence that fraud took place, admittedly slight, and the evidence that the laws of nature are false, then, since they are supported by so much evidence, the latter probability is far lower than the former. The main weaknesses in this argument are that it supposes the laws of nature to have been established in the region where extrasensory phenomena apply, and that it supposes a fundamental incompatibility between ESP and current physical laws. The argument suffers from another weakness, not specific to its application to ESP, and that is—it is too strong. If valid it would constitute an *a priori* disproof of any fundamental discovery that threatened previously established scientific systems—one thinks of Leverrier's observations on Mercury, for example. I have argued elsewhere that the relationship between current physical laws and extrasensory phenomena is that if accepted, the latter would require that the former be viewed as having a slightly more restricted range than one had carelessly supposed. It is only when the laws are extrapolated from the regions in which they have been directly supported by experimental evidence that they could come into conflict with ESP. Such an extrapolation is tempting, and appropriate enough in the absence of contrary evidence, but so weak that here—as on countless previous occasions—the first lot substantiated counterclaims in the extended range must be taken as having a very low antecedent improbability. Though it is, the evidence for the present laws of nature supports them in a range where they are not jeopardized by the new results. There are, in addition, some grounds for doubting whether any laws of nature are in any way jeopardized by the new results. It is true that certain vague general principles which characterize many of our laws are rejected by ESP supporters, but I would class these general principles as being at the level of philosophical rather than physical insights, and consequently even more readily subject to reformulation.

I now turn to a criticism that has been made of the experiments on statistical grounds. This is the so-called "optional stopping!" The argument goes as follows. It is a theorem in statistics that if one proceeds long enough with a random series one will be able to find a point at which the deviation from chance of the results so far is as unlikely as one wishes. This is a much more sophisticated kind of criticism than the "what about the negative cases?" criticism. It rests on a theorem which is regarded as counter-intuitive by many well trained mathematicians. It is not the theorem that sooner or later in a random series one will find a sequence of the most unlikely kind—for example, sooner or later in throwing an unbiased die one will come across a run of 600 sixes. It is a theorem that has the consequence that sooner or later in throwing an unbiased die the average number of sixes thrown will diverge from one sixth of the total number of throws by enough to make the divergence as unlikely as one likes. The application of this theorem to ESP work is as follows: it is suggested that the basic experiments proceed up to the point where this extremely probable divergence is observed and shortly thereafter are terminated, on the grounds that the subject is "losing his power." In reality, the subject is undergoing the to-be-expected drop back to his normal scoring rates. The reputation of this criticism is roughly that it cannot explain why the successful subject's performance is high at the beginning and continues at the same level throughout until the final terminating period. Subjects are not persisted with unless their initial performance is good. There is no policy of extensive testing of subjects who begin poorly, in the hope that they will ultimately turn in significantly deviant scores. Now the likelihood that a subject will *consistently* score at the level above chance that Mrs. Stewart achieved is not made any higher by the theorem. Hence we are correct to suppose that its improbability is so large as to require some alternative explanation.

The third kind of attack on the statistical theory involved in the interpretation of the results of the ESP tests is of an extremely fundamental kind. It involves nothing less than an attack on the meaningfulness of the concept of randomness itself. Whenever we interpret an ESP test, or any of a wide range of tests of the efficiency of fertilizers, the rate at which mathematics is learned, the reliability of the manufacturing process and so on, there is a stage at which we say "it is extremely unlikely, to such and such a degree, that the results observed could have come about by chance." If the degree mentioned is sufficiently high, then we commonly regard the case as proven for the existence of a significant and perhaps novel effect. The criticism now under consideration, put forward in its most widely-known form by Spencer Brown, suggests that this stage of the argument is faulty. No less an authority than R. A. Fisher gave this approach the sanction of his support at one stage. Now it *is* perfectly true that the concept of randomness is a rather elusive one, logically speaking. Moreover, and rather excitingly, Spencer Brown was able to uncover peculiarities in the tables of random numbers that experimenters usually employ to give their cards an unbiased sequence. These turned out to be due to the interference by the individuals responsible for publishing the tables, with the output of whatever device they were employing to give them a random sequence. This interference was prompted by the feeling that the sequence as it came from the apparatus was biased, e.g. because it had too many 9's in it. Hence the tables of "random numbers" were actually tables of mechanically produced sequences which looked random to their transcribers, a rather intuitive criterion.

However, to be practical about the matter, the logical difficulties do not have insuperable consequences for the practising scientist and the weaknesses in the tables are rather slight, and corrections can be applied to the interpretations based on them which adequately compensate for the degree of bias introduced by the touchiness of the various compilers. There are three other crushing arguments against viewing this kind of attack as constituting a serious difficulty for the ESP work.

Firstly, exactly the same statistics are used in the analysis of this work as elsewhere in science. And the use of these simple statistics in developing better hybrid corns, better stamping machinery and vaccines, etc., has for a long time borne so much fruit in practical benefits that we can have great confidence in its overall reliability. This rebuttal would not be satisfactory if the effects in question were of a very marginal kind. But they are, on the contrary, of a very clear-cut kind, at least as significant as any of the results uncovered in ordinary statistical experimentation.

Secondly, we need not rely in any way on an abstract analysis of randomness, nor on the use of random tables. We may just set to work and find out how often one pack of cards will match another pack of cards. This is a case when nobody is making a guess, and where we may set about finding out what happens when there is no intention to make a telepathic or clairvoyant perception. Half a million cards have been matched in this way, in one of the major investigations, and the results are absolutely indistinguishable from those which our usual theory of probability leads us to expect. Yet when one of the gifted subjects in these experiments attempts to set down a list of cards to match a hidden pack, the results are quite different. We can only conclude that this difference is due to some special feature of the experimental set-up, and in the reliable designs it appears that the only real difference is the telepathic intent.

Thirdly, there is an internal feature of the results in the classic series that annihilates any kind of attack on these statistics. During the course of an experiment, and without informing the subject, the conditions were radically changed; instead of there being an agent who was examining the cards at the same time the subject was attempting to guess them, the agent would simply pass them from one pile to another without looking at them. Hence there was no opportunity for telepathy to occur. What was the effect on the scores by the subject at such times? The effect was striking and significant; the subject's scores would drop to the chance level whenever the conditions were changed in this way. That is, the subject was able to apprehend successfully the card on many occasions when there was somebody else in a distant place who knew what it was, but was not able to do this when there was no such person. Yet the same statistics apply whether or not someone is looking at the card. The *difference* between the subject's score when telepathy is possible and when it is not cannot therefore be explained by any feature of the statistical analysis. There is really a fourth weakness in this kind of an attack. The suggestion is that statistical analysis is absolutely indispensable to getting these startling results. It is not. There was a memorable occasion in the Soal series where R. H. Thauless suggested stacking the deck, again without informing the subject. The first twelve cards of the 25 were arranged to be the same and the next thirteen were arranged to be the same, though different from the first thirteen. Under these conditions, we have the equivalent of what the communications engineer does when faced with the necessity for getting a message through a noisy line. He simply repeats the message a number of times, and the recipient picks out the most frequent symbol from each group of repetitions. In the experiment we are talking about, the results were unmistakable, and absolutely no use of statistics was involved. On each occasion where twelve or thirteen repetitions of the same signal were "sent," one symbol and only one occurred predominantly in the subject's responses. And this symbol was always the symbol that the agent was thinking about. It is worth adding that the conditions of this experiment were such as to bias it strongly against success. For the subject believed that she was guessing at a randomized pack, and was thus strongly motivated against producing multiple recurrences of the same "guess." Hence she was biased against uttering what was in fact the truth. The question is often asked why, if telepathy is possible, ordinary messages are not sent and received instead of these symbol codes. The answer is that it would be much easier to send them, and moreover in their most difficult form they have already been sent.

SUMMARY: I have now completed my listing of the criticisms that a thoughtful person would wish to hear answered before he would be satisfied to accept certain rather elementary claims of psychoanalysis and parapsychology—namely the claims that psychoanalysis does some good and that parapsychology studies something that exists. It is proper to be sceptical about the claims of these subjects if these criticisms cannot be met. It is not proper to suppose that because one does not know the answers to them oneself, the answers do not exist; a dull remark, but one which is really heated in these areas.

Now, what is the state of these two subjects in the light of the criticisms raised above? It seems perfectly clear that psychoanalysis has not met the appropriate objections, whereas parapsychology has met them. There is a brilliant paper in the literature which provides a detailed documentation of the parallelism between psychoanalysis and phrenology. I have here been concerned to stress the differences between psychoanalysis and another of the "disreputable subjects." I would sum up my conclusions in this way: psychoanalysis provides us with a great theory without a factual foundation; parapsychology, a factual basis on which there is yet to be built a great theory. I leave it to you to draw your own conclusions as to the scientific merits of these two conditions.

POSTSCRIPT

1. There are many cases of supposed extrasensory capacities on the part of animals. A number that have been carefully investigated turned out to be demonstrations of extreme sensory acuity, often on the unconscious level as far as the animal's owner was concerned. But there are areas—such as the homing of pigeons—where we have by no means eliminated the possibility of ESP as an explanation.

2. There is no strong evidence at the present moment for a correlation between extrasensory capacity and intelligence.

3. There is no strong evidence that ESP powers increase in individuals with any particular kind of brain damage. The evidence is slightly better

for the improvement of ESP powers under certain kinds of relaxing treatment e.g., drugs, alcohol, and hypnosis.

4. The discovery of fraud on the part of a medium in the conventional seance phenomena is not adequate ground for supposing that she is capable of nothing but fraud. Any professional medium is under considerable pressure to produce phenomena on schedule. It is extremely unlikely that the kinds of phenomena we are concerned with can be produced on demand, hence it is extremely likely that a medium if she did have significant ESP powers would be constantly failing unless she were to "help them out" somewhat on some occasions. Of course one likes to breathe a sigh of relief when one uncovers fraud in these cases, but honesty requires a perpetual willingness to return to the investigation if any possibility of genuine phenomena still exists, in the light of the consideration I have just mentioned.

5. ESP could be regarded as action at a distance; and so could electromagnetic phenomena. On the other hand, both can be regarded as action through the medium of the field. The difference seems to me to be largely verbal, in the present state of the evidence. It is sometimes said that the velocity of propagation must be infinite for a phenomenon to constitute action at a distance. But the velocity of propagation of electromagnetic phenomena from the frame of reference of the signal itself is infinite (in the sense that no time passes, though distance is covered) and I rather think that is the crucial frame of reference for this issue.

6. We have no grounds for saying the telepathic propagation operates according to an inverse square of the distance law, but we also have no grounds for saying that it does not. The effects so far could be quite well explained by supposing that there is an inverse square law but that the receptor sensitivity is extremely high, just as they could be quite well explained by supposing that there is no fall-off at distance. Pratt's recent work has suggested that taking all the distance studies together one does find some support for an inverse square law.

7. The evidence for precognition seems to me substantially weaker than the evidence for telepathy or clairvoyance. The evidence for psychokinesis seems to me very much less satisfactory than for precognition. Propagation hypotheses that can handle precognition are of course extremely tricky.

8. When I say that psychoanalysis is a theory without a factual foundation, I do not intend to suggest that it is a theory without any facts to explain. It is indeed a theory about certain kinds of facts, notably facts

about the behavior of children and neurotics, and about our own aberrant behavior, as well as about normal adult behavior. But having facts to explain is not the same thing as having facts to support a theory. The facts which are supposed to support the claims of therapeutic efficacy on the part of psychoanalysis are at the moment more readily explicable in terms of less novel hypotheses. The various hypotheses in psychoanalysis that are concerned with process rather than outcome have not been discussed in this paper, and provide a very much more complicated problem. It must be stressed that the correctness of psychoanalytic process hypotheses would lend almost no support to the claim of psychotherapeutic efficacy, *and vice versa.*

II. The Last Frontiers

In Part I of this paper I discussed two subjects in which I am not professionally engaged and compressed them into a few pages, naturally producing considerable dissatisfaction amongst the professionals concerned with these subjects. Here, I am going to attempt something more closely connected with my own professional field and—naturally—these topics will not be dealt with exhaustively. Nevertheless, I am going at least to outline a certain section of the field of the philosophy of science and thus raise questions about certain parts which will not be answered here directly.

I began this Essay with an analogy between geographical exploration and intellectual exploration. In the course of expanding on that analogy I distinguished frontiers of three different kinds. First, those which we are at the moment attacking; second, those which seem to be within our power to conquer though we have not yet begun to fight on them; and third, those which might be said to represent the final limits of all future investigations.

Here I wish to discuss a number of candidates that have been suggested —I shall take ten of them—as last frontiers, impassable barriers to the progress of science, the science in this particular case being that concerned with the study of human beings. I shall discuss these candidates under three different headings. I shall first introduce them and explain them as they are intended by people who think they constitute insuperable difficulties. I shall then discuss, in the case of some of the more important ones, the arguments given by people who dismiss them as not being ultimate barriers. I shall then point out that this dismissal is unsound, at least in part, and attempt to provide some kind of synthetic view of the situation as I see it now.

It is not my purpose here to spend time on a detailed analysis of the conception of science, but I am going to begin by making one claim about the concept. It seems to me correct to say that the sciences are concerned with four tasks: description, prediction, control, and explanation, to arrange them in one natural order of difficulty.

The first claimant for the title of an ultimate frontier for psychology and the related behavioral sciences is the uniqueness of the individual. It is often argued that everybody is unique or that "people are different," a line of argument with which in a certain sense it is difficult to disagree. It is further argued, however, that this is incompatible with the possibility of an exact science. Now the usual reply to this is a very straightforward and powerful one. This reply consists in pointing out that even if every human being is importantly different from every other human being, it may also be that large groups of human beings are importantly similar to each other. It may be, for example, that individuals who have the same learning history, described in quite general terms, will find themselves capable of certain tasks and incapable of other tasks. In this case we would be able to predict their performance, and explain it, and to some extent, control it. Hence, there appears to be *no* incompatibility between uniqueness and the rule of scientific law.

Secondly, and independently, we have the complexity argument. These two arguments are often thought to be the same, though they are not. Supposing that, as a matter of fact, human beings are not unique, and that there are in fact only two kinds of them, namely men and women. All men behave in exactly the same way as all other men, all women behave in exactly the same way as all other women, and the only way you can tell people of one sex apart is from the numbers they carry around or their precise location at a particular time. Nevertheless, it might be that their behavior is so complex as to render a science of psychology inappropriate or impossible. That is, the fact that all men behave in the same way does not guarantee that their behavior will be predictable in advance, or explicable in retrospect. Life would still be interesting in certain respects, despite the absence of individuality; unpredictability would remain (and, of course, a difference between the sexes). Thus the suggestion is that the complexity of human behavior provides difficulties for the science of psychology today which are quite unlike the difficulties that astronomy has to face in the prediction of eclipses and planetary positions.

The counter to this, and it is by no means an easy one to meet, consists in saying that the suggestion that complexity constitutes a barrier to a

science of psychology is no better founded than a corresponding suggestion would have been had it been made about the prediction of chemical
behavior prior to the introduction of the great classificatory scheme of
the periodic table. Again it might be said that this suggestion constitutes
a kind of defeatism that might well have, indeed did, infect the thought
of the early astronomers in the days of epicycles, when the observations
looked extremely complicated. To have argued then that since things
were so complicated a science of predictive astronomy would never
emerge would have been to make a mistake of a rather serious kind, as
the event has proved. And to argue the same way in the case of psychology
today is just to argue from present ignorance. It is to express a pessimistic
attitude about the future of science, and it cannot be held to be an argument. The complexity is a passing phase, characteristic of the early days
of a science, but the complexity cannot in any sense be considered a last
frontier.

Third, fourth, and fifth, we take up a series of related points stemming
from the fact that psychology is distinguishable amongst the sciences as
one of those where the investigator is himself in a certain sense part of
the field of his investigations. This self-involvement gives rise to a series
of difficulties or alleged difficulties for psychology. The first of these, our
point three, is the likelihood that the biases we acquire in the course of
our behavior as human beings will carry over into our study of human
beings. For example, in the field of anthropology, and in social psychology
generally, as well as in personality theory, we have many cases in the
history of psychology where there were the most disastrous results for
the scientific investigations owing to the imposition on the data of some
cultural or personal bias of the investigators.

The normal counter to this consists in pointing out that bias (although
more likely here than in studying some new field of bacteriology where
we do not really have prejudices in favor of black bacteria as against
white bacteria, or vice-versa) is still such that we can apply corrections
to compensate for this extra risk. In the first place we can use trans-
cultural controls in judgments. In cultural studies, again we can use a
carefully formalized procedure in the interpretation of the data, and we
can develop our skills in the detection of bias by making it an explicit
object of study. Indeed, corresponding to this difficulty there might be
said to be an advantage, namely, that in psychology alone are we able to
make a direct investigation of the origins and effects of bias.

The second of the "self-involvement" difficulties is one that has to do
with the kind of understanding required in psychology. It has been argued

by a number of thinkers, Collingwood in particular, that in psychology and similar subjects such as history, we require a kind of understanding that we do not require elsewhere and without which we cannot have an adequate subject. This kind of understanding is called *empathy*, and it is obtained as well as required by virtue of the fact that we are studying individuals essentially like ourselves, possessing motives, the power of rational thought, and the sensitivities with which we ourselves are familiar. These qualities of human beings distinguish them from the inorganic realm which we study in the physical sciences, and they make necessary a kind of understanding in psychology that goes far beyond the mere comprehension of regularities, which suffices, so it is said, in the physical sciences.

For example, if you observe somebody leaving his house at a particular time, going outside, picking up some wood, bringing it back in and putting it on the fire which is burning low, you have observed a form of behavior whose meaning is quite transparent to a human observer. To the question, "Why did this man go out?" we reply that he went out to get some wood for the fire and we understand why he did that. This is something quite different from understanding that he did it, and of the greatest importance. On the other hand, in the case of planetary behavior, if we ask questions as to why certain things occur, all we can give in reply are sets of laws governing the forces and orbits of the planets. Now this special kind of understanding required for analysis of human behavior, so it is said, is not subject to precise laws of its own. Indeed, it is of its essence that it is not law-governed at all. Hence its existence and necessity constitute a barrier for psychology which will indefinitely prevent its conversion into a science like the other sciences.

The standard reply to this point about empathy is a very powerful one. On the one hand it is pointed out that people are often mistaken in the explanations that they give on the basis of having empathized with someone. That is, empathy is by no means a guaranteed procedure for obtaining understanding—it is, in fact, no different from any other kind of intuition. Subsumption of an event under a law, on the other hand, is an entirely objective procedure and leads either to immediate agreement or an immediate method of settling a disagreement. Secondly, it is pointed out that subsumption under a law *is* all that we need for understanding human behavior, contrary to our first impression of the matter. In the case of the human being going out to get some wood for his fire, we need a set of laws relating this form of behavior to the behavior of other people, when their need for warmth is and is not met, and to laws about cognitive perception of deficiency situations, etc. When we have these, the action will be fitted into a wider context in terms of which we would have all the appropriate kinds of understanding. Hence empathy is neither necessary nor sufficient for understanding, and so its involvement does not constitute an insurmountable barrier for psychology.

Thirdly, under this subgroup we have the so-called Oedipus effect. This unfortunate name for it does not refer to the Oedipus relationship which psychoanalysis has done so much to popularize; it is simply that Karl Popper drew the name from the same source. The Oedipus effect is the effect of a prediction upon its truth. In the myth, Oedipus was led to fulfill the prophecy which was made about him because of the steps he took to avoid fulfilling it. This was a case of a prediction whose announcement led to its own fulfillment. There is, of course, a converse case where the announcement of the prediction leads to its falsification, and the underdog effect which is sometimes thought to have contributed to the success of Harry Truman in 1948 is an example of this. The announcement of the results of the polls, which showed him losing, was enough to bring out supporters and keep his enemies at home, which, of course, confounded the predictors. These effects are called the "bandwagon" and "underdog" effects in the field of political competition. Now it is quite indisputable that planets do not react to predictions about their behavior in a way which either falsifies these or brings them about.

However, the psychologist is not usually very disturbed by the existence of these effects; he is likely to say that they simply demonstrate the existence of another relevant variable in the human, but that they in no way suggest that this variable's relationship to the final behavior is indeterministic. In other words, we must make a distinction between predictions which are not announced and those which are, and we may reasonably expect that on some occasions the actual behavior will be altered by the announcement that it will take a certain form. This alteration should itself be predictable, and the fact that we cannot announce what it is to the individual who is the subject without thereby having it falsified does not show that we cannot predict it.

By no means unrelated to the last of these three kinds of self-involvement difficulty is the oldest and perhaps the most interesting of all the candidates for a roadblock for scientific psychology—our sixth example— the freedom of the will. The connection with the last point about self-affecting predictions is through the way that both are related to the prediction of behavior. It is said traditionally that human beings alone amongst the animals have a capacity for free choice, which renders the possibility of exact prediction ephemeral.

There are two separate issues here, and before commenting on the one that concerns us particularly, I wish to clarify the distinction between them. The issues are the issues of determinism and of free will. In my view it is possible to have determinism without free will, free will without determinism, neither, or both. It so happens that in this world we have free will without determinism, but we *do not* have free will *because of the absence of* determinism. Recent developments in physics, in the opinion of almost all contemporary theoretical physicists, have demonstrated a fundamental uncertainty or indeterminism in the field of particle physics. It has been argued that this indeterminism does not carry over to the forms of human behavior, because such large numbers of particles are involved in any single piece of behavior that the uncertainties "cancel out." Not only is this directly false (although the number of the uncertainties will be diminished), but it can readily be shown that even if it had until now been true it could be falsified tomorrow. I shall return to this point later. We may conclude that there is an indeterminism about human behavior. However, this indeterminism is in no way connected with those slices of behavior which we refer to as decisions or choices, except in the tenuous way in which it is related to all forms of behavior. Choices are no more and no less determined than any other kind of human behavior.

One argument for the freedom of the will is based upon a direct perception of it within oneself, the feeling that one "can do either of two things" and that it is oneself and only oneself that determines which choice one makes, regardless of one's background or tendencies. Another line of argument here operates on the premises that morality is impossible without responsibility, that responsibility is impossible without free will, and that morality exists. From this it concludes that free will must exist. A similar argument begins from premises about the reality of regret.

The usual rebuttal of these lines of argument by the philosopher of science or the psychologist consists in identification of "free" acts as those which are determined by the individual himself and not by somebody else, i.e., to identify free acts as a subset of determined acts. If I seize someone and throw him through a plate glass window this will be a case of behavior which is determined, not by him but by me, hence will not be an example of a free act on his part. The free acts are those for which the determinants are internal to the organism, although they may have got there by virtue of his previous training, which is performed by some other person. The important thing is that they are *now* internal, and when he does something, as we say "voluntarily," it is these variables which are determining the actions. Hence the traditional distinction can be made, but within the framework of determinism.

An even more powerful attack on this sixth suggestion has been made by philosophers who have argued that freedom of the will is not only compatible with determinism but absolutely requires it. An action that was performed by an individual and which could be shown not to have been the outcome of his training and present character would be held to be one for which he was not responsible. It is the determination of our acts by our training and character that *makes* them our responsibility. Insanity often involves actions which are wholly out of character, and it is partly for this reason that we discharge the psychotic from responsibility. If quantum jumps in the brain were producing actions of ours, then we would say they were accidental just to the degree that the quantum jump is undetermined.

The seventh and eighth candidates are ones which I shall not be discussing at any length, but which raise some extremely familiar problems in the history of philosophy and psychology. They are the practical and theoretical difficulties posed by the nature of the mind. I shall refer to them as the problems of the inaccessibility and the non-physicality of the mind. The difficulties here are so profound that psychologists have sometimes been led to suppose that the best solution to them is to attempt to proceed as if there is not a mind. Of course such a view is absurd, but then so are most of the views on this subject propounded by great philosophers. They can only be understood when seen in the context of the arguments given by their authors *against* the alternative view. No view is absurd if it is the best view possible. The nonexistence of the mind might be forced on us unless we could overcome the difficulties by explaining what the mind is. I believe those difficulties can be overcome, so that we can avoid the absurdity; but they cannot be overcome easily.

Of course, other reactions besides denying the existence of the mind have been adopted by psychologists. They have maintained that it exists but has nothing to do with psychology; that it is relevant to psychology only insofar as it manifests itself in behavior; that psychology is concerned only with the brain and not the mind; and so on. The variety of these positions demonstrates to all clearly the unhappiness of psychologists with the mind. It is therefore quite understandable that people who are somewhat more pessimistic should suppose that the mind is by its nature either inaccessible or such that even if accessible, it could not be subjected to scientific psychological analysis. (Here you will recall that the psychoanalysts, about whose shortcomings we were enlarging above, are very much on the right side of the fence. They are not only willing to admit the existence of the mind but anxious to propose the existence of a second mind, namely the unconscious one. It is hardly surprising empirically-oriented psychologists have found this doubling of the undesirable to be grounds for a special skepticism about psychoanalysis.)

Notice the essential distinction between the seventh and eighth points. The mind might well be inaccessible, or very difficult to gain access to, but relatively simple in its internal workings. Or it might be relatively easy to gain access to, but extremely hard to handle when we had. Talking this way is of course to use a special analogy for what is at most a nonspecial entity. To give a specific example, it might be that a very simple mechanistic account of the connections between motives and manifestations of them is satisfactory, in the sense that when we know what a man's motives are we can readily predict his behavior; but it might still be very difficult to infer his motives from his behavior. Sixty diseases produce rises in the body temperature, and hence we cannot decide which is present from that symptom alone; but we can predict that symptom if we independently know which disease the patient has. This would be a case of inaccessibility without internal peculiarity. But on the other hand it might be, and has often been thought to be true, that the mind operates according to laws quite unlike those of diseases or chemical reactions; so that even if it were possible to "see into it" easily, we should be no better off for predicting its subsequent states and the consequent overt behavior.

I suppose the commonest reaction to people who raise this kind of point against psychology is to say that the mind is not something over and above all behavior, but rather a logical construction out of behavior, or a kind of theoretical entity of a rather different logical type from behavior but nevertheless inferable from it with reasonable facility. That is, the point is conceded that accessibility is difficult and its ontological status is unlike that of material objects. But it is pointed out that difficulty does not guarantee failure, and that we already have a very wide range of successful predictions to our credit in the study of behavior. May we not reasonably expect that with further research we shall find more? After all, nonphysical entities may also obey laws—and in particular, their connection with the ordinary observable aspects of behavior may be fully explained by laws. The various arguments about the relevance of ESP phenomena to psychology, supposing their existence is conceded for the moment, has amply illustrated the range of circumstances under which we might concede both points seven and eight without in any way conceding that psychology is up against some kind of barrier.

The ninth difficulty has probably at least as old a history as any other, and was discussed at considerable length by Aristotle. It is the problem of teleological causation. It is argued that in psychology and in psychology alone one of the main determining factors of behavior is the goal of that behavior. Now the goal of a pattern of behavior is in the future, and thus in psychology we must face the existence of causation operating from the future to the present, whereas in the rest of science we are concerned only with causation that operates from the past to the future. This not only places psychology in a unique position, but it may also require abandonment of the goal of prediction for scientific psychology.

However, there is a standard reply to this which contributes a great deal towards meeting the difficulty, if it does not finally eliminate it. It consists in saying that what really determines behavior is not the future goal, but the present state of anticipation or set towards that goal. Hence the science of psychology may proceed along strictly conventional lines so long as it recognizes that the causally effective agent in teleological behavior is in the present or past even though the realization of it may be in the future.

Tenth, and finally, we turn to the element of morality, which is in some sense a unique feature of the human causal system, by comparison with that of the animals or the inanimate objects inhabiting our world. It is held by some that moral considerations affect our behavior and clearly do not accord to physical laws, since they concern the realm of value rather than of fact and thus transcend any science of psychology. To this it is normally replied that morality may or may not be subject to study by the sciences but the behavior of human beings with moral ideas certainly is, and it is with this that we are concerned in psychology. The reply is along exactly the same lines as are appropriate when dealing with the alleged nonphysicality of the mind; *it* may be nonphysical, but it is only with its effects that we are concerned, and these are certainly physical.

A final footnote: it may be puzzling why in this list which surely includes some rather unpromising candidates, there should be no mention of the human characteristic of originality. This has certainly been held by many people to constitute a uniquely nonpredictive feature of human behavior. However, I am unable to see any respect in which it involves a different point from that of number eight (the nonphysicality of the mind) or possibly number two (the complexity of the individual). For the only sense of originality which is important for us is the sense in which it produces results that we could not have foreseen. And since it is clearly a product of the mind (*pace* radical behaviorism) its existence must be due to some special property of the mind. Naturally it meets the same difficulties as objection eight.

There, then, we have the ten candidates for the title "Last Frontiers of Psychology." And there we have the usual "tough-minded" treatment of these candidates. It is my belief that neither the candidates as stated nor the rebuttals as stated constitute satisfactory positions.

Here, I shall discuss two or three of these in some more detail, and illustrate the weaknesses that I have in mind. I shall begin with numbers two and five.

Is it really true that the argument from the complexity of human behavior to the limitations of psychology is identical to the argument from the complexities of chemical behavior to the impossibility of precise chemistry? It is not I think true, and the reasons why it is not true are now available to us. In psychology, unlike in chemistry, we already know the existence of a number of crucial variables which are either inaccessible themselves or related to other variables which are in turn inaccessible. This was not so in chemistry; it was not so in astronomy, and it was not so in other subjects which at one stage looked complicated and turned out to be simple.

Let me see if I can make this a little more precise.

It is clear that an important type of problem in psychology is the problem of the prediction of behavior by an individual at a date substantially later than the date at which the prediction is made using data which is, of course, separated by a similar interval from the predicted act or state. In this respect psychology is like astronomy, where long-term predictions are important. Typical examples of such problems are problems about the success of a particular student in his college career, based upon his high school performance; the problem of predicting the success of a marriage given all data that we can currently gather about the personality of the prospective partners; the effect in the long run of a particular kind of diet or drug on people with a particular character or problem; the effect on morale or work output of sustained noise at a certain level or a variation in the controlling attitudes in the power group, etc., etc. Now some psychologists are unwilling to accept this kind of problem as a fair task for their subject. I want to make clear that although I do not consider it to be the only task of psychology, it seems to me a definitional matter that it is one of the tasks for psychology. Questions of a "pure" kind, such as whether instrumental learning occurs in the invertebrates or whether certain kinds of latent learning occur in the white rat strains or whether nonsense syllables can be better retained under certain laboratory conditions, such problems are indeed part of the province of psychology, but they are not the only ones it must try to handle. Predictions about behavior under rigidly controlled conditions and over short intervals are predictions and they are important, but they are less important, practically speaking, than the examples that I have mentioned. Certainly they are not more important unless one thinks of psychology as concerned only with laboratory behavior. Psychology cannot altogether abandon its connection with the applied problems, without abandoning its claims to be a science concerned with such problems. Now it is quite clear that with respect to problems of this kind psychology is never going to achieve the success in prediction that astronomy does because—to put the matter in one kind of technical jargon—the human being in his environment is an open system, constantly interfered with by variables from outside whose behavior we cannot fully predict. One might put it in another way by saying that a human being is no more predictable than the changes in his environment which affect him significantly. These include, of course, the weather, wars, health, love, job changes, and a large number of other variables which clearly are not predictable by the working psychologist. The girl that happens to sit next to you in the library in your first year and whom you marry in your second year (or don't marry in the second year but as a result do no work in the second year) certainly affects your behavior in college no matter what your high school scores are—and the fact that she will sit next to you is quite beyond the predicting power of any psychologist now or in the future.

The complexity of human behavior is never better demonstrated than by its sensitivity to a wide range of environmental variables; and this sensitivity is what constitutes the serious threat for psychology's ultimate success as a predicting instrument.

Supposing we were to move to what we might call conditional predictions. Given enough data about an individual could we not be certain that we could say of him exactly what he would do under such and such specified conditions, without any commitment to conclusions as to whether these conditions arise or not?

However, we here come up against other kinds of difficulties. For example, it is well-known that there are a number of late-maturing genes which are determinants of crucial areas of behavior, and whose presence cannot be detected by any measurements of behavior up until the time they begin to take effect. Again there are dietary and other changes which can lead to the formation of a brain tumor, with its consequent effect on behavior and on one's conditional predictions. One of the sources of brain tumors is presumably radiation, and the same radiations have another effect of some significance for the scope of successful hypothetical or conditional predictions. They mutate the genes in the germ plasm, and the result of this is that the behavior of the next generation may be different from that of the present one in a way which is not predictable from the present generation, even if we were to throw in all the laws of Mendelian inheritance as well.

Hence I am arguing that psychology by its very nature is concerned with, i.e., committed to, the treatment of unconditional predictions in a way very like the way astronomy is so concerned. It is not like the way in which chemistry is oriented, because there we are mainly interested in the properties of various substances, examples of which can be constructed at any time and must by definition have the same properties. There will be within psychology, as there is within the general study of the heavens, a pure branch, corresponding to astrophysics, whose concern will be with conditional predictions. These conditional predictions will, of course, convert into unconditional predictions under controlled conditions, e.g., in the laboratory or in ideal thought experiments. But there is a very large part of psychology which will never be amenable to treatment by the simple application of the laws that apply in the controlled circumstances. The secret of the success of observational astronomy is just exactly that the ideal conditions of astrophysics are very nearly realized in the heavens. But the gap between the ideal conditions in psychology and actual circumstances of learning and emotional interaction is enormous. This simple fact about the distance between the ideal case and the actual case has been very poorly recognized. The pathetic attempts of mathematical economics to produce an exact formal subject perfectly illustrate the point. A subject is not made exact by the use of exact procedures in the discussion of a model. The important question is how far the model is from reality. In the case of mathematical economics—by and large—the model is boringly distant from reality. (An interesting analogy arises in a field far distant from the physical sciences: the mathematical analysis of logical processes, the discipline referred to as mathematical or formal logic, which itself suffers sadly from this concentration on formal precision at the expense of applicability.)

Now all these difficulties arise simply because of the complexity of human behavior and its interaction with the environment. But as a result of studying them with a little more care, we are able to see that the analogy with the development of some of the other sciences is quite remote, and consequently that the pessimist about the future predictive efficiency of psychology may well be justified although quite able to concede that in other subjects this has not been the course of events. Not only mutations, but minor injuries, alterations in the diet, coincidences in the people one meets at a cocktail party, the weather on a particular day, and so on—all of these tiny, highly unpredictable events may seriously or crucially affect one's future actions or indeed one's future life. The human organism is indeed an open system, but this is not the important point; it is an open system which is extraordinarily sensitive to variations in the input. One might, of course, argue that none of this is of great importance because these environmental changes are themselves in principle predictable. Anyone who argues in this way has failed to see that the probability of correct prediction becomes vanishingly small, if it is really unlikely that we shall never in fact be able to predict these environmental changes. There may be some point to the remark that we can in principle track down a full explanation of any given human act. There is virtually no point to the remark that we could in principle predict every human act. It is an empty recitation of the formula of determinism, and unlike the other remark which does at least have in its favor the advantages of restriction to a specific finite act, the corresponding claim that prediction, extending as it does into the indefinite future, becomes increasingly absurd as we become conscious of the way in which minor unpredictabilities pile upon each other to produce gross divergencies of the actual future from any future which we shall ever be in a position to predict.

Psychology suffers from the fact that we know too many of the simple things about human behavior before we consider the possibility of a science of psychology. By this I mean that we are unwilling to say that facts, such as the fatiguing effect on human performance of running a mile, the interest in role-playing, the existence of enormous variations in social morality, the psychophysiological gross facts about the limits of acuity and tolerance amongst humans, are all known to us from common experience. Psychology has to go on from this point, and it has to go on in staggeringly complex fields.

So the difficulties with psychology and the social sciences arise from two sources. First, there is this definitional trick which steals from psychology the kind of information that would be counted as scientific if it were not already known. The kind of information which we already know about human beings would constitute part of the scientific study of comparative behavior if it were known about Martians. The mating behavior of the eel is scientifically a discovery; but the mating behavior of human beings is not—at least in its gross features—something which we can regard as a contribution of psychology. And on the other hand there is this problem of complexity. At a matter of fact the analogy between the behavior in the physical sciences is really very close, with regard to this second point. It is not at all close if we take Newtonian dynamics, or astrophysics as the typical physical science. But the working of the physical scientist currently employed by one of the large research laboratories, whether financed by industry or by an institute, is not the dealing with problems and solutions that are even approximate to the simplicity and precision of the astronomical ones. In aerodynamics, particularly dealing with speeds beyond Mach 1, in turbulent flow hydrodynamics, in elasticity work, conductivity work, metallurgy, etc., there are very powerful limitations on practical predictability, and even on theory-based conditional predictability. I add the qualification "theory-based," because in these practical fields in the physical sciences it is frequently possible to achieve conditional predictions, where the conditions simply specify a repetition of a set of conditions whose effect we have already examined. It is commonly though by no means universally possible to reproduce conditions in physical sciences (the exceptions are very noticeable where working with fatigue effects, for example), whereas in the behavioral sciences the very unit of investigation—the individual human organism or some group containing these as elements—is constantly changing in its dispositional properties and hence potential reactions. Nevertheless, in a subject such as meteorology we find a physical science with problems virtually identical to those of the behavioral sciences. One of the crucial problems forced on the subject by its relationship to other fields of man's activities is the prediction of precipitation, and it is this kind of event which exhibits the same sensitivity to minor variations in the accessible variables which themselves exhibit the same disinclination to recur in identical configurations, with the result that there are extremely significant limitations on the maximum efficacy of precipitation-predictions. This is not simply due to weaknesses in our meteorological theories, nor is it due to shortages of information in any real sense. We *could* improve our theories, and we could improve our supply of data, but it is now foreseeable that improvements of this kind will only give us an asymptotic approach to a level of predictive success that is quite far from being satisfactory.

Let us now turn from the assessment of the complexity problem to the set of problems connected with the free-will area and self-affecting predictions—what Popper has called, in talking about one kind, the Oedipus effect.

It is usually conceded quite readily that in the social sciences we must face the possibility of a prediction interacting with itself so as to bring about its own truth or falsehood. But the point is not thought to be one of great gravity, because it is usually said that we must simply make a distinction between behavior which is announceably predictable, i.e., behavior where the statement that it will follow a certain path has no effect upon the path that it follows, and behavior which is affected by statements about it. It is quite true, psychologists grant, that we cannot always tell people just what they are going to do without risking being wrong, in circumstances where if we had kept quiet and simply written our prediction down, we would have been correct. But although this is a special feature of the behavioral subjects, it is not an insuperable barrier to their progress, because the prediction can always be made (in principle) even if it cannot always be announced to those to whom it refers.

But this dismissal is far too quick. In fact there is an extremely serious problem here.

Let us look into the question whether there may not be a rather wider range of cases that constitute difficulty than merely those in which a prediction is announced to the people whom it concerns. Suppose that instead of announcing the prediction the predictor announces that he has made a prediction. Or suppose that he simply sits in the corner and smirks, in a way which makes clear to the predictee that he has made a prediction. Now the predictee might reason to himself as follows: if it had not been for the fact that the predictor thinks he knows what I am going to do, I would have done X. Now however I am tempted to do Y, just to show the predictor that he is wrong. However, may it not be that the predictor has taken account of this possible reaction by me and consequently has predicted Y? So perhaps I should go ahead with my first plan. On the other hand, it may be that he has foreseen that I shall argue in the way I have just argued, and has predicted X after all. Now it is clear that nothing the predictee can do will *guarantee* the frustration of the prediction, since in fact the predictor may have all these wiles at his command. But there is a strategy open to the predictee, which enormously increases the likelihood that he will falsify the prediction. Hereafter I shall refer to the predictee in these circumstances where his dominant motivation is to falsify the prediction as the Avoider. We are thus involved in a competition between the Predictor and the Avoider and we may refer to these two competitors as P and A. A knows that, however comprehensive P's knowledge of A's psychology is, P does not have complete knowledge about the future behavior of everything in the universe. A's preferred strategy then is to arrange that his selection be dominated by some physical system that is highly unpredictable by P. In a very simple case it would be sensible for him, supposing that he has to choose between X and Y, to flip a coin. He may be confident that P cannot predict the flip, and he knows that this will reduce to one chance in two the likelihood of success by P. Typically, these P—A situations are ones where A has open to him more than two alternatives. If he has N alternatives open to him, he may then switch to the use of a standard gambling device to reduce P's chance of success to one in N. This is a nice case of the distinction between conditional and unconditional prediction; it is easy to predict, given the motivational structure of A, that he will do whatever the turn of the wheel indicates he will do. But this is no good for P, because P wishes to predict what he will in fact do, and hence needs to know how the wheel will come up. It is easy to demonstrate, incidentally, that the range of important cases where the conditions we are talking about are met is very large; most major strategic problems in times of war, most important decisions in a complex game of chance or semi-chance, such as poker or bridge, many interpersonal dominance conflicts, most of the great battles for control of a market or a company in the business world, critical fights in the political field, etc., all yield the counter-prediction motivation and the multiple alternative possibilities.

At this stage in the development of the strategies and counter strategies it must be noted that one might well turn, not to a physical randomizing device such as dice, a roulette wheel, cards, or a coin, but one might instead use some human randomizer. For example, one might select one square on a large sheet of squared paper, with perhaps forty thousand squares on it, and one might ask an artist to use the sheet of paper for an abstract painting of some kind, and one might then select from one's alternative courses of possible action in terms of the following code: if the square has only one color showing on it in the resultant painting, and this color is blue, then one will select alternative 1; if green, then alternative 2 ... if it has two colors discernible on it then one will select the alternative corresponding to the sum of the numbers allotted to the pure shades, etc. In this way we are making use of a very important kind of unpredictability

—the unpredictability of original creations. The idea that one can "in principle" predict the details, or even the key elements in every future original idea or creation, seems to me to place so great a strain on the use of the term "in principle" as to constitute a reduction of it to triviality. But triviality is a long way from falsehood, and to have pointed out that psychologists are unlikely ever to render the thought of physicists superfluous by predicting all the new physical theories, is not to have pointed out that the behavior of the physicist transcends discoverable laws of behavior. These laws may be so complex, or require for their application such complex and inaccessible conditions, that the task is beyond any practical achievement; but this is not to say that it could not in principle be done. I believe that we can make a stronger point against the thesis that human behavior is in principle predictable.

As a preliminary step let us take account of the possible reply to our last case by abandoning the use of ordinary physical randomizers, which might be said themselves to be predictable in principle, and switch to the use of what we might call a "fundamental randomizer." In terms of our present conception of quantum theory it is not in principle possible to predict the moment at which a radioactive atom will radiate an electron. By setting up a Geiger counter in proximity to a small quantity of radioactive salt, we can readily arrange a system which will ring a bell or make a mark at a moment which is in this very strong sense unpredictable. And by setting up a suitable code, the Avoider can translate the result from the apparatus into a selection of one of his alternative courses of action. With this level of practice we are, of course, far and away ahead of any actual practicable predictions by P. However, we have not yet reached the last stage in the examination of the possibilities of avoidance behavior. But as a practical point one should note that the practical success of A's strategy in switching to the fundamental randomizer can be extended to a wide range of cases by a careful analysis of elementary choice situations, directed at converting them into choices between a wide range of equally satisfactory alternatives. The typical choice situation is one in which there is a slight utility difference between the alternatives that are open to one, especially if one takes account of a wide range of these. But this utility difference is typically far less than the disutility of having one's choice predicted by P. Consequently, it is typically best to regard the range of alternatives as equally satisfactory, provided one can practically guarantee surprising P. One is then in a position to increase the number N, referred to above as a large enough value to ensure the virtual certainty of P's failure. At this stage it is also appropriate to notice that our range of cases may be extended to include, not only those where A does not know what P has predicted but only that P has made a prediction, but also those cases where A is not certain that a P exists, but is certain that he wishes to act in a way that would not be predictable by P if he does exist.

We have so far been considering a strategy on A's part that might be called hitching a ride with the most unpredictable part of the universe. That is, A can clearly switch his behavior so that it is critically dependent upon the most unpredictable element in the universe. We shall shortly go on to a rather more complicated type of strategy. But might it not be suggested that there is some sense of "unpredictable" in terms of which everything in the universe is predictable in principle. To hold such a view is, of course, to renounce the usual interpretation of modern fundamental physics. It is in fact to have a hope about the future which should really be placed in the class of faiths rather than reasonable beliefs along with the view that mankind will survive. It expresses a commitment to a kind of physics which we now appear to have abandoned. It is no more than this, it has no scientific sanction, but only a metascientific one. And this metascientific sanction is entirely based on optimism. It is always nicer to have theories of a kind that predict everything; but this is hardly grounds for supposing that they are more likely than the other kind, or that they must ultimately always be possible.

We now turn to a very interesting development of the P-A competition. This strategy applies to a more general class of cases than the preceding ones, namely to the class where the range of choices is two or more, and it furthermore offers the possibility of a very high likelihood of falsifying P's prediction. But it is not quite so easy to manage. Its genesis may be understood if we imagine that A decides he is tired of utilizing the unpredictability of some other phenomenon and decides to utilize his own capacity to act contrary to any known prediction. The strategy consists in making a shadow-prediction *for* P, and then acting contrary to it. It is a sophistication of the very earliest kind of consideration in these avoidance situations. In its most elementary form, the procedure is for A to obtain knowledge of the data and laws that P is using in predicting A's behavior, and using these, to make the same prediction that P is making about A, and then to act differently. This is not, of course, in general feasible. However, there is a wider range of cases in which A has access to the same text books and sources of data as P, and uses these in order to make the shadow-prediction, which he then falsifies. But naturally he can only falsify these predictions once or twice without P realizing what is going on. Or, to put it another way, P cannot be using as data the fact that A has made a shadow-prediction, and this cannot be a very general condition. It appears clear that as long as either P or A is one jump ahead of the other with respect to information about basic laws or data as to the complexity of the strategy that the other is employing, just so long he will be able to win the competition at that trial. In practice, there will always be a very substantial gap in the data on each side. But for the enthusiast about the predictive possibilities in the social sciences this should not be serious, since he should be able to fill in the gap by making predictions from the data and laws he already has. Otherwise, of course, we will be insisting that the data includes everything that happens in the universe up till the time of the decision, and this will, of course, include knowledge as to the Avoider's views and as to the Predictor's predictions, and hence will guarantee—given the state of motivation of the Avoider—the final action. This would clearly be frustrating the conditions of "fair competition." Or, looking at it from the point of view of the Avoider, *his* data will have to include the Predictor's prediction, and hence will guarantee that the Avoider can falsify it. One side or the other must be favored in such provision of data. There is no such situation as one in which both sides are given all the data up to the moment when the final prediction is made by the Predictor and the final decision made by the Avoider, since the action of each is altered by this information about the other, in an entirely non-convergent way, (apart from special cases, such as predicting the behavior of a compulsive, which we are not considering).

Now, if there were laws which fully determined the behavior of human beings from certain initial conditions and if these laws and conditions could be known and combined, then one of two things would follow: either it *would* be possible for the Predictor to predict the Avoider's behavior, and the Avoider would know this and not be able to act otherwise, i.e., he would have lost his freedom of action—he would, so to speak, be a prisoner in his own body, seeing himself do what he does not want to do; or, on the other hand, the laws would not yield a univocal solution, which is to say that they are not deterministic laws at all. Now, to finish the argument off quickly, it is a fact of our experience that under certain motivational conditions, we simply can and do act so as to falsify any predictions which we have grounds for believing have been made about our behavior. It necessarily follows from this that either there cannot be laws and antecedent conditions which do fully determine our behavior, or they cannot be known to us. The moment that laws are uncovered which would enable a P to predict the behavior of an A, from that moment the A will act contrary to the predictions based on these laws (because he makes a shadow-prediction using them, and hence acts contrary to it, since he believes that P will be making a prediction in terms of them). So we might say that laws about human behavior (in this field) are true until applied!

The situation is actually slightly more complicated, because A will know that P is aware of A's motivation, and hence will simply not make a prediction using these laws, unless he believes they are unknown to A. The reflex nature of the problem is again apparent. What is quite clear, however, is that this is not a problem with a closed solution; once one has got to the point where the oscillations appear, there is no diminution of them, no convergence to a definite answer. The exception to this, of course, is when one side has laws or data the other does not. In such cases, the best strategy for the other side, once he sees that he is losing after a number of trials, is to switch to the randomizing procedure. Meanwhile, he would, of course, undertake the kind of research that would be required to provide for him the information which the other is using in making his predictions. Having acquired this, he might then switch back into the big game, where there is a definite chance of his wholly escaping the predictions of the other side. (I have now switched into symmetrical language, because it is clear that in the P-A competition, each is acting as a predictor and—in a certain sense—each is acting as an avoider, i.e., one who wishes either to act contrary to the prediction of the other or to predict contrary to the prediction of the other. Taking predicting as an action, we have a general symmetry between the two sides.)

The general family of cases is now widened further. Not only may the prediction not be announced, not only may it not be announced that a prediction has been made, but *no action can be taken that shows that a prediction has been made successfully by P*, without it very rapidly becoming the case that P will fail in his prediction since A will switch to randomizing. (We here see the one element of asymmetry in the situation, since if *P* switches to randomizing his predictions, upon discovering that A is shadow-predicting correctly, then he will probably do worse than he was doing before.)

Summing the situation up then, we see that we can operate according to unknown laws, laws known only to God, or even laws known to people who do not disclose them or disclose that they have them by their behavior. But there cannot be universally known laws governing all human behavior, and I take this to be a logical point of considerable importance, which goes beyond the point that one cannot *announce* predictions and expect them not to be falsified. It cannot be known that there *are* predictions without it being almost certain that they will be falsified, and it certainly cannot be known that there are predictions and how they were made, without it being virtually certain that they will be falsified.

Of course, there is nothing peculiar about human beings, by comparison with machines, in this complexity. It is perfectly easy to program a pair of machines to play the game of predictor and avoider, and it is, I think, easy enough to see that the programs would have to be indeterminate at some point. Popper has described a mild version of this, where we have a computer which is aiming to predict whether a certain light will be on or off at a certain time, and the light switch is governed by a mechanism which responds to the computer's prediction by switching the light on if the output tape says the light will be off, and vice-versa. In such a case, it is clear that the computer can never be right. This, of course, is only half of the situation that we have been talking about, and it also involves a very much simplified arrangement, in that, for example, the computer is not smart enough to see what is happening, whereas a human being could, and after a suitable analysis of the switch-controlling mechanism, would be able to devise an output tape which would make the prediction, though in language which would not bring about its falsification. This kind of dodge, and various other ones appropriate to that situation, will not save the predictor's position in the case we are talking about. (Popper has also discussed a more complex case, interestingly related to ours.)

So there cannot be laws which can determine the behavior of a human being completely, unless they are unknown to him. The moment that the set is announced, he can, of course, at least with respect to many kinds of law—falsify it or them by acting contrary. I take this to constitute an important part of the claim for free will. People do have the freedom to do the opposite of what it is predicted they will do, in many cases; they do have the freedom to invalidate any purported law of human behavior, in many large areas of behavior. And it is this freedom which people have intuitively felt, though often incorrectly described, when they support the free-will position with the so-called subjective argument.

I do not think that the situation described constitutes a disproof of determinism. I take determinism to be the thesis that all behavior is governed by precise laws, and not the thesis that these can be known. Any attempt to connect determinism with predictability, as has frequently been done, will however run into the kind of trouble I have been talking about. For it is not true that in principle one could predict the behavior of the avoider, unless one restricts his information compared with one's own. And, of course, it is hardly interesting that by restricting information one can predict behavior. If you tell somebody that the only way he can live is by acting in a certain way, and you do this under circumstances where he has no choice but to believe you, it is then possible to predict with great reliability that he will act in that way, provided that it does not infringe any other deeply ingrained aversions.

It is also true, I believe, that determinism is compatible with moral responsibility, though I do not agree with Dickinson Miller that moral responsibility or free will necessarily require determinism in the sense described. A very weak kind of determinism, of the kind that we already know to exist from observation, is all that is necessary; i.e., just enough to make it possible to identify people by their behavior and in terms of their characters. An important feature of the considerations just adduced seems to me that they do not impugn the possibility of giving an explanation of everything that happens, what we might call retroactive determination, but they do make predictive determinism quite limited in its scope. Explanatory accounts will always be possible, because—apart from independent grounds for suspecting the nonexistence of precise laws, such as quantum mechanics—there is no reason to deny that laws have operated up to the point where they are deliberately infringed upon. These laws may be used in explaining new events prior to their discovery. (And also some events after their discovery, viz. those by people unaware of them, unable to avoid their force or to discover their application.) There are many ears to whom it will sound odd to talk of explanation in terms of a law with a finite range in time. To examine this point would take us too far afield here, and I shall simply say that insofar as subsumption under laws can constitute explanation, it is nearly always perfectly satisfactory that the laws have a limited scope, or even that they involve reference to individuals. We are perfectly familiar with the fact that in our own lives a certain consideration may have constituted a compelling reason for action up to a particular age, and thereafter lose its force. The same possibility exists for unconscious motivation, indeed for inanimate objects too, not because of the possibility of counterpredictive behavior, but because laws may change or cease to hold with time. The urge to deny this springs from the attempt to build into the notion of law an answer to all the questions that lie behind the request for an explanation of a particular event, whereas an explanation undertakes to answer only one or a few of them.

What is the overall effect of these considerations? The frontiers of psychology are played down by its nature and by man's nature, and they will eternally prevent it from attaining the status of Newtonian dynamics, astrophysics, and other highly precise long-range predictive sciences. If, on the other hand, one is prepared to see the ideal of science not in these terms, but in terms of providing explanations that can be thoroughly grounded, providing highly reliable statistical predictions of a very useful kind in nearly all cases, providing classifications of an enlightening and fruitful kind, facilitating control in the practical sphere, and at all times subscribing to the requirements of testability and simplicity, then there are no barriers to the development of psychology. I have attempted to stress that the instinctive and often poorly expressed response of scholars in the humanities and those with religious or anti-scientific axes to grind cannot be dismissed as easily as empirical scientists have supposed, a supposition shared by many of the empiricist philosophers. They cannot be accepted either, in the form presented, but there remains a residue of truth in them which does indeed constitute a sound basis for constructing a careful distinction between the kind of science psychology is and can be and the kind of science that we sometimes think of as the proper or fully-developed ideal of science. Notice that I am not suggesting that there is a definite limit of accuracy in prediction or adequacy in explanation which we shall reach and beyond which we shall not be able to progress. I see us as continually increasing the range and efficiency of the science of psychology, but only asymptotically with respect to a degree of accuracy which falls far short of that which other sciences have attained. My view of the future is thus one of continual progress, of indefinite improvement, but not of improvement past every level of accuracy. Into the higher reaches of precision we shall never push psychology, without converting it into an inapplicable subject, or into neurophysics with its intrinsic limitations. These limitations are three: quantum uncertainty, unmanageable complexity of data, and problems of access to the data in the relevant circumstances (people just *won't* keep wearing ten thousand channel electro-encephalographs all the time).

Any student of the history of science knows very well the extent to which the conception of what that science ought to do and ought to be dominates the time and organization of research, in the field, often for decades or centuries. I am attempting to divert the attention of the practising social scientist from one goal to another. I believe that the effect of this point, in itself a relatively simple one, may be very considerable. That is the constructive side of my criticisms. On the laudatory side let me conclude by saying that the last few decades of work in psychology have produced a set of refinements and extensions of the idea of scientific method without parallel in the history of the physical sciences, and without parallel in history for its potential contribution to human welfare. The sophistication and efficiency of modern experimental design and analysis in psychology is comparable with anything that physics has to offer, and comparable not only in difficulty but in fertility. I only hope that we are able to utilize the magnificent tools that have been created for us in psychology. If we do, we shall have no need to regret the fact that humans are both complicated and self-conscious and its attendant consequence that psychology will never be like Newtonian astronomy.

Chapter 4 | **On the Conceptual Basis
of the Biological Sciences**

*Ernst Caspari
Professor and Chairman
Department of Biology
University of Rochester*

But the zoologist or morphologist has been slow, where the physiologist has long been eager, to invoke the aid of the physical or mathematical sciences; and the reasons for this difference lie deep, and are partly rooted in old tradition and partly in the diverse minds and temperaments of men. To treat the living body as a mechanism was repugnant, and seemed even ludicrous, Pascal; and Goethe, lover of nature as he was, ruled mathematics out of place in natural history. Even now the zoologist has scarce begun to dream of defining in mathematical language even the simplest organic forms. When he meets with a simple geometrical construction, for instance in the honeycomb, he would fain refer it to psychical instinct, or to skill and ingenuity, rather than to the operation of physical forces or mathematical laws; when he sees in snail, or nautilus, or tiny foraminiferal or radiolarian shell a close approach to sphere or spiral, he is prone of old habit to believe that after all it is something more than a spiral or a sphere, and that in this 'something more' there lies what neither mathematics nor physics can explain. In short, he is deeply reluctant to compare the living with the dead, or to explain by geometry or by mechanics the things which have their part in the mystery of life.

D'ARCY WENTWORTH THOMPSON, *On Growth and Form*

On the Conceptual Basis of the Biological Sciences

If one reads the recent literature on the Philosophy of Science, one is struck by the fact that it deals almost exclusively with the inorganic sciences, particularly physics. The reason seems to be that physics is the oldest and most basic of the modern natural sciences, and has as a consequence developed further than the others. It is often implied that the differences between the different branches of natural science are fundamentally only differences in degree of development, and that the same concepts are applicable to all of them.

Furthermore, much of the writings on the Philosophy of Science deal with classical physics, and omit references to developments of the past 20 or 30 years. This is probably necessary, since it would be very hard for a professional philosopher to keep up with all the advances and movements in physics while at the same time following the developments in modern philosophy. The impression is, however, sometimes obtained that the conceptual basis of the natural sciences is relatively static. This impression is reinforced by the fact that many practising scientists are not consciously aware of changes going on in their own conceptual framework during their own time.

The life sciences, on the other hand, have not been extensively treated as a separate object of philosophical inquiry in recent times. Around the turn of the century, there existed a vigorous controversy about the philosophical basis of biology. But the further development of biology has made many of the questions raised obsolete, and few biologists at present are interested in the old topics of discussion.

Biology, during the past 20 years, has undergone changes which have revolutionized our understanding of the life processes, particularly at the molecular level which is closest to the realm of physics. The question may therefore be raised whether we can still speak of a specific conceptual basis of biology, or whether we are dealing only with an aspect of a common conceptual basis of all natural sciences. Since great progress has been made in recent years in the explanation of life processes in physical terms, a reconsideration of the concepts of biology from the point of view of modern biology seems indicated.

Biology, as a natural science, shares the fundamental characteristics and aims of all natural sciences. The raw material of all sciences consists in statements about observations. The task of any science is to bring these statements about observations into a systematic order which can be grasped by the human mind. The unspoken assumption behind this ordering activity is the belief that some kind of order which can be formulated by the human mind exists in reality. This assumption is based on faith, but few people who do not share this faith in the first place will choose to become natural scientists.

In biology two methods for the obtaining of observations and ordering the statements about them are used. One consists in the comparison of existing organisms, species, or organs with each other, or with remains of extinct organisms. The other one derives its statements about observation from experiments. Both types of statement form an integral part of biology. The method of comparison leads to the establishment of similarities and dissimilarities between objects: individuals or structures. It has sometimes been called the "order-analytical" method. The experimental method leads ideally to the establishment of causal connections, and is therefore called the "causal-analytical" method. *Mainx* (1955) objects to both of these terms, because neither method leads to analytical statements but both lead to predictions. "Search for order" and "search for causal connections of processes," according to *Mainx*, would be better expressions. But both methods involve fundamentally a search for order, and differ from each other in the way in which observations are obtained and in the ordering principles employed.

Whatever name is given to these two methods, the difference between them and the results to which each one of them leads are obvious. The method of comparison finds its main biological applications in taxonomy and comparative anatomy, to which comparative physiology and biochemistry may be added as more recent fields. The method of comparison has in many older discussions been regarded as the typical method of biology, since 19th century biology was predominantly concerned with questions of this type. The existence of different types of organisms, species, of plants and animals, and their greater or less similarity with each other constitutes certainly one of the most striking aspects of the living world, and is obvious even to the unsophisticated observer. It should not be concluded, however, that the method of comparison, the "order-analytical" method, is restricted to biology. It has been applied repeatedly, and with good success, in the inorganic sciences.

One example is the periodic system of the chemical elements proposed by Mendeléeff. If the elements are arranged in the order of their relative atomic weights, elements with similar chemical characteristics occur at regular intervals, so that an orderly descriptive system of the elements can be established. This system had predictive value in so far as the existence of elements not yet found at the time could be deduced from the table, and their chemical and physical properties predicted. Another system established on the basis of the "order-analytical" method is the *Russell* diagram relating the luminosity of different stars to their color, i.e. their emission spectrum. This diagram again has predictive value since stars which have not yet been measured are expected to fall on one of the two lines of the diagram, and would not be expected to be distributed in the diagram at random. (fig. 1)

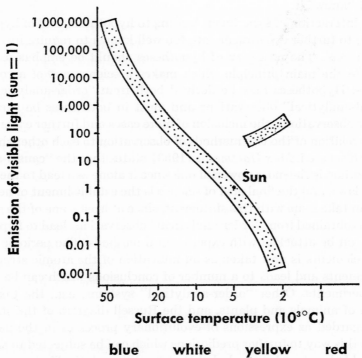

FIGURE 1. The Russell diagram of distribution of stars; the shaded portions indicate the highest frequencies of stars.

The experimental or "causal-analytical" method of inquiry has been the main method of research in the inorganic sciences, and has become increasingly more prominent in biology during the 20th century. It was introduced by Galileo, who called it "metodo risolutivo," and consists in the experimental analysis of individual cases which are assumed to stand for a whole range of cases. Galileo was quite aware of having invented a new method of approach, and his analysis of free fall is still as good an example of the procedure as any other. It is important to realize that his quantitative observations on free fall led him to the formulation of a new concept, "acceleration," the change of velocity in time. This concept leads on to more general hypotheses on the behavior of bodies in motion, e.g. sliding down on inclined surfaces, which can be tested by further observation. It should be emphasized that the equivalence of the two types of motion, viz. free fall and sliding down an inclined plane, is by no means as obvious as it appears to us who have taken an elementary physics course and have been exposed to the danger of flunking the course if we did not "know" it.

The interaction of experiment leading to hypothesis, and of hypothesis leading to further experiments are too well known to require further discussion here. The necessity of hypotheses should be emphasized, since they are the main principle which makes a science out of a collection of data. Hypotheses may be derived both from "order-analytical" and "causal-analytical" observations and must in both cases be verified by further observations, the inclusion of more cases and further experiments.

The relation of the two methods of observation to each other should be briefly discussed. *Max Hartmann* (1953) states that the "causal-analytical" method is the more powerful one since it alone can lead to the finding of new laws, and the final goal of science is the establishment of new laws. One can take issue with this statement, since at least some of the generalizations obtained from "order-analytical" observations lead to hypotheses which can be attacked with experimental methods. The periodic system of the elements is now taken as an indication of the atomic structure of the elements and leads to a number of conclusions which can be verified by experiments. Other "order-analytical" systems, e.g., the taxonomic system of animals and plants, and the Russell diagram of the stars, are now regarded as expressions of evolutionary processes in the past, and lead in this way to further predictions which can be subjected to analysis. It should therefore be concluded that "order-analytical" statements are a valid method of inquiry which lead to valid generalizations; they may be finally reduced to statements which are based on generalizations obtained from experimental data.

Both methods which have been discussed up till now are common to all of the sciences, and biology may at most be distinguished by the fact that it uses "order-analytical" observations more extensively than the inorganic sciences. The question may be raised whether there exist any methods or concepts which are used exclusively in the biological sciences and not in the inorganic sciences. In this connection the problem of purpose and function is important and crucial.

In antiquity, particularly in Plato and Aristotle, purpose is regarded as an explanatory principle. Aristotle states that "to know is to know by means of causes" (Posterior Analytics 94 a 20) and the Greek word "aitia" which is usually translated as "cause" has a teleological flavor and might be better translated as "reason." Aristotle's scientific method as applied to biology is set forth in the first book of *De partibus animalium*. There he argues: "Therefore another point for us to decide is which of these two Causes (i.e. Final Cause and Efficient Cause) stands first and which comes second. Clearly the first is that which we call the "Final" Cause— that for the sake of which the thing is formed—since that is the logos of the thing—its rational ground—and the logos is always the beginning for products of Nature as well as for those of Art." (*Part. Animal.* I 639 b 13-17.) The "Final Cause" here can definitely be rendered by the word purpose, a goal which exists prior to the thing. Aristotle was, of course, aware of the existence of cause-effect relations in the modern sense, and the "Efficient" or "Motive" Cause, the Cause which sets a process in motion, is an example of this. Most cause-effect relations, however, are designated by Aristotle by a different term, "ananke," necessity. "In the theoretical sciences (e.g. Mathematics), we begin with what already *is*; but in Natural Science with what is *going to be*: thus, we say, *Because* that which is going to be—health, perhaps, or man—has a certain character, *therefore* of necessity some particular thing, P, must be or must be formed; not *Because* P is now, or has been formed, *therefore* the other thing (health, or man) of necessity is now or will be in the future." (*Part. Animal.* I 640 a 1-6). In other words, necessity is not accepted as an explanatory concept, but as a means by which the "Final Cause" can express itself. "We point out that although Respiration takes place for such and such a *purpose* any one stage of the process follows upon the others *by necessity*." (*Part. Animal.* 642 a 31.)

Since the scientific revolution of the 16th and 17th centuries the attitude of scientists towards explanatory principles has completely changed. The scientific description of natural processes has centered around the establishment of cause-effect relations. Explanation by means of Final Cause or purpose is regarded as unscientific and meaningless. This has certainly gone so far in the physical sciences that any teleological question strikes us as meaningless. We cannot ask about the purpose of the planets for the sun, the purpose of electrons for an atom, or why it is *best* for the earth to be round. These questions would have been legitimate for

Plato and Aristotle, and the former actually raises the third question in *Phaedo.*

But in biology the need for corresponding questions persists and has given rise to a set of nonphysical concepts which are generally used: organ and function. An organ means a part of a living organism which has a specific function, and a function is an activity which is in some way necessary or useful for the organism. The use of the term "function" in physiology has definitely teleological implications and can in many instances be rendered by the word "purpose." If we say, e.g., that the function of the eye is the perception of light, we do not mean only that it is a structure which absorbs light, but also that it is used by the organism for the purpose of perceiving light.

It should be emphasized here that the teleological implications of the term "function" are not identical with the teleological principles of Aristotle. Function is not an explanatory term, but more a heuristic concept which enables us to ask meaningful questions. It is certainly not implied that it is a design (logos) which exists prior to the entity, as expressed in the quotation from Aristotle. It only means that in a biological system we may ask for the function of a part with respect to the whole, and that on this question we will obtain a meaningful answer. For example, in a well-known textbook of zoology (*Claus, Grobben and Kühn*, p. 675) Tömösvary's organ, an organ of the Diplopoda, a group of Millipedes, is described as "a sense organ with unknown function." To a biologist this means that it is an organ found in these animals, that its structure (nerve-supply, etc.) leads us to suspect that it has a sensory function and that the particular type of stimuli to which this organ responds has not been investigated. The possibility that this organ may have no function at all is not taken seriously.

It is sometimes claimed that the concept of function is only an auxiliary concept of heuristic value in describing the very complex biological systems. The implication of this claim is that we need the term to help us in the analysis of a complex system, but that as the analysis proceeds to a complete understanding of the system, the need for the use of this concept will disappear. It is therefore necessary to point out that the concept is also applicable in biological systems of the lowest degree of complexity, at the molecular level.

When the first electron micrographs of bacteriophages (viruses attacking bacteria) were published, it became immediately obvious that some of them have a complex form. They possess a "head" and a "tail." (fig. 2) For the biologist the question arose immediately: what are the functions

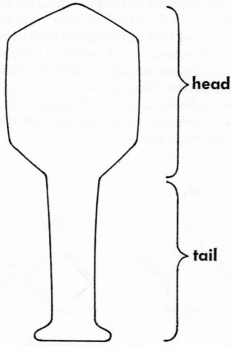

FIGURE 2. Sketch of bacteriophage T2. Drawn after electron micrographs by Dr. T. F. Anderson.

of the head and of the tail? This has turned out to be a meaningful question, because it leads to a meaningful answer. The head contains all the genetic information of the virus, i.e. the information necessary to produce more virus particles of the same kind. The tail is actually not a tail at all but an organ of attachment by which the virus makes contact with the host bacterium. The tail itself can be further analyzed in terms of function (*Garen and Kozloff* 1959, *Brenner et al.* 1960). The length of the tail contains a contractile sheath, consisting of about 200 protein molecules of molecular weight 50,000. This sheath surrounds a hollow core at the end of which there are numerous fibers which become attached to specific sites at the surface of the host bacterium. After attachment the tail releases an enzyme which digests the cell wall of the bacterium at the place of attachment. Finally, the genetic material from the head is injected through the hollow canal of the tail into the host bacterium, a process in which contraction of the sheath of the tail is apparently important. In general, the tail is composed of a certain number of molecules of different species, each with different physical characteristics and potentialities. All of them can be described with reference to their function, the role they play in the transfer of genetic material from the free virus to the host cell.

The functional point of view can be driven even further, since it can be applied to parts of molecules active in biological systems. Hemoglobin is a protein molecule found in the red blood cells of vertebrates which has the function of carrying oxygen from the lung, the seat of respiration, to the organs. It is known to consist of a protein proper, globin, to which are attached four identical molecules of smaller size, called heme, whose structural formula is as shown in Figure 3.

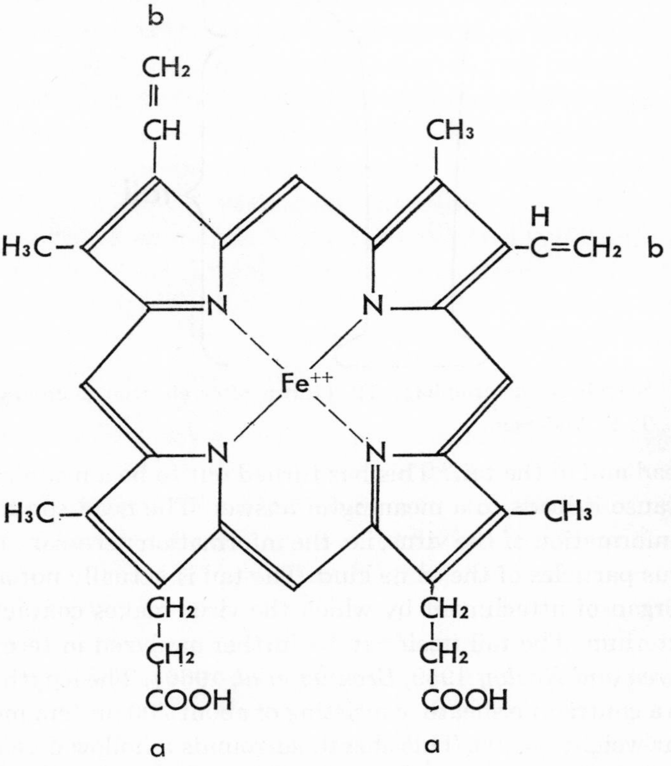

FIGURE 3. Structural formula of heme, the pigment moiety of hemoglobin.
    a. propionic acid side chains
    b. vinyl side chains

It can be seen that the molecule consists of a symmetrical ring structure surrounding an atom of Fe. To this ring structure are attached two propionyl-chains (a–a) and two vinyl-chains (b–b). The question may be asked: what is the function of the Fe atom, and what are the functions of the two kinds of side chains? The function of the Fe atom has been known for a long time: it combines reversibly with oxygen and carries it in the blood stream. The functions of the side chains have been analyzed by Granick and his collaborators (*Granick and Gilder* 1946, 1947). It could be shown that the propionyl-groups, together with the Fe atom, attach the heme molecule to the globin protein, and insure its correct orientation. The vinyl groups, because of their electronic arrangement, are necessary for the incorporation of the Fe atom into the ring, and for keeping it in its position. Again, the question as to the function of the side chains of heme leads to a meaningful answer, by relating their properties to the structure of a system of a higher order, in this case the hemoglobin molecule. It is clear that the same question cannot be asked of any organic molecule which is found outside the context of a living organism.

These examples show that the concept of function is not simply an auxiliary term which helps us to ask the right questions concerning very complex systems. It is, rather, an integral part of biological analysis. If, in the case of the tail of bacteriophage, one describes its molecular structure completely without mentioning the fact that it is an organ of attachment and fulfills a specific function in the life cycle of the organism, an important part of the description of the system is missing. In other words, the complete description of a biological structure or process consists of two parts: an analysis of its structure, composition and activity in physical and chemical terms, plus its function with respect to the superordinate system of which it forms a part.

The fact that biology is obliged to ask questions and use concepts which do not make sense if applied to inorganic systems has given rise to the dispute between vitalists and mechanists which raged in the second part of the 19th century. Vitalism argues that, since we can legitimately ask questions concerning organisms and organic structures which we do not use in the inorganic sciences, there must be something inherent in living organisms which is not present in inorganic systems. The mechanistic point of view proposes that all life processes can be reduced ultimately to physical and chemical terms and that it is the task of Biology to do this. Wherever concepts are used which cannot be reduced to chemical and physical terms they are preliminary and an expression of our present ignorance.

The doctrine of vitalism has been most consistently and clearly stated by Hans Driesch. His form of vitalism deals with the problem of the whole. As stated earlier, the concept of function implies that biological structures and processes have to be described with reference to the whole of which they form a part. Driesch admits that biological processes proceed in conformity with the causal laws of physics and chemistry, but he postulates that in addition life has some characteristic of its own which regulates the physical process in such a way that they proceed in a direction which tends towards the maintenance of the whole. This characteristic property of life is called "entelechy"; the similarity of the relation of entelechy and physical process and of "aitia and ananke" in Aristotle's system is striking. In Driesch's thinking there is always in the background the analogy with the machine which follows physical laws but needs an engineer to construct and direct it. Similarly, in Aristotle's arguments, the analogy with the artist or craftsman producing an object recurs over and over again.

Driesch proceeds to argue that there are certain biological problems which cannot in principle be explained in terms of physical and chemical mechanisms, and which constitute proof that an entelechy exists. Among these the most important are: 1. the ability of organisms to regulate, i.e. the ability, particularly at embryonic stages, to develop two complete wholes out of a divided organism; 2. the ability of identical reproduction; and 3. the behavior of organisms. Of these three main problems, the second one, identical reproduction, has found a simple and elegant explanation in purely physicochemical terms in the Watson-Crick model of DNA. Progress is being made in the description of behavioral processes and variables at the cellular and biochemical level, and although we cannot describe animal behavior in these terms at the present time, there is certainly hope that this problem will yield to such analysis in the future. The problem of regulation has not yet been successfully attacked in terms of chemical and physical concepts; but embryology in general has not been as fruitful a field of biological inquiry in the last 20 years as genetics and biochemistry.

Most biologists have continued to work on mechanistic premises, i.e. they have tried to analyze biological processes in terms of chemistry and physics at an increasingly fundamental level. This procedure has been eminently successful, and the revolutionary progress of biology in the past 20 years has been achieved on the basis of this attitude. Vitalism, on the other hand, has been quite sterile in furthering our understanding of life processes. This is in part due to the fact, mentioned above, that it assumes that certain questions which cannot be attacked at the time are in principle and will remain forever unanswerable. But in addition, vitalism severely restricts the questions which can be asked. Actual vitalistic statements tend to be tautological, since what is to be explained is already included in the definition. They do not therefore lead to hypotheses which can be tested by observation. Furthermore, vitalistic definitions are metaphysical and not operational. Entelechy, for example, is defined as "immaterial and nonspatial," and can therefore not be measured or observed. It does not lead, therefore, to empirical statements subject to observations, but to "explanations" which cannot be further analyzed. It is in this sense that the assumption of an "entelechy," a "life force," an "élan vital" (*Bergson*) begs the question which it is supposed to answer, and cannot lead to analyses of life processes which go beyond these defined terms.

In biology, the most rapidly advancing field at present is molecular biology. This term refers to the postulate that biological processes should be described at the molecular level. The implication is that if a process has been completely described at the molecular level, there is nothing else to describe. This approach has been very successful and has led to an understanding of gene structure, of the energy turnover in the cell, of the process of nerve conduction, and many other phenomena. In addition, molecular biology has contributed more than any other single factor to the development of the unity of the natural sciences which we are witnessing at present.

It still leaves open, however, the problem of function, and how we can account for it. We have seen that this question must be asked at all levels of biological inquiry, down to the molecular level. There appears, therefore, to exist here a real difference between the inorganic and biological sciences which has to be accounted for.

The answer appears to lie in some of the well-understood characteristics of living systems. Living matter exists in the form of open systems which are in a steady state equilibrium with their nonliving environment; they constantly exchange matter with their environment. Furthermore, organisms consist of molecules of high molecular weight which are arranged in an orderly way; in other words, living matter shows organization. The maintenance of this highly organized state requires the constant expenditure of energy which must be taken up from the environment. In other words, the highly organized state of living matter is unstable, and may occasionally break down, losing the characteristics of living matter, i.e. organization and the ability for reproduction. Organisms can die or lose their reproductive ability partially or completely.

The ability of living matter to reproduce its own kind, which is well understood at the molecular level, leads to the possibility of a parent-progeny chain which has a unique history. The possibility of death and loss of reproductive capacity defines the process which we call natural selection. Because of the inherent instability of biological systems, selective pressure will act in a direction which will tend to stabilize the system.

Mechanisms which insure the stability of a biological system have been thoroughly investigated, particularly in physiology. The physiologist Cannon has designated the maintenance of the state of equilibrium, in which an adult organism finds itself, by the term "homeostasis." Much research has been done in exploring the functioning of homeostatic systems, and they have, at least in many cases, turned out to be feedback systems. Feedback systems can be described completely in physical and chemical terms, but they must also be described with reference to the systems to be maintained, i.e. in terms of function.

The following generalization may, then, be proposed. Living systems are organized systems with the ability for self-reproduction. They are inherently unstable, and are therefore subject to the possibility of breakdown of the system, death, and of lowered ability to reproduce. These phenomena result in differential reproduction, the fundamental basis of selection. Function must be understood as a consequence of natural selection. The question for the function turns out to be basically an historical one, the question for the origin of stabilizing mechanisms in the history of the species. The question of function becomes meaningful, because natural selection has acted upon the organization of living organisms in such a way that greater stability of the system is produced.

The question of function could conceivably be posed with respect to nonliving systems. We could consider as the "purpose" the remaining of the system in the state in which it happens to be. But in an inorganic system we are not really interested in this problem. We would express the stability of a system in terms of probability of change and direction of change under certain conditions. In living systems, on the other hand, the main problem is the system's ability to maintain its organization even though it is in an unstable state. All the characteristics by which we may distinguish living from nonliving systems rest on the ability of the latter to break down, and as a consequence, the possibility of natural selection. The question for function is therefore justified in biology, because it asks primarily for the mechanisms involved in keeping a biological system in its characteristic organized state. Furthermore, the question of history, the origin of structures and functions in the evolutionary history of a species, remains a legitimate problem of the biological sciences.

BIBLIOGRAPHY

Aristotle. *De Partibus Animalium.* transl. A. L. Peck. The Loeb Classical Library. Cambridge, Mass. and London: Harvard Univ. Press and Heinemann. 1955.

Brenner, S., G. Streisinger, R. Home, S. Champe, L. Barnett, S. Benzer and M. Rees. "Structural components of bacteriophage." J. Molecular Biol. 1: 281-292, 1960.

Cannon, W. B. *The Wisdom of the Body.* (2nd ed.) New York: Norton. 1939.

Claus, C., K. Grobben and A. Kühn. *Lehrbuch der Zoologie.* 10th ed. Berlin and Vienna: Springer. 1932.

Driesch, H. *Die Biologie als selbständige Grundwissenschaft und das System der Biologie.* Leipzig: Engelmann. 1911.

Garen, A. and L. Kozloff. "The initiation of bacteriophage infection." In: *The Viruses* (F. M. Burnet and W. M. Stanley eds.): 203-236. 1959.

Granick, S. and H. Gilder. "Distribution, structure and properties of the tetrapyrroles." *Advances in Enzymology,* vol. 7, pp. 305-368. 1947.

Granick, S. and H. Gilder. "The porphyrin requirements of Hemophilus influenzae and some functions of the vinyl and propionic acid side chains of heme." J. General Physiology 30: 1-13, 1946.

Hartmann, M. *Allgemeine Biologie, eine Einführung in die Lehre vom Leben.* 4th ed. Stuttgart: Fischer. 1953.

Mainx, F. "Foundations of Biology." *International Encyclopedia of Unified Science, 1955,* I, 567-654.

Chapter **5** | *The Nature of Time*

Adolf Grünbaum
Andrew Mellon Professor of Philosophy
University of Pittsburgh

There is no other way to solve the problem of time than . . . through physics. . . . If time is objective the physicist must have discovered that fact, if there is Becoming the physicist must know it; but if time is merely subjective and Being is timeless, the physicist must have been able to ignore time in his construction of reality.

H. REICHENBACH, *The Direction of Time*

The Nature of Time

1. INTRODUCTION.

There are conflicting accounts of the respective contributions made by science and by philosophy to the elucidation of the nature of time. Thus, the astronomer G. M. Clemence tells us: "It is not possible in a scientific journal (or anywhere for that matter) to say much about the nature of time itself. That subject belongs to philosophy rather than to science. . . . What we, as scientists, know about time itself is very little indeed. We can say much more about the measurement of it." [Clemence (7), p. 261].* And the philosopher Max Black writes [Black (5), p. 179]: "The modern advances in thermodynamics, relativity, cosmology, and information theory, instead of clarifying our insight into this basic notion [of time], seem so far only to have added to the general confusion." On the other hand, according to the philosopher H. Reichenbach, [Reichenbach (23), p. 16], "There is no other way to solve the problem of time than . . . through physics. . . . If time is objective the physicist must have discovered that fact, if there is Becoming the physicist must know it; but if time is merely subjective and Being is timeless, the physicist must have been able to ignore time in his construction of reality."

An examination of the relevant findings of the natural sciences in this essay will show that their temporal import extends far beyond the principles of chronometry, which codify the procedures and results of *measuring* time. For, as we shall see, in addition to bearing on *metrical* aspects of time, the results of the natural sciences also illuminate some of the cardinal *qualitative* features of physical, psychological, and common sense time. In fact, it will turn out that there are fundamental *qualitative* questions about time which philosophy cannot answer without detailed reliance on the discoveries of the natural sciences.

Our focus on the qualitative aspects of time prompts us to disregard all scientific and philosophical questions pertaining to the measurement of time intervals between events. Examples of *metrical* time problems arising within the natural sciences are the following: how can we allow

---

*The figures in parentheses within the text refer to *References* which are listed at the end of the chapter (p. 181ff.); superior figures refer to *Notes,* also listed at the end of the chapter (p. 177ff.).

for the effects of tidal friction on the rate of rotation of the earth so as to use the earth as a reliable clock? Or how can geochemists utilize deposits of radioactive materials to make age determinations? And what is the relation, if any, between the rate of metabolism and *psychological* estimates of duration? Or what are the respective effects of boredom and exhiliration on psychological estimates of duration? More generally, what is the mechanism underlying the successful operation of "biological clocks?"[1] As for *philosophical* questions that have arisen in *chronometry* and which we shall leave aside as well, mention should be made of such issues as the status of temporal congruence (isochronism of clocks) and of simultaneity.[2]

2. THE ANISOTROPY OF TIME.

The qualitative feature of time to which we shall now turn our attention is encountered in the following kind of commonplace experience: When hot water and cold water are poured into an essentially closed container, their temperatures will equalize so as to yield lukewarm water, but, at least in our ordinary experience, lukewarm water in a closed container does *not* undergo separation into hot and cold portions of water. Similarly, we find that while the young grow old, the aged do not then regain their youthful vigor. Neither do the dead rise from their graves, nor do cigarettes reconstitute themselves from their ashes. We shall soon see that *"irreversible"* kinds of processes like temperature equalization and biological decay are a source of one of the most striking qualitative attributes of the segment of cosmic time constituting the current epoch in our spatial region of the world.

Precisely what do we mean when calling the aforementioned kinds of physical and biological processes "irreversible?" There is both a weak sense and a strong sense in which a process might be claimed to be "irreversible." The weak sense is that the *temporal inverse* of the process in fact never (or hardly ever) occurs with increasing time for the following reason: certain particular *de facto* conditions ("initial" or "boundary" conditions) obtaining in the universe independently of any law (or laws) combine with a relevant law (or laws) to render the temporal inverse *de facto* nonexistent, although no law or combination of laws itself disallows that inverse process. The strong sense of "irreversible" is that the temporal inverse is *impossible* in virtue of being ruled out by a law alone or by a combination of laws. In contexts calling for the distinction between these two senses of "irreversible," we shall essentially follow H. Mehlberg, [Mehlberg (22)], and shall speak of the stronger, law-based kind of irreversibility as "nomological" while referring to the weaker kind of irreversibility as being *"de facto"* or "nomologically contingent." In the absence of these qualifications, the ascription of irreversibility to a process commits us to no more than the nonoccurrence or virtual nonoccurrence of its temporal inverse and leaves it open whether the irreversibility is *de facto* or nomological in origin. Thus, the processes of masticating food and mixing cream with coffee are irreversible in this neutral sense. Hence if a silent film of a dinner party were to show a whole beef steak being reassembled from "desalivated" chewed pieces or the mixture of coffee and cream unmixing, we would know that it has been played backward.

Let us consider graphically the significance of the presumed fact that there are kinds of sequences of states ABCD, occurring with increasing time, such that the *opposite* sequence DCBA would *not* also occur with increasing time. Suppose, for example, ABCD in the diagram are successive kinds of states of a house that burns down completely with increasing or later time. Then there will be no case of the *inverse* kind of sequence DCBA with increasing time, since the latter would constitute the resurrection of a house from debris. Thus, this *opposite* kind of sequence DCBA would exist only in the direction of *decreasing* or *earlier* time, while the first kind of sequence ABCD would *not* obtain in the latter direction.

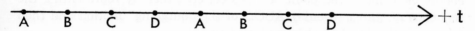

Accordingly, comparison of the structures of the opposite directions of time shows that, at least for the segment of cosmic time constituting the current epoch in our spatial region of the world, the kinds of sequences of states exhibited by the one direction are *different* from those found in the other. Hence we say that, at least locally, time is *anisotropic* rather than isotropic. It will be noted that the *anisotropy* of physical time consists in the mere structural *differences* between the *opposite directions* of physical time and constitutes no basis at all for singling out *one* of the two opposite directions as "the" direction of time.

The dependence of such anisotropy as is exhibited by time on the irreversible character of the processes obtaining in the universe can be thrown into still bolder relief by noting what kind of time there would be, if there were no irreversible processes at all but only reversible processes whose reversibility is not merely nomological but also *de facto*. That is to say the temporal inverses would not only be *allowed* by the relevant laws but would actually *exist* in virtue of the obtaining of the required initial (boundary) conditions. To forestall misunderstandings of such a hypothetical eventuality, it must be pointed out at once that our very existence as human beings having *memories* would then be impossible, as will become clear later on. Hence, it would be entirely misconceived to engage in the inherently-doomed attempt to imagine the posited eventuality *within* the framework of our actual memory-charged experiences, and then to be dismayed by the failure of such an attempt. As well try to imagine the *visual* color of radiation in the infrared or ultraviolet parts of the spectrum.

To see that if *all* kinds of natural processes *were* in fact *de facto* reversible, time would indeed be *isotropic*, we now consider an example of such a *reversible* physical process: the frictionless rolling of a ball over a path AD in accord with Newton's laws, say from A to D.[3] This motion is nomologically reversible, because Newton's laws likewise allow another motion over the same path but from D to A, which is the temporal inverse of the motion from A to D. And there are actual occurrences of this inverse motion, since the requisite initial conditions do obtain.

Let us plot on a time axis the special case in which a particular ball rolls from A to D and is reflected so as to roll back to A, the zero of time being chosen for the event of the ball's being at the point D. The letters A, B, C, and D on the time axis in our diagram denote the respective *events* of being at the point A in space, etc., thereby representing the sequence of states (events) ABCD of the "outgoing" motion and then the states DCBA of the "return" motion.

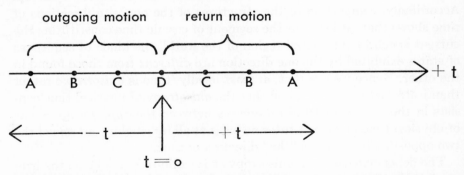

Mathematically, the nomological *reversibility* of the processes allowed by Newton's laws expresses itself by the fact that the form of the Newtonian equations of motion remains unaltered or *invariant* upon substituting $-t$ for $+t$ in them. We say, therefore, that Newton's laws for frictionless motions are *time-symmetric*. And hence our diagram shows that for every state of the ball allowed by Newton's laws at a time $+t$, these laws allow precisely the same *kind* of state at the corresponding time −t. In other words, in the case of reversible processes, the sequences of (allowed) states along the *opposite* directions of the time-axis are, as it were, *mirror-images* of each other. Hence, if all of the processes of nature were *de facto reversible*, time would be *isotropic*.

Thus, it is further apparent that the structure of time is *not* something which is apart from the particular kinds of processes obtaining in the universe. Instead, the nature of time is rooted in the very character of these processes.

We must clearly distinguish the *anisotropy* of physical time from the feature of common sense (psychological) time which is rendered by such terms as "the transiency of the Now" or "becoming" and by such metaphors as the "flux," "flow," or "passage" of time. The transient division of the time continuum into the past and the future depends on the transient Now and is *not* furnished solely by the relation of "earlier than" or its converse "later than." Thus the year 1910 is earlier than the year 1920, no less than 1950 is earlier than 1970, and than 1970, in turn, is earlier than 2850. And yet, at this writing (3 p.m., June 7, 1962), which is at the focus of my immediate experience, the events of 1970 and 2850 belong to the future and those of the other years we mentioned belong to the past. For by the past we mean the class of events earlier than those events which constitute the Now, i.e., the past is constituted by the events which "no longer exist." And by the future we mean correspondingly the set of events that are later than now, i.e., the occurrences which are yet to "acquire existence," as it were. But, as Hugo Bergmann has tellingly shown [H. Bergmann (1), pp. 27-28], the Now with respect to which the distinction between the past and the future of common sense and psychological time acquires meaning has no significance at all apart from the egocentric perspectives of a *conscious* (human) organism and from the immediate experiences of that organism.[4] Hence the *transient* division of the time continuum into *past* and *future* as effected by the *shifting* Now depends for its very *existence* on the perspectival role of consciousness. And the coming *into* being or becoming of an event is thus no more than the entry of its effect(s) into the immediate awareness of a sentient organism (man). On the other hand, the obtaining of the relation "later than" between two physical events or states does *not* depend at all on the transient Now of the ego-perspective of any sentient organism. The latter *independence* cannot, of course, be gainsaid on the grounds that in the case of those pairs of events which *cannot* be linked by causal chains, the usual choice of a definition of simultaneity made in the special theory of relativity[5] leads that theory to affirm a dependence of the existence of the relations "later than" and "simultaneous with" on the inertial system, which is inanimate.

The transiency of the Now is a feature of psychological (and common sense) time in the sense that there is a *diversity* of the Now-contents of immediate awareness. Hence it is a matter of fact that the Now "shifts" in conscious awareness to the extent that there is a *diversity* of the Now-contents. But since these diverse Now-contents are ordered with respect to the relation "earlier than" no less than with respect to its converse "later than," it is a mere *tautology* to say that the Now shifts *from* earlier *to* later. For this metaphorical affirmation of shifting *in the future direction along the time-axis* tells us no more than that later Nows are later than earlier ones, just as earlier Nows are earlier than later ones! By the same token, the assertion that the "flow" of time is *unidirectional* is a tautology, as is the claim that time "flows" from the past to the future. The factual emptiness of the latter formulations must not tempt us into overlooking the following: a directionally-*neutral* claim of the transiency of the Now does codify an actual feature of psychological (common sense) time, and, because of its inherent dependence on consciousness, this feature is *not* also possessed by physical time.

Hermann Weyl has given a metaphorical rendition of the dependence of coming *into* being on consciousness by writing [Weyl (27), p. 116]: "The objective world simply *is*, it does not *happen*. Only to the gaze of my consciousness, crawling upward along the life [i.e. world-] line of my body, does a section of this world come to life as a fleeting image in space which continuously changes in time." This poetic declaration has given rise to serious misunderstandings, as shown by the following objection from Max Black [Black (5), pp. 181-2]:

> But this picture of a "block universe," composed of a timeless web of "world-lines" in a four-dimensional space, however strongly suggested by the theory of relativity, is a piece of gratuitous metaphysics. Since the concept of change, of something happening, is an inseparable component of the common-sense concept of time and a necessary component of the scientist's view of reality, it is quite out of the question that theoretical physics should require us to hold the Eleatic view that nothing happens in "the objective world." Here, as so often in the philosophy of science, a useful limitation in the form of representation is mistaken for a deficiency of the universe.

But contrary to Black, Weyl's claim that the time of inanimate nature is devoid of *happening* in the sense of *becoming* is not at all tantamount to the Eleatic doctrine that *change* is an illusion of the human mind! It is of the essence of the relativistic account of the inanimate world as embodied in the Minkowski representation that there is change in the sense that different kinds of events can (do) occur at different times: the attributes and relations of an object associated with any given world-line may be different at different times (e.g., its world-line may intersect with different world lines at different times). Consequently, the total states of the world (when referred to the simultaneity criterion of a particular Galilean frame) are correspondingly different at different times, i.e., they change with time. It is Black's own misidentification of mere change with becoming ("happening") which leads him to the astonishing and grotesque supposition that Weyl's mentalistic account of becoming bespeaks Weyl's unawareness that "the concept of change . . . is . . . a necessary component of the scientist's view of reality." Black refers to the web of earlier-later relations represented by the world-lines as "timeless" just because they do not make provision for becoming. And he suggests that Weyl conceives of them as forming a four-"space" in the sense in which physical space *excludes* the system of temporal relations obtaining with respect to "earlier than." It is apparent that Black's use of the terms "timeless" and "space" in this context is misleading to the point of conveying question-begging falsehoods. Weyl's thesis is that coming *into* being ("happening"), as contrasted with simply being, is only coming into the present awareness of a sentient organism. And that thesis is *not* vulnerable to Black's charge of having mistaken "a useful limitation in the form of representation" for "a deficiency of the universe."

It was none other than the false assumption that "flux" must be a feature of physical no less than of psychological (common sense) time that inspired Henri Bergson's misconceived polemic against the mathematical treatment of motion, which he charged with having erroneously *spatialized* time by a description which leaves out the flux of becoming and renders only the "static" relations of earlier and later.[6] The failure to be cognizant of the *physical* irrelevance of the "Now" found in consciousness and of such other temporal categories as depend in an essential way on this "Now" is not confined to Bergson. For this very failure also vitiates a good deal of philosophical writing on time which takes as its point of departure the conceptual commitments of the prescientific temporal discourse of common sense in which the "Now" of conscious experience is enshrined.[7] Thus, we shall see presently that P. W. Bridgman's critique of A. S. Eddington's account of the anisotropy of time is rendered nugatory by Bridgman's unawareness of the physical irrelevance of the "Now" and by his resulting erroneous identification of the anisotropy of physical time with the "unidirectional flow" of psychological time. Preparatory to our impending examination of Bridgman's objection to Eddington, mention must be made of the concept of entropy, which serves to provide a succinct characterization of the presumed irreversibility of processes like temperature equalization.

Specifically, suppose that a physical system is created such that one end is hot and the other cold and is then essentially *closed* off from the rest of the world. In ordinary experience, we do *not* find that the hot end becomes hotter at the expense of the increased coolness of the cool end. Instead, the system tends towards an *equilibrium* state of *intermediate* temperature. And, at least as far as ordinary physical experience is concerned, this entire process of temperature equalization is *irreversible*. It is possible to characterize this irreversibility more precisely by associating with each momentary state of the closed system a certain quantity, called the "entropy." For the entropy provides the following relative measure of the degree of temperature-equalization attained by the system in the given state: the irreversible temperature-equalization associated with the transition from the initial to the final state corresponds to an *increase* in the entropy. Accordingly, for a closed system not already in equilibrium, the second law of thermodynamics affirms an increase of the entropy with time. And therefore Eddington [(9), pp. 69ff.] attempted to use this law of thermodynamics to account for the *anisotropy* of time. But by his very unfortunate choice of the name "time's arrow" for the latter feature of physical time, he ironically invited the very misunderstanding which he had been at pains to prevent, viz., that he was intending to offer a thermodynamic basis for the "unidirectional flow" of psychological time [(9), pp. 68, 87-110]. Eddington maintained that the entropic behavior of closed physical systems distinguishes the two *opposite* directions of time *structurally* in regard to *earlier* and *later* respectively as follows: of two states of the world, the *later* state is the one coinciding with the *higher* entropy of a closed nonequilibrium system, whereas the earlier state corresponds to the state of *lower* entropy. [8] Thus, according to Eddington, the anisotropy of physical time would derive from the supposed fact that in one of the two opposite directions of time—which we call the direction of *"later"*—the entropy *increases*, whereas in the opposite direction, the entropy *decreases*. Upon generalizing the definition of "entropy," we find a great variety of processes in closed systems other than temperature equalization which involve an increase in entropy. Examples of this increase are: the scattering of energy concentrations which are then unavailable for work, frictional dissipations of mechanical energy, radio-active decay, burning, and processes of biological deterioration such as the increase of arteriosclerosis and its sequelae.

We are now ready to state and appraise Bridgman's objection to Eddington's thesis. A statement of our grounds for rejecting Bridgman's critique as unjustified will be instructive even though we shall find Eddington's claim wanting later on for reasons *other than* those given by Bridgman. Bridgman contends that the anisotropy of time cannot be founded on irreversible physical processes because the entropy increase cannot be regarded with Eddington as the fundamental indicator of the relation "later than." And his reason for the latter assertion is the follow-ing: "how would one go to work in any concrete case to decide whether time were flowing forward or backward? If it were found that the entropy of the universe were decreasing, would one say that time was flowing backward, or would one say that it was a law of nature that entropy de-creases with time?" [(6), p. 165].

We see that Bridgman takes Eddington to have offered an entropic basis of the "forward flow" of psychological time rather than of the anisotropy of physical time, because he falsely identifies these two different concepts. And we shall now show that his purported *reductio ad absurdum* argu-ment against Eddington's entropic account of the anisotropy of physical time derives its plausibility but also its lack of cogency from the conjunc-tion of precisely this illegitimate identification with a contrary-to-fact assumption. Thus, we ask Bridgman: under what circumstances could it be found that the entropy of the universe "were decreasing"? This situa-tion would arise in the contrary-to-fact eventuality that physical systems or the universe would exhibit *lower* entropy states at times which are *psychologically later*, and *higher* entropy states at times which are *psycho-logically earlier*, such as in the hypothetical case of finding that lukewarm water separates out into hot and cold portions as time goes on psycho-logically. To appreciate the import of this contrary-to-fact assumption, we note that an experience B is *psychologically-later* than an experience A under one of the following two conditions: (i) the awareness-and-memory content constituting experience A is a *proper part* of the memory-content of experience B, or (ii) experience B contains the memory of *the fact* of the occurrence of another experience A (e.g. the fact of having dreamt), but the memories ingredient in B do *not* contain the *content* of experi-ence A (e.g. the details of the dream having been forgotten).[9] Thus, psychologically later times are either times at which we do, in fact, have more memories or information than at the correspondingly earlier ones, or they are times at which it would be possible to have a richer store of memories even if the latter did not, in fact, materialize because of partial forgetting. Accordingly, Bridgman's posit of our finding that the entropy "were decreasing" would require the entropy increase among physical systems and the future direction of psychological time to be *temporally-counterdirected* as follows: temporally, the direction of increasing entropy among *physical* systems would *not also* be the direction of actual or possible *memory* (information) increase among *biological* organisms, since (actually or possibly) *"richer"* memory states would be coinciding temporally with *lower* entropy states of physical systems.

What is the logical force of Bridgman's contrary-to-fact assumption as a basis for invalidating Eddington's account of the anisotropy of physical time? Bridgman's objection is seen to be devoid of cogency in the light of the following reasons. In the first place, quite apart from the fact that Eddington was not concerned to account for the "forward flow" of psychological time, *in actual fact* the very production of memories in biological organisms depends, as we shall see, on entropy *increases* in certain portions of the external environment. And since Eddington was offering his criterion as an account of what does, in fact, obtain, the adequacy of this account cannot be impugned by the contrary-to-fact logical possibility of counterdirectedness envisioned by Bridgman. But even if the situation posited by Bridgman were to materialize in actuality, it would certainly *not* refute Eddington's claim that (i) the entropic behavior of physical systems renders the opposite directions of physical time anisotropic, because the entropy of each of these systems decreases in the one direction and increases in the other, and (ii) the direction of increasing entropy can be called the direction of "later than" or time increase. Although Eddington had left himself open to being misunderstood by using the misleading term "time's arrow," he had also sought to spike the misunderstanding that entropically characterized physical time "is flowing forward" in the sense of there being a physical becoming. For he makes a special point of emphasizing [(9), pp. 68-69 and ch. 5] that this becoming, so familiar from *psychological* time, eludes conceptual rendition as an attribute of physical processes, because it involves the concept "now." Contrary to Bridgman, there can be no problem of *physical* time flowing backward rather than forward, since the metaphor "flow" has no relevance to physical time. *Physically*, certain states are later than others by certain amounts of time. But there is no "flow" of *physical* time, because physically there is no egocentric (psychological) transient *now*. Moreover, as applied to *psychological* time, the locution "flow backward" is self-contradictory, since the assertion that the Now shifts forward (in the future direction) is a tautology, as we saw. A fluid can flow *spatially* up or down, because the meaning of spatial "flow" is *independent* of the meaning of "spatially up" or "down." But as applied to psychological time, the meaning of the action-verb metaphor "flow" *involves* the meaning of the metaphor "forward," i.e., of "from earlier to later." For the *flowing* here denotes metaphorically the shifting of the "now" from earlier to later or "forward." Hence if Bridgman's hypothetical situation of counterdirectedness could actually materialize, we would say that the entropy is decreasing with increasing psychological time without damage to Eddington's account and *not* that time is "flowing backward."[10]

Furthermore, if the situation envisioned by Bridgman did arise, we might well not survive long enough to be troubled by it. Poincaré has explained, in a qualitative way, why prediction and action would probably become impossible under the circumstances posited by Bridgman: two bodies *initially* at the same temperature would then acquire different temperatures at psychologically later times, while we would be unable to anticipate which of these bodies will become the warmer one, and thus we might be burnt severely if we happen to be in touch with the one that turns out to be the hot one. Or imagine taking a bath in lukewarm water and then not being able to predict which portion of the bathtub will turn out to be the boiling hot end. By the same token, whereas in actuality friction is a *retarding* force, because its dissipation of mechanical energy issues in an increase of the entropy with increasing psychological time, on Bridgman's contrary-to-fact assumption friction would be an *accelerating* force that sets stationary bodies into motion in unpredictable directions. Thus, with increasing psychological time, heat energy would convert itself into mechanical energy of a previously stationary body such as a heavy rock, and prediction of the direction in which the rock would start moving would then be well-nigh impossible. And even if we escaped destruction most of the time by *not* being in the paths of these unpredictable motions, we might well succumb to the anxiety induced by our inability to anticipate and control daily developments in our environment which would constantly threaten our survival.

Finally, suppose that we supplement the hypothetical conditions posited by Bridgman by assuming that in addition to his hypothetical human species A whose members are supposed to experience *higher* entropy states of physical systems as psychologically *earlier* than lower ones, there is another human species B possessing our actual property of experiencing these same higher entropy states as psychologically later.

Then, as Norbert Wiener has noted, a very serious difficulty would arise for communication between our two species A and B whose psychological time senses are counterdirected. Wiener writes [(29), p. 45]: "it is a very interesting intellectual experiment to make the fantasy of an intelligent being whose time should run the other way to our own. To such a being all communication with us would be impossible. Any signal he might send would reach us with a logical stream of consequents from his point of view, antecedents from ours. These antecedents would already be in our experience, and would have served to us as the natural explanation of his signal, without presupposing an intelligent being to have sent it. . . . Our counterpart would have exactly similar ideas concerning us. *Within any world with which we can communicate, the direction of time is uniform.*"

In amplification of Wiener's statement, consider a situation in which our species A and B have distinct habitats, which are represented respectively by the regions A and B of our diagram.

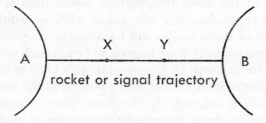

We can then show that any particle or signal which would be regarded as *outgoing* by one of the two species would likewise be held to be *departing* by the other, and any object or message which is *incoming* in the judgment of either species will also be held to be *arriving* by the other. For—to take the case of the *outgoing* influence—suppose that, as judged by the members of A, the particle reaches the point Y of its trajectory (see diagram) *later than* the point X and is therefore held to be departing by the men in A. Then the members of B will conclude that the particle is *leaving* them as well, since they will judge that it reaches point X *after* reaching point Y. And thus, if as judged by the A-men, they hurl a rock toward the B region such that the rock comes to rest and remains at rest in B indefinitely, then the B-men, in turn, will judge that a rock, having been at rest in their region all along, suddenly left their habitat and traveled to A, where it was then received by the A-men with ready, open arms. And if the B-men were struck by the discrepancy between the dynamical behavior of that rock and the behavior of other rocks in their habitat—assuming that the latter obey the familiar dynamical principles

—they might conceivably conclude after a number of such experiences that the dynamically aberrant rocks are linked to the presence elsewhere of temporally counterdirected beings.[11]

Although Bridgman's critique of Eddington's treatment of the anisotropy of time is unjustified, there are fundamental difficulties in Eddington's treatment of the problem. These arise from the following facts:

(1) with the development of the kinetic theory of gases, it became clear that such phenomena as temperature equalization among gases that mix in a closed container must be understood on the basis of a *statistical* treatment of the motions of the particles composing the gas, temperature equalization being a concomitant of the equalization of molecular speeds,

(2) the resulting statistical analogue of the entropy law *for a permanently closed system* then failed to yield the pervasive anisotropy of time affirmed by Eddington.

We shall now discuss the bearing of the statistical form of the entropy law on the anisotropy of time in four stages. We shall

(i) sketch the reasoning underlying the statistical analogue of the law,

(ii) demonstrate that the range of validity of the statistical analogue of the entropy law for a *permanently* closed system is so narrow as to render it *incompetent* to confer anisotropy on time, thus invalidating Eddington's treatment,

(iii) explain how a physical principle to be stated, which is not deducible from the statistical entropy law alone, does confer anisotropy on at least the physical time of our galactic system during the current epoch of the universe,

(iv) point out precisely what light the latter principle throws on each of the following: (1) the recordability of the past as opposed to the unpredictability of the future, (2) the relation of *psychological* time to *physical* time, and (3) the controversy between the philosophical mechanist and the teleologist.

3. The Statistical Analogue of the Entropy Law.

(i) If we compare a gas in a highly *unequalized* state of temperature with a near-equilibrium state from the standpoint of the kinetic theory of gases, we note that the molecular speeds will be much more *equalized* in the near-equilibrium state of *high* entropy than in the disequilibrium state of relatively low entropy.

Hence, a *high* entropy corresponds to

(1) a high degree of molecular equalization
(2) great homogeneity
(3) a well-shuffled state
(4) *low macro*-separation
(5) low order, where "order" means *not* smoothness or homogeneity, but rather inhomogeneity.

The application of the principles of Newtonian particle mechanics to the constituent molecules of idealized gases takes the following form: each of the n molecules of the gas in the closed system has a position and a velocity, or more accurately, three position coordinates x, y and z, and three components of velocity. Hence the *micro-state* of the gas can be characterized at any given time by specifying the six position and velocity attributes corresponding to each of the n molecules, each value being given to within a certain small range. The microstate of the gas at any given time may then be thought of as represented by points in the cells of a six-dimensional position-velocity space or "phase space." And each of the n molecules will then be in some one of the finite number m of cells compatible with the given volume and total energy of the gas.

A particular *arrangement* of the n individual molecules among the m cells constitutes a micro-state of the gas. Thus, if two individual gas molecules A and B were to exchange positions and velocities, a different arrangement would result. However, the *macroscopic* state of the gas, i.e., its being in a state of nearly uniform temperature or very uneven temperature, does *not* depend on whether it is molecule A or B that occupies a particular point in the container and has a given velocity. What matters *macroscopically* is whether *more* fast molecules are at one end of the container than at the other end or not, thereby making the one end hotter, or as hot as the other. In other words, the macro-state depends on *how many* molecules are at certain places in the container, as compared to the number in other places, and also depends on their respective velocities. Thus, the macro-state depends on the numerical spatial and velocity distribution of the molecules, *not* on the particular *identity* of the molecules having certain positional or velocity attributes. It follows that the *same* macrostate can be constituted by a *number* of *different* microstates, as in the case of the mere interchange of the microscopic roles played by our two molecules A and B. It is a basic postulate of statistical mechanics that each one of the m^n possible arrangements or micro-states occur with the same frequency in time or have *the same probability* $\frac{1}{m^n}$. This equiprobability postulate is called the quasi-ergodic hypothesis and gives the socalled probability metric of the Maxwell-Boltzmann statistics, since it asserts what occurrences are equally probable or frequent in time.[12]

It is of *basic importance* to see now that the number of micro-states W corresponding to a macro-state of near-equilibrium (uniform temperature) or high entropy is overwhelmingly *greater* than the number corresponding to a disequilibrium state of *non*-uniform temperature or quite low entropy. A drastically oversimplified example will make this fact evident.

Consider a position-velocity or phase-space of only four cells, and let there be just two different distributions (macro-states) of four particles among these cells as follows:

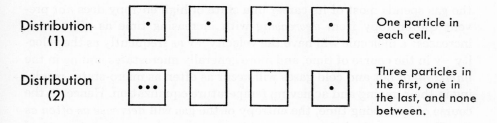

Distribution (1) — One particle in each cell.

Distribution (2) — Three particles in the first, one in the last, and none between.

The number of different permutations of four particles in a row is $4! = 4 \cdot 3 \cdot 2 \cdot 1 = 24$. And thus the number W of different arrangements or micro-states corresponding to the *homogeneous, equalized* macro-state given by distribution (1) is 24. But for the case of the second *inhomogeneous, unequalized* distribution, W is not 24, since the permutations of the three particles *within* the first cell do *not* issue in different arrangements. Hence, for the second case, W has the smaller numerical value $\frac{4!}{3!} = 4$.[13] And since the entropy S is given by $S = k \log W$, where k is a constant, the entropy will be lower in the second case than in the first.

It now becomes evident that in the course of time, high entropy states of the gas are enormously more probable or frequent than low ones. For (1) all arrangements are assumed to be equiprobable, i.e., to occur with the same frequency, and (2) many more arrangements correspond to macro-states of high entropy than to states of low-entropy. Saying that high entropy states are very probable means that the gas spends the overwhelming portion of its indefinitely long career in the closed system in states of high entropy. This then is the statistical analogue of the law of entropy increase.

(ii) To appreciate the import of this statistical entropy law for the anisotropy of time, we recall that according to Newton's laws, the motions of particles are completely *reversible*. And all other known laws governing the behavior of the *elementary* constituents of physical processes likewise affirm the *reversibility* of that behavior. Thus, Maxwell's equations for electromagnetic phenomena, and the fundamental probabilities of state transitions of quantum mechanical systems are *time-symmetrical*.[14] Accordingly, we can discuss the case of a gas constituted by Newtonian particles behaving reversibly as the paradigm case for answering the following question: can the *statistical* form of the entropy law for a permanently-closed system form a basis for the anisotropy of time?

Our answer will now turn out to be in the negative. For the fact that the gas spends most of its career in a state of high entropy does *not* prevent the entropy from *decreasing* with increasing time as often as it increases: a molecule will have the velocity +v as frequently as the velocity −v in the course of time, and more generally microstates issuing in the *unmixing* of hot and cold gases will occur as often as micro-states resulting in their mixing and achieving temperature equalization. Hence, in the course of increasing time, the entropy of the gas will *decrease as often as it will increase*. And this means, of course, that the usual statement of the second law of thermodynamics is false. To be sure, if we consider a large number of low entropy states of the gas, then we will find that the vast majority of these will soon be *followed* by high entropy states. And in *that* sense, we can say that it is highly probable that a *low* entropy state will soon be followed by a high one. But it is no less true that a low entropy state was *preceded* by a state of high entropy with equally great probability!

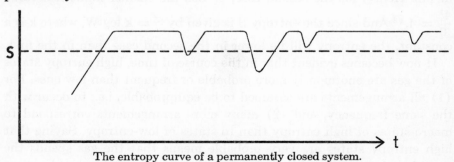

The entropy curve of a permanently closed system.

This *equality* among the probabilities of *higher* entropies in the *past* and in the future destroys the possibility of saying with Eddington that the *earlier* states are characterized by the lower entropies of a permanently closed system. And we are thus compelled to reach the following fundamental conclusion: *no pervasive anisotropy could possibly be conferred on time by the entropic evolution of a single, permanently-closed system.* Hence even if the entire universe qualified as a system whose entropy is defined—which a spatially-*infinite* universe does *not*, as we shall see in §4 below—its entropic behavior could *not* confer any pervasive anisotropy on time.

But, it might be objected that actual physical experience presents us with entropy increases in quasi-isolated systems far more frequently than with corresponding decreases: if 10,000 people sat down together to dinner and each poured some cream into a cup of black coffee, it is an incontestably safe bet that the cream will mix with the coffee in all cases and that no one will report a subsequent *unmixing* of them *for ordinary intervals of time.* And hence it could be argued that this kind of phenomenon of entropy increase confers anisotropy at least on the time of our galactic system during the current epoch. But this kind of phenomenon of entropy increase is not incompatible with the statistical form of the entropy law for a *permanently* closed system, since we restricted ourselves to ordinary intervals of time. Yet it is correct to conclude, as we shall now see in detail, that such phenomena do furnish a viable physical basis for a *statistical* anisotropy of time.[15]

(iii) We begin with an account of certain features of the physical world having the character of initial or boundary conditions within the framework of the theory of statistical mechanics. The sought-after basis of the statistical anisotropy of time will then emerge from principles of statistical mechanics relevent to these *de facto* conditions.

The universe around us exhibits striking disequilibria of temperatures and other inhomogeneities. In fact, we live in virtue of the nuclear conversion of the sun's reserves of hydrogen into helium, which issues in our reception of solar radiation. As the sun dissipates its reserves of hydrogen via the emission of solar radiation, it may heat a terrestrial rock embedded in snow during the day time. At night, the rock is no longer exposed to the sun but is left with a considerably higher temperature than the snow surrounding it. Hence, at night, the *warm* rock and the *cold* snow form a quasi-isolated subsystem of either our galactic or solar system. And the relatively low entropy of that subsystem was purchased at the expense of the dissipation of the sun's reserves of hydrogen. Hence, *if* there is some quasi-closed system comprising the sun and the earth, the branching off of our subsystem from this wider system in a state of low entropy at sunset involved an entropy increase in the wider system. During the night, the heat of the rock melts the snow, and thus the entropy of the rock-snow system increases. The next morning at sunrise, the rock-snow subsystem merges again with the wider solar system. Thus, there are subsystems which branch off from the wider solar or galactic system, remain quasi-closed for a limited period of time, and then merge again with the wider system from which they had been separated. Following Reichenbach, [(23), p. 118] we shall use the term "branch system" to designate this kind of subsystem.

Branch systems are formed not only in the natural course of things, but also through human intervention: when an ice cube is placed into a glass of warm gingerale by a waiter and then covered for hygienic purposes, a subsystem has been formed. The prior freezing of the ice cube had involved an entropy increase through the dissipation of electrical energy in some larger quasi-closed system of which the electrically-run refrigerator is a part. While the ice cube melts in the covered glass subsystem, that quasi-closed system increases its entropy. But it merges again with another system when the then chilled gingerale is consumed by a person. Similarly for a cold room that is closed off and then heated by burning logs.

Thus, our environment abounds in branch-systems whose initial relatively low entropies are the products of their earlier coupling or interaction with outside agencies of one kind or another. This rather constant and ubiquitous formation of a branch-system in a relatively low entropy state resulting from interaction often proceeds at the expense of an entropy increase in some wider quasi-closed system from which it originated. And the *de facto*, nomologically-contingent occurrence of these branch systems has the following *fundamental consequence*, at least for our region of the universe and during the current epoch: among the quasi-closed systems whose entropy is relatively low and which behave as if they might remain isolated, the vast majority have not been and will not remain permanently-closed systems, being branch systems instead.

Hence, upon encountering a quasi-closed system in a state of fairly low entropy, we know the following to be overwhelmingly probable: the system has *not* been isolated for millions and millions of years and does *not* just *happen* to be in one of the infrequent but ever-recurring low entropy states exhibited by a permanently-isolated system. Instead, our system was formed not too long ago by branching off after an interaction with an outside agency. For example, suppose that an American geologist is wandering in an isolated portion of the Sahara desert in search of an oasis and encounters a portion of the sand in the shape of "Coca-Cola." He would then infer that, with overwhelming probability, a kindred person had interacted with the sand in the recent past by tracing "Coca-Cola" in it. The geologist would not suppose that he was in the presence of one of those relatively low entropy configurations which are assumed by the sand particles spontaneously but very rarely, if beaten about by winds for millions upon millions of years in a state of effective isolation from the remainder of the world.

There is a further *de facto* property of branch systems that concerns us. For it will turn out to enter into the temporally asymmetrical statistical regularities which we shall find to be exhibited in the entropic behavior of these systems. This property consists in the following *randomness* obtaining *as a matter of nomologically-contingent fact* in the distribution of the W_1 micro-states belonging to the initial macro-states of a *space*-ensemble of branch-systems each of which has the same initial entropy $S_1 = $ k log W_1: For each class of *like* branch-systems having the *same* initial entropy value S_1, the micro-states constituting the identical initial macro-states of entropy S_1 are *random samples* of the set of all W_1 micro-states yielding a macro-state of entropy S_1.[16] This attribute of randomness of micro-states on the part of the initial states of the members of the space-ensemble will be recognized as the counterpart of the following attribute of the micro-states of one single, permanently-closed system: there is equiprobability of occurrence among the W_1 micro-states belonging to the *time*-ensemble of states of equal entropy $S_1 = $ k log W_1 exhibited by one single, permanently-closed system.

We can now state the statistical regularities which obtain as a consequence of the *de facto* properties of branch systems just set forth, when coupled with the principles of statistical mechanics. These regularities, which will be seen to yield a temporally-asymmetric statistical behavior of the entropy of branch-systems, fall into two main groups as follows.

Group 1. In most space-ensembles of quasi-closed branch-systems each of which is initially in a state of nonequilibrium or relatively *low* entropy, the majority of branch systems in the ensemble will have *higher* entropies *after* a given time t.[17] But these branch systems simply did not exist as quasi-closed, distinct systems at a time t *prior to* the occurrence of their initial, branching off states. Hence, not existing then as such, the branch systems did in fact *not* also exhibit the same higher entropy states at the *earlier* times t, which they would indeed have done then had they existed as closed systems all along.

The increase after a time t in the entropy of the overwhelming majority of branch systems of initially low entropy—as confirmed abundantly by observation—can be made fully intelligible. To do so, we note the following property of the *time*-ensemble of entropy values belonging to a single, permanently-closed system and then affirm that property of the space-ensembles of branch systems: since *large* entropic downgrades or decreases are *far less* probable (frequent) than moderate ones, the *vast majority* of *non*-equilibrium entropy states of a permanently-closed system are located either at or in the immediate temporal vicinity of the *bottom* of a *dip* of the one-system entropy curve. In short, the vast majority of the *sub*-maximum entropy states are on or temporally very near the *upgrades* of the one-system curve. The application of this result to the space-ensemble of branch-systems whose initial states exhibit the aforementioned *de facto* property of *randomness* then yields the following: among the initial low entropy states of these systems, the vast majority lie at or in the immediate temporal vicinity of the bottoms of the one-system entropy curve at which an upgrade begins.

Group 2. A decisive *temporal asymmetry* in the statistics of the temporal evolution of branch-systems arises from the further result that in most space ensembles of branch systems each of whose members is initially in a state of *equilibrium* or very *high* entropy, the vast majority of these systems in the ensemble will *not* have *lower* entropies *after* a finite time t, but will still be in equilibrium.[18] For the aforementioned randomness property assures that the vast majority of those branch systems whose initial states are equilibrium states have maximum entropy values lying somewhere *well within* the plateau of the one-system entropy curve, rather than at the extremity of the plateau at which an entropy *decrease* is initiated.[19]

We see therefore that in the vast majority of branch systems, either one end of their finite entropy curves is a point of low entropy and the other a point of high entropy, or they are in equilibrium states at both ends as well as during the intervening interval. And it is likewise apparent that the statistical distribution of these entropy values on the time axis is such that the vast majority of branch systems have the *same direction of entropy increase* and hence also the same opposite direction of entropy decrease. Thus, the statistics of entropy increase among branch systems assures that in most space ensembles the vast majority of branch systems will increase their entropy in *one* of the two opposite time directions and decrease it in the other. In this way *the entropic behavior of branch systems confers the same statistical anisotropy on the vast majority of all*

*those epochs of time during which the universe exhibits the requisite dis-
equilibrium and contains branch systems satisfying initial conditions of
"randomness."* [20]

Let us now call the direction of entropy increase of a typical representative of these epochs the direction of "later," as indeed we have done from
the outset by the mere assignment of higher time numbers in that direction but without prejudice to our findings concerning the issue of the
anisotropy of time. Then our results pertaining to the entropic behavior
of branch systems show that the directions of "earlier than" and "later
than" are not merely opposite directions bearing decreasing and increasing time coordinates respectively but are statistically *anisotropic* in an
objective physical sense. For I have shown elsewhere in some detail [21] that
increasing real numbers can be assigned as time coordinates in a physically meaningful way *without* any commitment to the existence of (*de
facto* or nomologically) irreversible kinds of processes. In fact, the use of
the real number continuum as a basis for coordinatizing time no more
entails the anisotropy of time than does the corresponding coordinatiza-
tion of one of the three dimensions of space.

It should be noted that I have characterized the positive direction of
time as the direction of entropy increase for a *typical representative* of
all those epochs of time during which the universe exhibits the requisite
disequilibrium and contains branch systems satisfying initial conditions
of "randomness." Accordingly, it is entirely possible to base the customary temporal description of fluctuation phenomena on entropic counterdirectedness with respect to the majority of branch systems, a description
which is *not* liable to *any* of the absurdities which led Bridgman to conclude that an entropic account of the anisotropy of time is unacceptable.
(iv) Our conclusions regarding the entropy statistics of branch systems
can now be used to elucidate (1) the conditions under which retrodiction
of the past is feasible while prediction of the future is not, (2) the relation
of *psychological* time to physical time, and (3) the merits of the controversy between philosophical mechanism and teleology.

1. Suppose we encounter a beach whose sand forms a smooth surface
except for one place where it is in the shape of a human footprint. We
know from our previous considerations with high probability that instead
of having evolved *isolatedly* from a prior state of uniform smoothness into
its present uneven configuration according to the statistical entropy
principle for a permanently-closed system, the beach was an *open* system
in *interaction* with a stroller. And we are aware furthermore that if there
is some quasi-closed wider system containing the beach and the stroller,

as there often is, the beach achieved its ordered low entropy state of bearing the imprint or interaction-indicator at the expense of an at least compensatory entropy increase in that wider system comprising the stroller; the stroller increased the entropy of the wider system by scattering his energy reserves in making the footprint.

We see that the sandy footprint shape is a genuine indicator and not a randomly-achieved form resulting from the unperturbed chance concatenations of the grains of sand. The imprint thus contains information in the sense of being a veridical indicator of an interaction. Now, in all probability the entropy of the imprint-bearing beach-system increases after the interaction with the stroller through the smoothing action of the wind. And this entropy increase is parallel, in all probability, to the direction of entropy increase of the majority of branch systems. Moreover, we saw that the production of the indicator by the interaction is likely to have involved an entropy increase in some wider system of which the indicator is a part. Hence, *in all probability the states of the interacting systems which do contain the indicators of the interaction are the relatively higher entropy states of the majority of branch systems, as compared to the interaction state. Hence the indicator states are the relatively later states as compared to the states of interaction which they attest.* And by being both *later* and indicators, these states have *retrodictive* significance, thereby being traces, records or "memories." And due to the high degree of retrodictive univocity of the low entropy states constituting the indicators, the latter are veridical to a high degree of *specificity.*

Confining our attention to indicators whose production requires only the occurrence of the interaction which they attest, we therefore obtain the following conclusion. Apart from two classes of *advance*-indicators requiring very special conditions for their production and constituting *exceptions,* it is the case that *with overwhelming probability, low entropy indicator-states can exist in systems whose interactions they attest only after and not before these interactions.*[22] If this conclusion is true (assuming that there are either no cases or not enough cases of *bona fide* precognition to disconfirm it), then, of course, it is not an *a priori* truth. And it would be very shallow indeed to seek to construe it as a trivial *a priori* truth in the following way: calling the indicator states "traces," "records" or "memories" and noting that it then becomes tautological to assert that traces and the like have only retrodictive and no predictive significance. But this transparent verbal gambit cannot make it true *a priori* that—apart from the exceptions just mentioned—interacting systems bear indicators attesting veridically only their *earlier* and *not* their later interactions with outside agencies.

Hence, the two exceptions apart, we arrive at the fundamental asymmetry of recordability: *reliable indicators in interacting systems permit only retrodictive inferences concerning the interactions for which they vouch but no predictive inferences pertaining to corresponding later interactions.*

2. We saw that the production of traces, records or memories is usually accompanied by entropy increases in the branch systems. And therefore it follows that the direction of increase of stored information or "memories" either in inanimate recording-devices or in *memory-gathering organisms like man* must be the same as the direction of entropy increase in the majority of branch systems. But we saw in §2 that the direction of the increase or accumulation of mental traces or memories is the *forward* direction of psychological time. Hence, what is *psychologically* later goes hand-in-hand with what is purely physically later on the basis of the entropic evolution of branch systems. And the anisotropy of psychological time *mirrors* the more fundamental anisotropy of physical time.

By way of concrete example, note that the vocal output of a lecturer increases the entropy of the lecture room *and* produces memories in his listeners at his physiological expense. At the start of his lecture, the lecturer had concentrated energy, and therefore the entropy of the lecture room was then relatively low. After his lecture much of that energy has been scattered in the form of sound waves, thereby increasing the entropy of the room and *also* registering memories in his listeners which enable them to tell that it is then later than it was when they first sat down for the lecture.

These considerations show that even if our physiological existence were possible in a state of total equilibrium—which it is not—we would then *not* be able to have the kind of temporal awareness that we do have. If we were unfortunate enough to be surviving while immersed in one vast cosmic equilibrium, it would then be unutterably dull to the point of loss of our psychological time sense.

3. The results of our discussion of the temporal asymmetry of recordability have a decisive bearing on the controversy between mechanism and teleology.

By mechanism we understand the philosophical thesis that all explanation must be *only a tergo*, i.e., that occurrences at a time t can be explained *only* by reference to *earlier* occurrences and *not also* by reference to later ones. And by teleology we understand a thesis which is the contrary rather than the contradictory of mechanism: all phenomena occurring at a time t (or, more narrowly, all phenomena belonging to a certain domain and occurring at a time t) are to be understood by reference to *later* occurrences only. We note that, thus understood, mechanism and teleology can *both* be false.

During our post-Newtonian epoch there is a misleading incongruity in using the term "mechanism" for the thesis of the monopoly of *a tergo* explanations. For in the context of the *time-symmetric* laws of Newton's mechanics, the given state of a closed mechanical system at a time t can be inferred from a state *later* than t (i.e., *retrodicted*) no less than the given state can be inferred from a state *earlier* than t (i.e., *predicted*). Instead of furnishing the prototype for mechanistic explanation in the philosophical sense, the phenomena described by the time-symmetric laws of Newton's mechanics constitute a domain with respect to which both mechanism and teleology are false, thereby making the controversy between them a *pseudo-issue*. More generally, that controversy is a pseudo-issue with respect to any domain of phenomena constituted by the evolution of closed systems obeying *time-symmetric* laws, be they deterministic or statistical.

But there is indeed a wide class of phenomena with respect to which mechanism is true. And one may presume that tacit reference to this particular class of phenomena has conferred plausibility on the thesis of the *unrestricted* validity of mechanism: traces or marks of interaction existing in a system which is essentially closed at a time t are accounted for scientifically by *earlier interactions* or *perturbations* of that system— which are called "causes"—and *not* by later interactions of the system.

In view of the demonstrated restricted validity of mechanism, we must therefore deem the following statement by H. Reichenbach as too strong: "We conclude: If we define the direction of time in the usual sense, there is no finality, and only causality is accepted as constituting explanation."[23]

We have now completed our discussion of the anisotropy of time insofar as it depends on processes for which an entropy is defined. It remains to consider whether there are not also *non*-entropic kinds of physical processes which contribute to the anisotropy of time.

4. NON-ENTROPIC, NOMOLOGICALLY-CONTINGENT IRREVERSIBILITY.[24]

In a series of notes, published in *Nature* during the years 1956-1958, K. R. Popper[25] has expounded his thesis of the "untenability of the widespread, though surely not universal, belief that the 'arrow of time' is closely connected with, or dependent upon, the law that disorder (entropy) tends to increase" (II). Specifically, he argues in the first three of his four notes that there exist *irreversible* processes in nature whose irreversibility does *not* depend on their involvement of an entropy increase. Instead, their irreversibility is *nomologically-contingent* in the following sense: the *laws* of nature governing elementary processes do indeed allow the temporal inverses of these irreversible processes, but the latter processes are *de facto* irreversible, because the *spontaneous* concatenation of the initial conditions requisite for the occurrence of their temporal inverses is well-nigh physically impossible. Noting that "Although the arrow of time is not implied by the fundamental equations [laws governing elementary processes], it nevertheless characterizes most solutions" (I), Popper therefore rejects the claim that "every nonstatistical or 'classical' mechanical process is reversible" (IV).

In response to the first two of Popper's four notes, E. L. Hill and I published a communication[26] in which we endorsed Popper's contention of the existence of nonentropic, nomologically-contingent irreversibility in the form of an existential claim constituting a generalization of Popper's contention.

In view of Popper's criticism (III) of the latter generalization, my aim in this Section is as follows:

(i) To appraise Popper's criticism,

(ii) To show that the generalization put forward in the paper by Hill and myself has the important merit of dispensing with the *restriction* on which Popper predicates his affirmation of nomologically-contingent irreversibility: the requirement of the *spontaneity* of the concatenation of the initial conditions requisite to the occurrence of the temporal inverses of the thus *conditionally* irreversible processes.

We saw in §3 that the obtaining of certain species of *nomologically-contingent* boundary conditions is a *necessary* condition for an entropically-grounded statistical anisotropy of time. Hence we shall be able to conclude that nomologically-contingent properties of the world enter integrally not only into the entropic kind of statistical irreversibility but also into the nonentropic kind of irreversibility affirmed by Popper as the physical basis for the anisotropy of time.

Independently of O. Costa de Beauregard, who had used the same illustration before him,[27] Popper (I) considers a large surface of water initially at rest into which a stone is dropped, thereby producing an outgoing wave of decreasing amplitude spreading concentrically about the point of the stone's impact. And Popper argues that this process is irreversible in the sense that the "spontaneous" (IV) concatenation on all points of a circle of the initial conditions requisite to the occurrence of a corresponding *contracting* wave is physically impossible, a "spontaneous" concatenation being understood to be one which is *not* brought about by coordinated influences emanating from a common center. Being predicated on the latter spontaneity, this nomologically-contingent irreversibility is of a *conditional* kind.

Now, one might object that the attribution of the irreversibility of the outgoing wave motion to this nomologically-contingent factor is unsound. The grounds would be that the statistical entropy law is *not irrelevant* to this irreversibility, because the diminution in the amplitude of the outgoing wave is due to the super-position of *two* independent effects as follows: (1) the requirements of the law of conservation of energy (*first* law of thermodynamics), and (2) an entropy increase in an essentially closed system through dissipative viscosity. To be sure, the entropy increase through dissipative viscosity is a *sufficient* condition (in the *statistical* sense of §3 above!) for the irreversibility of the outgoing wave motion, i.e., for the absence of a corresponding (spontaneously initiated) contracting wave motion. But this fact cannot detract from the soundness of Popper's claim that another, independent *sufficient condition* for the conditional kind of *de facto* irreversibility affirmed by him is as follows: the nomologically-contingent impossibility of the spontaneous occurrence of the coordinated initial conditions requisite for a contracting wave motion. We see that Popper rightly adduces the need for the *coherence* of these initial conditions as his basis for denying the possibility of their *spontaneous* concatenation, i.e., their concatenation *without* first having been coordinated by an influence emanating from a central source. Says he (III): "Only such conditions can be causally realized as can be organized from one centre. . . . causes which are not centrally correlated are causally unrelated, and can cooperate [i.e., produce coherence in the form of *isotropic* contraction of waves to a precise point] only by accident . . . The probability of such an accident will be zero."

In view of the aforementioned *conditional* character of Popper's nomologically-contingent irreversibility, E. L. Hill and I deemed it useful to point out (cf. fn. 26) the following: there does indeed exist an important class of processes in *infinite* space whose *irreversibility* is (1) nonentropic and nomologically-contingent, hence being of the kind correctly envisioned by Popper, yet (2) *not conditional* by *not* being predicated on Popper's proviso of spontaneity. Without presuming to speak for Professor Hill, I can say, for my part, that in making that existential claim I was guided by the following considerations:

(i) Popper (II) briefly remarks correctly that the eternal expansion of a very thin gas from a center into a spatially *infinite* universe does *not* involve an entropy increase, and the *de facto* irreversibility of this process is therefore *non*-entropic. For the statistical Maxwell-Boltzmann entropy is not even defined for a spatially infinite universe: the quasi-ergodic hypothesis, which provides the essential basis for the probability-metric ingredient in the Maxwell-Boltzmann entropy concept, is presumably *false* for an *infinite* phase-space, since *walls* are required to produce the collisions which are essential to its validity. In the absence of some kind of wall, whose very existence would assure the *finitude* of the system, the rapidly-moving particles will soon overtake the slowly-moving ones, leaving them ever further behind for all future eternity instead of *mixing* with them in a space-filling manner. Moreover, if the number of particles in the infinite universe is only finite, the equilibrium state of maximum entropy cannot be realized, since a finite number of particles cannot be *uniformly* distributed in a phase space of infinitely many cells. On the other hand, if the number of particles is denumerably infinite, the number W of microscopic arrangements in $S = k \log W$ becomes undefined or infinite (cf. fn. 13), and no entropy increase or decrease is defined.

(ii) Though *allowed* by the *laws* of mechanics, there seem to exist no "implosions" at all which would qualify as the temporal inverses of eternally progressing "explosions" of very thin gases from a center into infinite space. In the light of this fact, one can assert the *de facto* irreversibility of an *eternal* "explosion" *unconditionally*, i.e., *without* Popper's restrictive proviso of *spontaneity* in regard to the production of the *coherent* initial conditions requisite for its inverse. For in an infinite space, there is also no possibility at all of a *non*-spontaneous production of the coherent "initial" conditions for an implosion having the following properties: the gas particles converge to a point after having been moving through infinite space for all past eternity in a manner constituting the temporal inverse of the expansion of a very thin gas from a point for all future eternity. There can be no question of a *non*-spontaneous realization of the "initial" conditions required for the latter kind of implosion, since such a realization would involve a self-contradictory condition akin to that in Kant's fallacious First Antinomy: the requirement that a process which has been going on for all infinite past time must have had a finite beginning (production by past *initial* conditions) after all.

On the other hand, in a spatially *finite* system it is indeed possible to produce *non*-spontaneously the initial conditions for contracting waves and for implosions of gas particles which converge to a point. Thus, assuming negligible viscosity, there are expanding water waves in *finite* systems of which the temporal inverses could be produced *non*-spontaneously by dropping a very large circular object onto the water surface so that all parts of the circular object strike the water surface simultaneously. And hence there are conditions under which contracting waves do exist in finite systems. But there is no need whatever for Popper's spontaneity proviso to assert the *de facto* irreversibility of the eternal expansion of a *spherical light-wave* from a center through infinite space! If space is infinite, the existence of the latter process of expansion is assured by the facts of observation in conjunction with electromagnetic theory; but despite the fact that the *laws* for a homogeneous and isotropic medium *allow* the *inverse* process no less than the actual one,[28] we never encounter the inverse process of spherical waves closing in isotropically to a sharp point of extinction.

In view of the decisive role of the *infinitude* or "*openness*" of a physical system (the universe)—as opposed to the finitude of *closed* systems—in rendering Popper's spontaneity proviso dispensable, Hill and I[29] made the following existential claim concerning processes whose irreversibility is *non*-entropic and *de facto* in "open" (infinite) systems:

> In classical mechanics the closed systems have quasi-periodic orbits, whereas the open systems have at least some aperiodic orbits which extend to infinity. . . . there exists a fundamental distinction between the two kinds of system in the following sense. In open systems there always exists a class of allowed elementary processes the inverses of which are unacceptable on physical grounds by requiring a *deus ex machina* for their production. For example, in an open universe, matter or radiation can travel away indefinitely from the 'finite' region of space, and so be permanently lost. The inverse process would require matter or radiant energy coming from 'infinity,' and so would involve a process which is not realizable by physical sources. Einstein's example of an outgoing light wave and Popper's analogous case of a water wave are special finite illustrations of this principle.

It will be noted that Hill and I spoke of there being "at least some aperiodic orbits which extend to infinity" in the classical mechanics of open systems and that we were careful *not* to assert that *every* such allowed process extending to infinity is a *de facto* irreversible one. Instead, we affirmed the existence of a *de facto* irreversibility which is *not* predicated on Popper's spontaneity proviso by saying: "there always exists a class of allowed elementary processes" that are thus *de facto* irreversible. And, for my part, I conceived of this claim as constituting an extension of Popper's recognition of the essential role of *coherence* in *de facto* irreversibility to processes of the following kind: processes whose *de facto* irreversibility is *not* conditional on Popper's finitist requirement of spontaneity, because these processes extend to "infinity" in open systems and would hence have inverses in which matter or energy would have to come from "infinity" *coherently* so as to converge upon a point.

The communication by Hill and myself prompted the following puzzling dissent by Popper (III):

> In this connection, I must express some doubt as to whether the principle proposed by Profs. Hill and Grünbaum is adequate. In formulating their principle, they operate with two ideas: that of the 'openness' of a system, and that of a *deus ex machina*. Both seem to me insufficient. For a system consisting of a sun, and a comet coming from infinity and describing a hyperbolic path around the sun, seems to me to satisfy all the criteria stated by them. The system is open; and the reversion of the comet on its track would require a *deus ex machina* for its realization: it would "require matter . . . coming from 'infinity' ". Nevertheless, this is an example of just that kind of process which, I take it, we all wish to describe as completely reversible.

Popper's proposed counterexample of the comet coming from "infinity" into the solar system seems to me to fail for the following reasons: (1) neither the actual motion of the comet nor its inverse involve any *coherence*, a feature which I, for my part, had conceived to be essential to the obtaining of nonentropic *de facto* irreversibility in open systems. In my own view, the fact that particles or photons *came from "infinity"* in the course of an infinite past does *not per se* require a *deus ex machina*, any more than does their *going to "infinity"* in the course of an infinite future: in this context, I regard as innocuous the asymmetry that a particle which has already come from infinity can be said to have traversed an infinite space by *now*, whereas a particle now embarking on an infinite future journey will only have traversed a *finite* distance at *any* one time in the future. It is a *coherent* "implosion" from infinity that I believe to require a *deus ex machina*, i.e., to be *de facto* nonexistent, while coherent "explosions" actually do exist. (2) Even ignoring that the motion of Popper's comet does not involve coherence, the issue is *not*, as he seems to think, whether it would require a *deus ex machina* to realize the reversal of any given actual comet in its track; rather the issue is whether no *deus ex machina* would be needed to realize the actual comet motion while a *deus ex machina* would have been needed to have another comet execute *instead* a motion inverse to the first one. The answer to this question is an emphatic "no": unlike the case of outgoing and contracting waves (explosions and implosions), the two comet motions, which are temporal inverses of each other, are *on a par* with respect to the role of a *deus ex machina* in their realization. And even the reversal of the motion of an actual comet at a suitable point in its orbit might in fact be effected by an elastic collision with an oppositely moving other comet of equal mass and hence would *not* involve, as Popper would have it (III), "a *deus ex machina* who is something like a gigantic tennis player."

It seems to me, therefore, that far from being vulnerable to Popper's proposed counterexample, the existential claim by Hill and myself is fully as viable as Popper's, while having the merit of achieving generality through freedom from Popper's spontaneity proviso. I therefore cannot see any justification at all for the following two assertions which H. Mehlberg made in a very informative recent paper[30]: (a) He states incorrectly that Hill and I have claimed *de facto* irreversibility for "the class of all conceivable physical processes provided that the latter meet the mild requirement of happening in an 'open' physical system," and (b) Mehlberg asserts that "Popper has shown the untenability of the Hill-Grünbaum criterion by constructing an effective counter example which illustrates the impossibility of their sweeping generalization of his original criterion."

Mehlberg's critical estimate of Popper's own affirmation of nonentropic *de facto* irreversibility likewise seems to me to be unconvincing in important respects. After asking whether the irreversibility asserted by Popper is "lawlike or factlike"—a question to which the answer is: "avowedly factlike" — Mehlberg[31] concludes that Popper's temporal asymmetry "seems to be rather interpretable as a local, factlike particularity of the terrestrial surface than as a universal, lawlike feature . . . which may be expected to materialize always and everywhere." There are two points in Mehlberg's conclusion which invite comment: (i) the significance which he attaches to the circumstance that the irreversibility of certain classes of processes is *de facto* or factlike rather than nomological or lawlike, when he assesses the bearing of that irreversibility on the issue of anisotropy vs. isotropy of time, and (ii) the contrast between the epistemological parsimony of his characterization of Popper's irreversibility as a "local, . . . particularity of the terrestrial surface" and the inductive boldness of Mehlberg's willingness to do the following: affirm a cosmically pervasive nomological *isotropy* of time on the basis of attributing *cosmic* relevance, both spatially and temporally, to the fundamental *time-symmetric* laws which have been confirmed in modern man's limited sample of the universe.

As to the first of these two points in Mehlberg's denial of the anisotropy of time, I note preliminarily that human hopes for an eternal biological life are no less surely frustrated if all men are indeed *de facto* mortal, i.e., mortal on the strength of "boundary conditions" which do obtain permanently, than if man's mortality were assured by some *law*. By the same token, I see no escape from the conclusion that if *de facto* irreversibility does actually obtain everywhere and forever, such irreversibility confers pervasive anisotropy on time. And this anisotropy prevails not one iota less than it would, if its existence were guaranteed by temporally *asymmetrical* fundamental *laws* of cosmic scope. It is of considerable interest, of course, that such irreversibility as obtains in nature is *de facto* rather than nomological. But, in my view, when evaluating the evidence for the anisotropy of time, Mehlberg commits the following error of misplaced emphasis: he wrongly discounts *de facto* irreversibility vis-à-vis nomological irreversibility by failing to show that our warrant for a cosmic extrapolation of time-symmetric *laws* is actually greater than for a corresponding extrapolation of the factlike conditions making for observed *de facto* irreversibility. For on what grounds can it be maintained that the ubiquitous and permanent existence of the *de facto* probabilities of "boundary conditions" on which Popper rests his affirmation of temporal anisotropy is less well confirmed than those laws on whose time-symmetry Mehlberg is willing to base his *denial* of the anisotropy of time? In particular, one wonders how Mehlberg could inductively justify his contention that we are only confirming a "particularity of the terrestrial surface," when we find with Popper (III) that "Only such conditions can be causally realized as can be organized from one centre. ... causes which are not centrally correlated are causally unrelated, and can co-operate [i.e. produce coherence in the form of *isotropic* contraction of waves to a precise point] only by accident ... The probability of such an accident will be zero." If this finding cannot be presumed to hold on all planet-like bodies in the universe, for example, then why are we entitled to assume with Mehlberg that *time-symmetric* laws of mechanics, for example, are exemplified by the motions of binary stars throughout the universe? Since I see no valid grounds for Mehlberg's double standard of inductive credibility of pervasiveness as between laws and factlike regularities, I consider his negative estimate of Popper's nonentropic *de facto* anisotropy of time as unfounded.

Mehlberg's misplaced emphasis on the significance of lawlike vis-à-vis *de facto* irreversibility likewise seems to me to vitiate the following account which he gives of the import of *de facto* irreversibility in optics, a species of irreversibility which he admits to be of cosmic scope. He writes[32]:

> A less speculative example of cosmological irreversibility is provided by the propagation of light *in vacuo,* which several authors have discussed from this point of view. ... In accordance with Maxwell's theory of light conceived as an electromagnetic phenomenon, they point out that light emitted by a pointlike source, or converging towards a point, can spread on concentric spherical surfaces which either expand or contract monotonically. Yet, independently of Maxwell's theory, the incidence of expanding optical spheres is known to exceed by far the incidence of shrinking spheres. The reason for this statistical superiority of expanding optical spheres is simply the fact that pointlike light-emitting atoms are much more numerous than perfectly spherical, opaque surfaces capable of generating shrinking optical spheres, mainly by the process of reflection. If true, this ratio of the incidences of both types of light waves would provide a cosmological clue to a pervasive irreversibility of a particular class of optical processes. The bearing of this optical irreversibility upon time's arrow was often discussed. A long time before the asymmetry of expanding and contracting light waves was promoted to the rank of time's arrow, Einstein [A. Einstein, "Über die Entwicklung unserer Anschauungen über die Konstitution und das Wesen der Strahlung," *Physikalische Zeitschrift, 10,* 817-828, 1910] pointed out that the asymmetry of these two types of optical propagation holds only on the undulatory theory of light. Once light is identified instead with a swarm of photons, the asymmetry vanishes. This conclusion holds at least for a spatially finite universe or for optical phenomena confined to a finite spatial region.

> Once more, however, the decisive point seems to be that the asymmetry between the two types of light waves depends on factual, initial conditions which prevail in a given momentary cross section of cosmic history or at the 'boundaries' of a finite or infinite universe rather than on nomological considerations concerning this history: any other ratio of the incidences of expanding and shrinking light waves would also be in keeping with the relevant laws of nature contained in Maxwell's theory of electromagnetic phenomena. Of course, the aforementioned non-nomological conditions, responsible for the factual ratio of these incidences, are not 'local' either,

since the whole world is involved—they belong to cosmology. These conditions are nevertheless factlike rather than lawlike, as a comparison with the pertinent laws which can be derived from Maxwell's theory clearly shows.

Contrary to Mehlberg, the decisive point appears *not* to be that "the asymmetry between the two types of light waves depends on factual, initial conditions ... rather than on nomological considerations." He also asserts that "at least for a spatially finite universe or for optical phenomena confined to a finite spatial region" the corpuscularity of the photon, as conceived by Einstein, invalidates the optical asymmetry which obtains on the undulatory theory of light. I believe, however, that this claim should be amended as follows: "the optical asymmetry vanishes, *if at all*, *only* in a *finite* space." For suppose that one assumes with Einstein that the elementary radiation process is one in which a single emitting particle transfers its energy to only a single absorbing particle. In that case, the fantastically complicated *coherence* needed for the formation of a continuous contracting undulatory spherical shell of light is no longer required. Instead, there is then a need for the less complicated coherence among emitting particles located at the walls of a *finite* system and emitting converging photons. But, as Hill and I pointed out [(20)], the *de facto* irreversibility of the spatially symmetrical eternal propagation of a pulse of light from a point source into *infinite* space does *not* depend on whether the light pulse is undulatory instead of being constituted by a swarm of photons.

Neither does *this* irreversibility depend on the acceptance of the steady-state theory of cosmology which, in the words of T. Gold [(12), pp. 86-87], offers the following explanation for the fact that the universe is a nonreflecting sink for radiation:

> It is this facility of the universe to soak up any amount of radiation that makes it different from any closed box, and it is just this that enables it to define the arrow of time in any system that is in contact with this sink. But why is it that the universe is a non-reflecting sink for radiation? Different explanations are offered for this in the various cosmological theories and in some schemes, indeed, this would only be a temporary property.[33]
> In the steady state universe it is entirely attributed to the state of expansion. The red shift operates to diminish the contribution to the radiation field of distant matter; even though the density does not diminish at great distances, the sky is dark because in most directions the material on a line of sight is receding very fast ...

What Gold appears to have in mind here is that due to a very substantial Doppler shift of the radiation emitted by the receding galaxies, the frequency ν becomes very low or goes to zero, and since the energy of that radiation is given by $E = h\nu$, very little if any is received by us converging from these sources. And he goes on to say:

> This photon expansion going on around most material is the most striking type of asymmetry, and it appears to give rise to all other time asymmetries that are in evidence. The preferential divergence, rather than convergence, of the world lines of a system ceases when that system has been isolated in a box which prevents the expansion of the photons out into space. Time's arrow is then lost.

We see that Gold's account includes an appreciation of the decisive role played by the infinitude of the space in rendering irreversible the radiation spreading from a point. To be sure, he does emphasize that the Doppler shift due to the expansion makes for the darkness of the sky at night, which would otherwise be lit up by strong radiation. But the crucial point is the following: even if the energy of radiation from receding galaxies were not drastically attenuated by the Doppler shift, such radiation would still *not* be the inverse of a process in which a pulse of photons from a point source forever spreads symmetrically into infinite space from that point source. The inverse of the *latter* process of outgoing radiation would be a contracting configuration of photons that has been coming from "infinity," i.e., from no sources at all, and has been converging on a point for all infinite past time.

5. SUMMARY.

We have examined the following multifaceted problem: what are the physical bases of the anisotropy of both physical and psychological time? And by specifying these bases, we have endeavored to provide insight into one of the cardinal *qualitative* features of time, which is quite independent of the scales or metrics that are used to measure durations. We stressed that the anisotropy of *psychological* time does depend on at least some of those *physical* regularities which confer anisotropy on physical time. But we were careful to note that these regularities do not themselves explain such phenomena of psychological time as the striking (directionally-neutral) transiency of the "Now." And there are, of course, other impressive qualitative features of *psychological* time whose explanation would require highly complicated neurological theory. We need mention only such phenomena as melody awareness in which we have an *instantaneous* awareness of the temporal succession of sounds, which cannot be explained by the mere succession of states of awareness of the individual sounds. Thus, like most other deep problems, the problem of time confronts us with many remaining questions.

NOTES

1. Accounts of current theories of the operation of "biological clocks" are given in (10).

2. For recent discussions of these philosophical problems, see A. Grünbaum (13) and (14).

3. In the present context of exclusively reversible processes, the relation of "earlier than" implicitly invoked in the assertion that a ball moves *"from A to D"* (or, in the opposite direction, *"from D to A"*) must be *divested* of its customary anchorage in an anisotropic time. For as I have explained elsewhere in detail [Grünbaum (15), §3], in the world of exclusively reversible processes now under discussion, the assertion that a given motion of a ball was *"from A to D"* rather than *"from D to A"* expresses *not* an objective physical relation between the two terminal events of the motion, but only the *convention* that we have assigned a lower time-number to the event of the ball's being at A than to its being at D. By contrast, in the context of *irreversible* processes, the relation term "earlier than" names an *objective* physical relation between two states which is *different* from the converse objective relation named by "later than."

4. The dependence of the "Now" and, correlatively, of the transient division of the time continuum into "past" and "future" on the perspectival role of consciousness is *not* at all refuted by the use of the locutions "Here-Now," "Absolute Past," and "Absolute Future" in explaining the Minkowski diagram of the entirely *non*-psychological special theory of relativity. Neither does the use of these locutions show conversely that this theory makes essential use of psychological temporal categories. For the "Now" in the "Here-Now" of the Minkowski diagram designates no more than a kind of *arbitrary* zero or origin of temporal coordinates: we can make use of the Minkowski diagram at noon on June 1, 1962 to let "Here-Now" designate a certain event occurring after the extinction of the sun. And the "Absolute Past" and the "Absolute Future" are no more than the set of events respectively absolutely earlier and later than the event arbitrarily designated as the "Here-Now."

   For a critique of H. Reichenbach's attempt to provide a physical, as opposed to merely psychological, characterization of the Now *on the basis of indeterminist physics,* cf. [H. Bergmann (1), pp. 27-28, and A. Grünbaum (15), §4].

5. For details on the special theory of relativity relevant here, see A. Grünbaum (14), §2.

6. Cf. H. Bergson, [(2)] and [(3)]. Related criticisms of Bergson's treatment of other aspects of time are given in A. Grünbaum [(16), pp. 144-155].

7. W. Sellars [(24)] has provided a penetrating and detailed articulation of the logical commitments of pre-scientific temporal discourse, distinguishing it carefully from the logic of the temporal language of physics and giving an analysis of the latter as well.

8. Although we shall see below that Eddington's criterion of "later than" is vulnerable to serious criticism in the light of the statistical treatment of thermodynamic systems, it should be noted here that his criterion does *not* render the second law of thermodynamics tautologous [Grünbaum (17), p. 552]. Nor is Eddington open to the objection that his criterion is logically circular on the grounds that the concept of the *instantaneous* entropy state of an extended *closed* system presupposes the temporal concepts of simultaneity and temporal betweenness. For, as has been pointed out elsewhere [Grünbaum (17), pp. 552-553], there is no logical compulsion to make these temporal concepts logically dependent on the concept "later than."

9. I am indebted to my colleague Professor A. Janis for pointing out to me (by reference to the example of having dreamt) that condition (i) is only a sufficient and not also a necessary condition for the obtaining of the relation of being psychologically later. This caution must likewise be applied to the following two assertions by William James, if they are to hold: "our perception of time's flight, . . . is due . . . to our *memory* of a content which it [i.e., time] had a moment previous, and which we feel to agree or disagree with its content now" [(21), p. 619], and "what is past, to be known as past, must be known *with* what is present, and *during* the 'present' spot of time" [(21), p. 629].

10. The entirely *non*-metrical concept represented by the metaphor "forward flow" is not at all vulnerable to the metrical *reductio ad absurdum* offered by J. J. C. Smart [(25), p. 81] and by Max Black [(4), p. 57] in the following form: these authors ask irrelevantly "How fast does time flow?" and then go on to claim quite mistakenly that a nonexistent super-time would be needed to give meaning to the flow of psychological time. Max Black likewise supposes incorrectly that the metaphor "forward flow" commits one to saying that time is "changing" [(4), p. 57] and to the contention that it makes sense to speak of the cessation of the flow of psychological time. The absurdities which Black is then able to derive from the literal interpretation of these latter assertions can therefore *not* serve to discredit the concept of the transiency of the Now as understood in this essay.

11. Reichenbach [(23), pp. 139-140] discusses a situation envisaged by Boltzmann in which there are two entropically-counterdirected galactic systems each of

which contains intelligent beings whose positive sense of psychological time is geared to the direction of entropy increase in its own galactic environment. Says he [(23), p. 139]: "Let us assume that among the many galaxies there is one within which time goes in a direction opposite to that of our galaxy. . . . In this situation, some distant part of the universe is on a section of its entropy curve which for us is a downgrade; if, however, there were living beings in that part of the universe, then their environment would for them have all the properties of being on an upgrade of the entropy curve." And Reichenbach then offers the following quite incomplete hints as to how there might be physical interaction between the two sets of intelligent beings such that either set of beings would be able to secure information indicating the temporal counterdirectedness of the other [(23), p. 139 and p. 140]:

"That such a system is developing in the opposite time direction might be discovered by us from some radiation traveling from the system to us and perhaps exhibiting a shift in spectral lines upon arrival. . . . the radiation traveling from the system to us would, for the system, . . . not leave that system but arrive at it. Perhaps the signal could be interpreted by inhabitants of that system as a message from our system telling them that our system develops in the reverse time direction. We have here a connecting light ray which, for each system, is an arriving light ray annihilated in some absorption process."

12. The socalled quasi-ergodic hypothesis is *not* an assertion based on our lack of knowledge as to the actual relative frequency of the different micro-states: instead it has the logical status of a theoretical claim concerning a presumed fact. What is a matter of our lack of knowledge in this context, however, is which one of the many micro-states that can underly any given macro-state does, in fact, obtain when the system exhibits the specified macro-state.

13. More generally, Bernoulli's formula for W is $W = \dfrac{n!}{n_1! \, n_2! \, n_3! \, \ldots \, n_m!}$, where $\sum_i^m n_i = n$. If we wished to *normalize* the thermodynamic probability (which is a large number) so as to be less than 1, then we would have to divide it by the total number of arrangements for all distributions. Hence the (normalized) probability W_p of a *particular* distribution is given by $W_p = \dfrac{W}{m^n}$.

14. For a more detailed discussion of this time-symmetry, see Mehlberg [(22), Section 2, pp. 112-120], and A. Grünbaum [(15), §3].

15. I draw here on material contained in my earlier publication [Grünbaum (18), §2].

16. Cf. R. C. Tolman [(26), p. 149].

17. Cf. R. Fürth, [(11)].

18. Ibid., p. 270.

19. Although the decisive asymmetry just noted was admitted by H. Mehlberg [(22), p. 129], he dismisses it as expressing "merely the factual difference between the two relevant values of probability." But an asymmetry is no less an asymmetry for depending on *de facto,* nomologically-contingent boundary conditions rather than being assured by a *law* alone. Since our verification of laws generally has the same partial and indirect character as that of our confirmation of the existence of complicated *de facto* boundary conditions, the assertion of an asymmetry depending on *de facto* conditions is generally no less reliable than one wholly grounded on a law. Hence when Mehlberg [(22), p. 117, n. 30] urges against Schrödinger's claim of entropic asymmetry that for every pair of branch systems which change their entropy in one direction, "there is nothing to prevent" another pair of closed subsystems from changing their entropy in the opposite direction, the reply is: Mehlberg's criticism can be upheld only by gratuitously neglecting the statistical asymmetry admitted but then dismissed by him as "merely" factual. For it is the existence of the specified boundary conditions which statistically prevents the existence of entropic time-symmetry in this context.

20. Readers familiar with Reichenbach's "hypothesis of the branch structure" as set forth in his *The Direction of Time* [(23), p. 136] will note that though heavily indebted to Reichenbach, my treatment of the assumptions regarding branch systems departs from Reichenbach's in several *essential* respects. A statement and justification of these departures is given in A. Grünbaum [(15), footnote 97].

21. A. Grünbaum [(15), §2].

22. The two exceptions, which I have discussed elsewhere in some detail [Grünbaum (18), pp. 152-155], are constituted by the following two classes of advance indicators: (i) veridical predictions made and stored (recorded) by human (or other sentient, theory-using) beings, and physically-registered, *bona fide* advance indicators produced by computers, and (ii) advance indicators (e.g., sudden barometric drops) which are produced by the very cause (pressure change) that also produces the future interaction (storm) indicated by them.

23. Reichenbach [(23), p. 154].

24. The material in this §4 is drawn from §1 and §2 of my earlier paper [Grünbaum (19)].

25. K. R. Popper, *Nature 177,* 538 (1956); *178,* 382 (1956); *179,* 1297 (1957); *181,* 402 (1958). These four publications will be cited hereafter as "I," "II," "III" and "IV" respectively.

26. E. L. Hill and A. Grünbaum, *Nature 179,* 1296 (1957).

27. O. Costa de Beauregard [(8), p. 402].

28. Cf. G. J. Whitrow, [(28), pp. 8-10 and 269]; also E. Zilsel [(30), p. 283].

29. Cf. footnote 26.

30. H. Mehlberg [(22), p. 128].

31. H. Mehlberg [(22), p. 126].

32. H. Mehlberg, *op. cit.,* pp. 123-124.

33. Presumably Gold is referring here to models of spatially closed or finite universes.

REFERENCES

(1) H. Bergmann, *Der Kampf um das Kausalgesetz in der jüngsten Physik,* Braunschweig, 1929.

(2) H. Bergson, *Creative Evolution,* New York, 1944.

(3) H. Bergson, Matière et Mémoire, Geneva, 1946.

(4) M. Black, "The 'Direction' of Time," *Analysis* XIX, 54 (1959); this paper is reprinted in M. Black, *Models and Metaphors,* Cornell University Press, 1962, pp. 182-193.

(5) M. Black, "Review of G. J. Whitrow's *The Natural Philosophy of Time,"* *Scientific American,* vol. 206, April, 1962, pp. 179-185.

(6) P. W. Bridgman, *Reflections of a Physicist,* New York, 1950.

(7) G. M. Clemence, "Time and Its Measurement," *American Scientist 40,* p. 260 (1952).

(8) O. Costa de Beauregard, "L'Irréversibilité Quantique, Phénomène Macroscopique," in A. George (ed.), *Louis de Broglie,* Paris, 1953.

(9) A. S. Eddington, *The Nature of the Physical World,* New York, 1928.

(10) L. Frisch (ed.), *Biological Clocks, Cold Spring Harbor Symposia on Quantitative Biology,* vol. XXV, 1960, Cold Spring Harbor, L. I., New York.

(11) R. Fürth, "Prinzipien der Statistik," *Handbuch der Physik,* vol. 4, 1929, pp. 270 and 192-193.

(12) T. Gold, "The Arrow of Time," in *La Structure et L'Évolution de l'Univers* (Proceedings of the 11th Solvay Congress), Brussels, 1958.

(13) A. Grünbaum, "Geometry, Chronometry and Empiricism," in *Minnesota Studies in the Philosophy of Science* (eds. Feigl and Maxwell), vol. III, Minneapolis, 1962.

(14) A. Grünbaum, "Logical and Philosophical Foundations of the Special Theory of Relativity," in *Philosophy of Science: Readings,* A. Danto and S. Morgenbesser, eds. New York: Meridian, 1960, pp. 399-434.

(15) A. Grünbaum, "Carnap's Views on the Foundations of Geometry," in *The Philosophy of Rudolf Carnap,* P. A. Schilpp, ed., LaSalle, Illinois: Open Court, 1962.

(16) A. Grünbaum, "Relativity and the Atomicity of Becoming," *The Review of Metaphysics,* vol. 4 (1950), pp. 143-186.

(17) A. Grünbaum, "Time and Entropy," *American Scientist 43* (1955), pp. 550-572.

(18) A. Grünbaum, "Temporally Asymmetric Principles, Parity Between Explanation and Prediction, and Mechanism versus Teleology," *Philosophy of Science,* vol. 29, (1962), pp. 146-170.

(19) A. Grünbaum, "Popper on Irreversibility," in: M. Bunge (ed.), *The Critical Approach,* Essays in Honor of Karl Popper, The Free Press, Glencoe, Illinois (1963).

(20) E. L. Hill and A. Grünbaum, "Irreversible Processes in Physical Theory," *Nature,* vol. 179 (1957), pp. 1296-1297.

(21) W. James, *The Principles of Psychology,* New York, 1950.

(22) H. Mehlberg, "Physical Laws and Time's Arrow," in: H. Feigl & G. Maxwell (eds.), *Current Issues in the Philosophy of Science,* New York, 1961, pp. 105-138.

(23) H. Reichenbach, *The Direction of Time,* Berkeley, 1956.

(24) W. Sellars, "Time and the World Order," *Minnesota Studies in the Philosophy of Science,* vol. III, Minneapolis, 1962, pp. 527-616.

(25) J. J. C. Smart, "The Temporal Asymmetry of the World," *Analysis XIV,* 81 (1954).

(26) R. C. Tolman, *The Principles of Statistical Mechanics,* Oxford, 1938, p. 149.

(27) H. Weyl, *Philosophy of Mathematics and Natural Science,* Princeton: Princeton University Press, 1949.

(28) G. J. Whitrow, *The Natural Philosophy of Time,* London, 1961.

(29) N. Wiener, *Cybernetics,* New York, 1948.

(30) E. Zilsel, "Über die Asymmetrie der Kausalität und die Einsinnigkeit der Zeit," *Naturwissenschaften,* vol. 15, (1927), pp. 280-286.

Chapter **6** | *Problems of Microphysics*

P. K. Feyerabend
Professor of Philosophy
University of California

Descartes who seemed to me to be jealous of the fame of Galileo had the ambition to be regarded as the author of a new philosophy, to be taught in academies in place of Aristotelianism. He put forward his conjectures as verities, almost as if they could be proved by his affirming them on oath. He ought to have presented his system of physics as an attempt to show what might be anticipated as probable in this science, when no principles but those of mechanics were admitted: this would indeed have been praiseworthy; but he went further, and claimed to have revealed the precise truth thereby greatly impeding the discovery of genuine knowledge.

HUYGHENS

` ACKNOWLEDGMENTS

For support of research the author is indebted to the National Science Foundation and to the Minnesota Center for the Philosophy of Science.

Problems of Microphysics

(1) INTRODUCTION.

When the formalism of the elementary quantum theory was first conceived it was unclear how it was to be related to experience and what intuitive picture should be connected with its application. "The mathematical equipment of the . . . theory," writes Heisenberg about this period,[1] "was . . . complete in its most important parts by the middle of 1926, but the physical significance was still extremely unclear." There existed a variety of interpretations. However, in the course of time each of these interpretations turned out to be unsatisfactory. Only the suggestions of Niels Bohr and of his collaborators, which later on were presented in a more systematic manner and which then received the name "Copenhagen Interpretation"[2] seemed to succeed in solving most of the problems that had been fatal for its rivals. It was this interpretation which was finally accepted by the great majority of physicists, including some of those who had first objected to it on philosophical grounds.[3] From about 1930[4] (or rather from about 1935[5]) to 1950 the Copenhagen Interpretation was *the* microphilosophy, and the objections of a few opponents, notably of Einstein and Schrödinger[6] were taken less and less seriously. During these years the idea of complementarity was developed and proved to be fertile in such fields as psychology[7] (Jung's included), biology,[8] ethics,[9] and theology.[10] The most decisive argument for the soundness of this idea of complementarity derived from its application (and its success[11]) in the domain of physics itself. Here it led to the development of a variety of theories such as Dirac's theory of the electron and the quantum theory of fields. The belief that these theories could not have been developed without support from the basic principles of the Copenhagen Interpretation,[12] and their empirical fruitfulness, seemed to show the soundness of the philosophy that had been developed by Bohr and his disciples. Here at last the practicing physicist was given a point of view which contained no arbitrary element, which allowed him correctly to interpret many applications of a fairly complicated theory, viz. the wave-mechanics, which was capable of providing a guide in research and all of whose basic assumptions were directly taken from experience. "We are here not presented," writes Professor Rosenfeld,[13] "with a point of view which we may adopt, or reject, according to whether it agrees, or does not agree with some philosophical criterion. It is the unique result of an adaptation of our ideas to a new experimental situation in the domain of atomic physics. It is therefore completely on the plane of experience . . . that we have to judge whether the new conceptions work in a satisfactory way." Considering the success of the theories which were built in accordance with the idea of complementarity, this judgment most certainly was believed to be a positive one.

And yet we are now witnessing the development of a counter-movement which demands that the basic assumptions of the Copenhagen Interpretation be given up and be replaced by a very different philosophy. The critics do not deny the *initial* success of the elementary theory, of Dirac's theory of the electron and of the field theories. They mainly point out two things. First, that at the present moment all these theories are in difficulty as far as empirical adequacy is concerned and that they are also not as simple and straightforward as they perhaps ought to be.[14] And secondly, they question the argument from empirical success itself. Complementarity is successful—let us take this for granted. This does not show that it is a reasonable point of view for its empirical success, the fact that it is confirmed by all actual, and perhaps even by all conceivable experimental results may well be due, not to its correctness, but to its being void of empirical content.[15] Nor would its empirical success prove the non-existence of valid *alternatives* to complementarity. Indeed, one of the most valuable contributions of the revolutionaries consists in their having shown that there is not a single sound argument, empirical or mathematical, establishing that complementarity is the last word in matters microphysical and that a theoretician who intends to improve quantum theory will be successful only if he works with theories that possess inbuilt uncertainties. At least to this writer it is now clear that future research need not (and should not[16]) be intimidated by the restrictions which some high priests of complementarity want to impose upon it.

It is unfortunate that the majority of physicists is still opposed to these very clear results. There are various reasons for this situation. The most prominent reason is the soporific effect which partial empirical success seems to have upon many physicists. Also many physicists are very practical people and not very fond of philosophy. This being the case, they will take for granted and not further investigate[17] those philosophical ideas which they have learned in their youth and which by now seem to them, and indeed to the whole community of practicing scientists, to be the expression of physical common sense. In most cases these ideas are part of the Copenhagen Interpretation.

A second reason for the persistence of the creed of complementarity in the face of decisive objections is to be found in the *vagueness* of the main principles of this creed.[18] This vagueness allows the defendants to take care of objections by *development* rather than by *reformulation*, a procedure which will of course create the impression that the correct answer has been there all the time and that it was overlooked by the critic. Bohr's followers, and also Bohr himself, have made full use of this possibility even in cases where the necessity of a reformulation was clearly indicated. Their attitude has very often been one of people who have the task to clear up the misunderstandings of their opponents rather than to admit their own mistakes. A very important instance of this kind of behavior which will be discussed later in the paper is Bohr's answer to Einstein's very decisive objection of 1935.[19] Here I want to mention another example where this attitude is exhibited most clearly. Before Bohm published his well-known paper on hidden variables[20] it was commonly assumed that the quantum theory was incompatible with any interpretation that employed hidden parameters and that this character of the theory was guaranteed by experience.[21] "There is *only one* interpretation," writes Pascual Jordan,[22] "which is capable of conceptually ordering the . . . totality of experimental results in the field of atomic physics." In defending his interpretation against Einstein's remarks Bohr points out that, in his opinion, "there could be no other way to deem a logically consistent mathematical formalism as inadequate than by demonstrating the departure of its consequences from experience, or by proving that its predictions did not exhaust the possibilities of observation, and Einstein's argumentation could be directed to neither of these ends."[23] Considering the idea of hidden parameters Pauli writes:[24] "In this connection I may also refer to von Neumann's well known proof that the consequences of quantum mechanics cannot be amended by additional statements on the distribution of values of observables, based on the fixing of values of some hidden parameters, without changing some consequences of present quantum mechanics." Von Neumann went even further. Thus summarizing his often quoted but otherwise little known "proof" he writes:[25] "Not only is the measurement impossible [of the hidden parameters] *but so is any reasonable theoretical definition,* i.e., any definition which, although incapable of experimental proof, would also be incapable of experimental refutation." The gist of all these statements is that the Copenhagen Interpretation is the only interpretation that is empirically adequate and formally satisfactory. This contention was refuted in Bohm's paper. Has this fact been admitted by the Copenhagen school? It has not been admitted. On the contrary, Bohm's paper was attacked in a manner that suggested he had overlooked some essential elements of the idea of complementarity. Thus Heisenberg remarked that the model "says nothing about physics that is different from what the Copenhagen language says,"[26] and he also insinuated that it was *ad hoc.*[27] It has also been said that "given the ψ-function, the values of the parameters cannot manifest themselves, neither directly, nor indirectly";[28] and that they are for this reason to be regarded as "purely metaphysical."[29] As regards the first assertion we need only return to Bohr's reply to Einstein which we have quoted above. For if Bohr's interpretation is unassailable by virtue of the fact that it satisfies the criteria outlined in this quotation (full empirical adequacy, and formal satisfactoriness), then so is Bohm's which, as Heisenberg explicitly admits, is empirically equivalent with it and formally without reproach. This refutes the idea, expressed, among others, by Jordan, that there exists only one interpretation that possesses these desirable characteristics.[30] And as regards the second assertion, we must point out that, as is evident from the quotation, von Neumann asserted that even metaphysical hidden parameters could not be made to agree with the formalism of the theory. All this is a good example of the way in which complementarity has been reinterpreted in the light of objections, thereby giving the impression that these objections had really missed the point.[31]

A third reason for the persistence of the creed of complementarity is to be sought in the fact that many objections against it are irrelevant. Most critics interpret the two main principles of the Copenhagen Interpretation, viz., the principle of the indeterminateness of state descriptions and the principle of the relational character of quantum mechanical states not as *physical* assumptions which describe objective features of physical systems; they interpret them as the direct result of a positivistic *epistemology* and reject them together with the latter.[32] Now it is of course quite correct that this is the way in which some members of the Copenhagen Circle have introduced these principles, but it should also be clear that this is not the only way to justify them and that much better arguments are available, arguments which are directly derived from physical practice. This situation, by the way, accounts for the strangely unreal character of many discussions on the foundations of the present theory. The members of the Copenhagen school are confident that their point of view with whose fruitfulness they are well acquainted is satisfactory and superior to a good many alternatives. But when writing about it, they do not draw sufficient attention to its physical merits, but wander off into philosophy and especially into positivism. Here they become an easy prey to all sorts of philosophical realists who quickly (or not so quickly) exhibit the mistakes in their arguments without thereby convincing them of the incorrectness of their point of view—and quite justly so, for this point of view can stand upon its own feet and does not need any support from philosophy. So the discussion between physicists and philosophers goes back and forth without ever getting anywhere.

In the paper to follow I shall try to get out of this vicious circle. I shall try to give a purely physical explanation of the main ideas behind the Copenhagen Interpretation. It will turn out that these ideas and the physical arguments leading up to them are much more plausible than the vague speculations which were later used in order to make them more acceptable. But it will also turn out that despite this plausibility none of the arguments is powerful enough to guarantee the absolute validity of these ideas and to justify the demand that the theories of the microscopic domain will forever have to conform to a certain pattern.[33] Such restrictions are possible only if certain *philosophical* ideas are used as well. *These* philosophical ideas will be investigated in the second part of the present paper. The result of our investigation will be that while the physical arguments dealt with in the first part are sound and ingenious, the philosophical ideas needed to confer absolute validity upon them are neither correct nor reasonable. The result of the criticism is, of course, that now as ever we are free to consider whatever theories we want when attempting to explain the structure of matter.

(2) THE EARLY QUANTUM THEORY: WAVE-PARTICLE DUALITY.

Not long after Planck had introduced the quantum of action[34] it was realized that this innovation was bound to lead to a complete recasting of the principles of motion of material systems. It was Poincaré[35] who first pointed out that the idea of a continuous motion along a well-defined path could no longer be upheld and that what was needed was not only a new *dynamics*, i.e., a new set of assumptions about the acting forces, but also a new *kinematics*, i.e., a new set of assumptions about the kind of motion initiated by these forces. Both Bohr's older theory and the dual nature of light and matter further accentuated this need. One of the problems arising in the older quantum theory was the treatment of the interaction between two mechanical systems.[36] Assume that two systems, A and B, interact in such a manner that a certain amount of energy, ϵ, is transferred from A to B. During the interaction the system A+B possesses a well-defined energy. Experience shows that the transfer of ε does not occur immediately, but that it takes a finite amount of time. This seems to suggest that both A and B change their state gradually, i.e., A

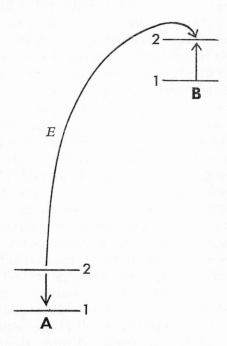

gradually falls from 2 to 1, while B gradually rises from 1 to 2. However, such a mode of description would be inconsistent with the *quantum postulate* according to which a mechanical system can be only either in state 1, or in state 2 (we shall assume that there are no admissible states between 1 and 2), and it is incapable of being in an intermediate state. How shall we reconcile the fact that the transfer takes a finite amount of time with the non-existence of intermediate states between 1 and 2?

This difficulty was resolved by Bohr[37] on the basis of the assumption that during the interaction of A and B the dynamical states of both A and B cease to be well defined so that it becomes *meaningless* (rather than *false*) to ascribe a definite energy to either of them.[38]

This simple and ingenious physical hypothesis has so often been misrepresented that a few words of explanation seem to be needed. First of all it must be pointed out that in the above formulation the term "meaning" has not entered, as has been asserted by various critics, because of some connection with the now customary attitude of preferring semantical analysis to an investigation of physical conditions.[39] After all, there are well-known classical examples of terms which are meaningfully applicable only if certain physical conditions are first satisfied and which become inapplicable and therefore meaningless as soon as these conditions cease to hold. A good example is the term "scratchibility" (Mohs scale), which is applicable to rigid bodies only and which loses its significance as soon as the bodies start melting. Secondly, it should be noted that the proposed solution does not contain any reference to *knowledge,* or *observability*. It is not asserted that during the time of transfer A and B may be in some state which is unknown to us, or which cannot be observed. For the quantum postulate does not merely exclude the knowledge or the observability of the intermediate states; it excludes these intermediate states themselves. Nor must the argument be read as asserting, as is implied in many presentations by physicists, that the intermediate states do not exist *because* they cannot be observed. For it refers to a postulate (the quantum postulate) which deals with existence, and not with observability. The emphasis upon the absence of *predictability* is not satisfactory either. For this way of speaking would again suggest that we could predict better if we only knew more about the things that exist in the universe, whereas Bohr's suggestion denies that there are such things whose detection would make our knowledge more definite. The third remark concerns a suggestion for getting around the kinematics of ill-defined states which has often been made in connection with wave mechanics and which will be discussed in detail later in the present paper. According to this suggestion, the difficulties which arise when we try to give a rational account of processes of interaction are due to the fact that the classical point mechanics is not the correct theory for dealing with atomic systems, and the state descriptions of classical point mechanics are not the adequate means for describing the state of systems upon the atomic level. According to this suggestion, we ought not to retain the classical notions, such as position and momentum, and make them less specific. What we ought to do is rather to introduce completely new notions which are such that when *they* are used states and motions will again be well defined. Now if any such new system is to be adequate for the description of quantum phenomena, then it must contain means for expressing the quantum postulate which is one of the most fundamental micro-laws, and it must therefore also contain adequate means for expressing the concept of energy. However, once this concept has been introduced, in the very same moment all our above considerations apply again with full force: while being part of A+B, neither A nor B can be said to possess a well-defined energy, from whence it follows at once that also the new and ingenious set of concepts will not lead to a well-defined and unambiguous kinematics. "It would," therefore, "be a misconception to believe," writes Bohr,[40] "that the difficulties of the atomic theory may be evaded by eventually replacing the concepts of classical physics by new conceptual forms." This last remark will be of great importance in connection with the interpretation of Schrödinger's wave mechanics.

The empirical adequacy of the proposed solution is shown by such phenomena as the natural line breadth which in some cases (such as in the absorption leading to states preceding Auger effect) may be quite considerable.

Its consequence is, of course, the *renunciation of the kinematics of classical physics.* For if during the interaction of A and B neither A nor B can be said to be in a well-defined state, then the change of these states, i.e., the *motion* of both A and B will not be well defined either. More particularly, it will no longer be possible to ascribe a definite trajectory to any one of the elements of either A or B. One may now attempt to retain the idea of a well-defined motion and merely make indefinite the relation between the energy and the parameters characterizing this motion. The considerations in the next paragraph show that this attempt encounters considerable difficulties.

The reason is that the *duality of light and matter* provides an even more decisive argument for the need to replace the classical kinematics by a new set of assumptions. It ought to be pointed out, in this connection, that dealing with both light and matter on the basis of a single general principle, such as the principle of duality, may be somewhat misleading. For example, whereas the idea of the position of a light quantum has no definite meaning,[41] such meaning can be given to the position of an electron. Also, no account is given in this picture of the coherence length of light. It is therefore advisable to restrict the discussion of duality to elementary particles with a rest mass different from zero, for example to electrons.

Now it has been asserted[42] that the interference properties of light and matter, and the duality resulting from them, are but an instance of statistical behavior in general, which latter is then thought to be best explainable by reference to such classical devices as pin boards and roulette games. According to this assertion the elementary particles move along well-defined trajectories and possess a well-defined momentum at any instant of their motion. It is sometimes admitted that their energy may occasionally undergo sudden and perhaps individually unexplainable changes. But it is still maintained that this will not lead to any *indefiniteness* of the state that experiences these sudden changes.

I shall now try to show that this assumption cannot give a coherent account of the wave properties of matter and of the conservation laws. It is sufficient, for this purpose, to consider the following two facts of interference: (1) interference patterns are independent of the number of particles which at a given moment are dwelling in the apparatus. To use an example: We obtain the same pattern on a photographic plate whether

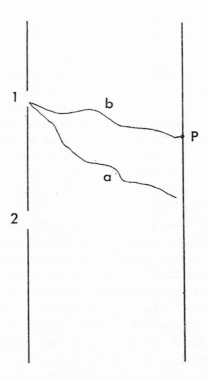

we now use strong light and short time of exposure or whether we use very weak light and a long time of exposure.[43] (2) The two-slit interference pattern is not simply the arithmetical sum of the patterns created by each single slit. It is quite possible for the two-slit pattern to possess a minimum in a place, say *P*, in which the one-slit pattern shows a finite intensity. (1) allows us to neglect the mutual interaction (if any) between the particles. Considering (2) we may reason as follows: If it is correct that each particle always possesses a well-defined trajectory, then the finite intensity in P is due to the fact that some particles arrived there along the path b. As long as slit two remains closed there will always be some particles which, having passed slit one, will travel along b. Assume that E is such a particle, for example an electron, and that it is about to enter slit one. Now if we open slit two at this very moment we have thereby (by virtue of fact (2) above) created conditions which are such that E must not arrive at P. Hence, the process of opening slit two must lead to a change in the former path of E. How can this change be accounted for?

It cannot be accounted for by assuming action at a distance. There is no room in the conservation laws (which are valid also in the quantum theory) for energies deriving from such an action. Furthermore,[44] the alleged action works not everywhere in space, but only along those surfaces which in the wave picture are surfaces of equal phase and is therefore nothing but a misleading way of bringing in wave-notions.

According to Popper[45] and Landé[46] the change of path of the *individual* particle is not in need of explanation. What *can* be explained, by reference to the change of physical conditions (opening of slit two), is the emergence of a new stochastic process that leads to a new interference pattern. This position is *indeterministic*, as it admits the existence of uncaused individual changes and its indeterminism is about as radical as that of the Copenhagen point of view. It also shares with that point of view its emphasis on the importance of the *experimental situation:* predictions are valid only for certain experimental conditions, they are not universally valid (this point will be explained in greater detail in section (6)). However, it *differs* from the Copenhagen point of view insofar as it works with well-defined states and well-defined trajectories. This being the case it must and does admit[47] that the conservation laws are valid only for large ensembles of particles in a certain situation and that they may be violated in the individual case. It is here that the difficulties arise. For, as is well known,[48] energy and momentum are conserved in each individual case of interaction also for elementary particles. This point of view must therefore be rejected *unless* it is developed in such detail that an alternative account can be given of all those experiments which have convinced the physicists of the individual validity of the conservation laws. *Until* such a more detailed account has been given (and nobody can say in advance that it is impossible!) we must again regard the assumption of the indefiniteness of state descriptions as the most satisfactory explanation. Let it be noted, by the way, that this restriction applies to all the arguments we are going to develop in favor of the assumption of the indeterminateness of state descriptions. All these arguments presuppose the validity of certain experimental findings such as the quantum postulate, the laws of interference, the individual validity of the conservation laws; and the arguments show that *given* these experimental findings we are forced to reject various interpretations which do not work with intrinsically indefinite state descriptions. It follows that an alternative to the idea of complementarity is likely to be successful only if it implies that at least some of these experimental results are not strictly valid without, of course, contradicting them inside the domain (of error, or experimentation) where they were first found to apply. The issue concerning the foundations of the quantum theory can therefore be solved only by the construction of a *new theory* as well as by the demonstration that this new theory is experimentally at least as valuable as the theory that is being used at the present time; it cannot be solved by alternative *interpretations* of the present theory.[49]

Now it is the belief of many followers of the "orthodox" point of view that such a new theory is impossible. To be more specific, they believe that such a theory will either be internally inconsistent, or inconsistent with some very important experimental results. They therefore not only suggest an interpretation of the known experimental results in terms of indefinite state descriptions. They also suggest that this interpretation *be retained forever* and that it be the foundation of any future theory of the microlevel. It is at this point that we shall have to part company. I am prepared to defend the Copenhagen Interpretation as a physical hypothesis and I am also prepared to admit that it is superior to a host of alternative interpretations. The whole first part of the present paper will be devoted to showing its superiority as a physical hypothesis. But I shall also show that any argument that wants to establish this interpretation more firmly is doomed to failure. Now, as ever, the future development of physics is a completely open matter.

However, if we are not prepared, at the present stage at least, to doubt the validity of the conservation laws and of the laws of interference then the only possible account of the properties of interference patterns seems again to be in terms of the assumption that the behavior of the particles between the slits and the screen is no longer well defined. In the case of a single slit this lack of definiteness can even be roughly calculated. As is well known[50] the result is that the indefiniteness Δx of position and the indefiniteness Δp_x of momentum required for circumventing the described difficulties are related by the formula

$$\Delta x \cdot \Delta p_x > h \tag{1}$$

This result can be shown to possess universal validity. Indeed, whenever the conditions of experimentation are such that interference effects are to be expected, the definiteness of state descriptions will have to be restricted just to the extent to which the wave picture remains applicable. The exact amount of this restriction can be calculated if we combine de Broglie's ideas with the mathematics of the Fourier analysis.[51] The result is again given by formula (1)[52] which thereby has been shown to possess universal validity: *inherent indefiniteness is a universal and objective property of matter.*[53] Only *after* this basic assumption has been adopted, can Heisenberg's discussions, and his attempt to derive various forms of (1) from an analysis of methods of measurement,[54] lead to a proper interpretation of the relations thus obtained as well as to the realization that the reference, made in this analysis, to the process of *measurement* is purely accidental.[55] It is of course true that arrangements such as systems with slits, or Geiger counters, can be used for measuring properties of physical objects. However the idea of the indefiniteness of state description and, more specifically, the uncertainty relations emerge, not because the arrangements can be thus used, but because of the peculiarity of the physical processes going on in them. If this is not taken into account, then it is always possible to raise the objection that what has been derived is a restriction of our ability to know the exact state of the dynamical system, or of our ability to *predict*, but not a restriction of the dynamical states themselves. Such a conclusion is the more likely to be drawn, as many discussions of the matter are subjectivistic in the sense that they first interpret (1) as restrictive of *knowledge,*[56] which interpretation is then reconciled with the objective validity of the quantum postulate and of other empirical laws by identifying knowledge with physical reality,[57] or by declaring that the idea of a real external world is "metaphysical."[58] This, by the way, explains the strange unreality of so many discussions on the foundations of the quantum theory: the defenders use bad and irrelevant arguments for a point of view with whose physical fertility they are intimately acquainted and of whose value they have therefore a very high opinion. The opponents, ignorant of the features of physical practice but well acquainted with the irrelevant descriptions of it, set out to destroy these irrelevant arguments and believe that they have thereby destroyed the point of view these arguments were supposed to support. This, of course, will not be admitted by the physicists, and so the battle goes on and on without any hope of being resolved in a satisfactory manner. It is mainly this feature of which I think when hearing the fashionable *bon mot* that nowadays physics and philosophy are much closer than they ever were in the 19th century.[59]

(3) WAVE MECHANICS.

The older quantum theory, although experimentally quite successful and also extremely fruitful in its power to unite a host of otherwise disconnected facts,[60] was yet regarded as unsatisfactory by many physicists. Its main fault was seen to lie in the manner in which it combined classical and non-classical assumptions and which made a coherent interpretation impossible.[61] For many physicists it was therefore nothing more than a stepping stone on the way to a really satisfactory theory, i.e., to a theory which could give us not only correct predictions, but also some insight into the nature and dynamics of microscopic entities. It is quite true that Bohr, Kramers, Heisenberg, and others worked along very different lines. Their main objective was not the construction of a new physical theory about a world that existed independently of measurement and observation; their main objective was rather the construction of a logical machinery for the utilization of those parts of classical physics which could still be said to lead to correct predictions.[62] The inspiration for this lay no doubt in the surprising fact that many classical laws remained *strictly valid* even on the quantum level. This suggested that what was needed was not the elimination, and complete replacement, of classical physics but rather a modification of it. However that may be—the philosophical spirit behind the "Korrespondenzdenken" was not shared by everybody. Thus de Broglie and Schrödinger tried to develop an entirely new theory for the description of the nature and the behavior of atoms, molecules, and their constituents. When this theory was finished it was hailed by many as the long expected coherent account of the microcosmic level. The hypothesis of the indefiniteness of state descriptions, so it was thought, had only reflected the indefiniteness and incompleteness of the early theory, and it was now no longer necessary. More especially, it was assumed either that the states were now new, but well-defined entities (the ψ-waves), or it was assumed that whatever incompleteness occurred was due to the statistical character of the theory, i.e., it was due to the fact that wave mechanics was "primarily a variety of statistical mechanics, similar to the classical statistical mechanics of Gibbs."[63] These two interpretations still survive. I hope that our arguments in the last section have made it clear that any such interpretation of wave mechanics is bound to lead into inconsistencies. The only presupposition of the hypothesis of indefinite state descriptions is the quantum postulate and the dual nature of light and matter (taken together with the individual con-servation of energy and momentum). Both these facts are contained in the wave mechanics which will therefore be equally in need of the said hypothesis.[64] A closer analysis of the two main alternatives shows that this is indeed correct.

Let us first consider the suggestion that the quantum theory provides new types of complete and well-defined states, viz., the ψ-waves which are to replace the descriptions, in terms of trajectories, of the classical point mechanics. This assumption has been made, and elaborated in some detail, by Planck. It is also identical with Schrödinger's original interpretation of his theory. According to Planck[65] (and Schrödinger) "the material waves constitute the primary elements of the new world picture. . . . In general the laws of the matter waves are basically different from those of the classical mechanics of material points. However the point of central importance is that the function characterizing matter waves, i.e., the wave function . . . is fully determined for all places and times by initial and boundary conditions."

Two objections must be raised against this point of view. The first objection is that it does not remove the indeterminateness of such magni-tudes as the energy, or the momentum, or the position of a material particle; the reason is that the relation between the ψ-wave and the values of these magnitudes is purely statistical.[66] It can of course be asserted that now the ψ-waves are the states. However it must then be also admitted that these states do not uniquely determine the physical properties of the system concerned. But even if we were satisfied with the verbal manoeuvre implicit in this move we would still not have solved the case from which the whole difficulty arose, i.e., the case of the inter-action of two systems. For it can be shown[67] that only in very special circumstances it is possible to break up the ψ-function for two systems into two ψ-functions, one for each of the components. In general, the ele-ments of a large system of interacting particles cannot be said to be in any state whatever.[68] This makes it obvious that the wave mechanics does not provide any means for getting around the indeterminateness which we discussed in the previous section. The most decisive objection against Planck's proposal is however this. Planck assumes that the only changes of the wave function are those which occur in accordance with Schrödinger's equation. This omits the reduction of the wave packet, which does not obey Schrödinger's equation[69] but which is necessary if we want to utilize the results of measurement for future calculation. A closer analysis of this process of reduction shows that it cannot be interpreted in a simple, realistic manner.[70]

We now turn to the second suggestion according to which "the description of the quantum theory" must be regarded as "an incomplete and indirect description of reality," such that the ψ-function "does not in any way describe a state which would be that of a single system; it rather relates to many systems, to an 'ensemble of systems' in the sense of statistical mechanics."[71] According to this interpretation the single system is always in a well-defined (classical) state, and any indeterminacy that is introduced is due to our lack of knowledge of this state. Quite obviously this assumption is inconsistent with Bohr's hypothesis, and it is also not easy to see how it could be made compatible with the quantum postulate. However, let us not forget that for anybody who does not know of the qualitative arguments presented in the last sections, and this includes a good many philosophers, there are strong reasons to assume that it is correct. These reasons consist above all in the fact that within wave mechanics the connection between the theory and "reality" is established by *statistical* rules (Born's rules): "It has not till now been taken sufficiently into account," writes Popper in his analysis of the uncertainty relations,[72] "that to the mathematical derivation of the Heisenberg formulae there must correspond, precisely, a derivation of the *interpretation* of these fundamental equations." And he points out that, given Born's rules *and nothing else*, we must interpret Δx and Δp_x in formula (1) as the standard deviations, within large ensembles, of quantities, *which are otherwise well defined*, and *not* as "statements imposing limitations upon the attainable precision of measurement."[73] This point of view seems to derive further support from von Neumann's systematic application of the frequency theory to wave mechanics whose statistical ensembles "make again possible an objective interpretation (which is independent of . . . whether one measures, in a given state, the one or the other of two not simultaneously measurable quantities)."[74] Hence, "if we start from the assumption that the formulae which are peculiar to the quantum theory are . . . statistical statements, then it is difficult to see how prohibitions of single events could be deduced from a statistical theory of this character. . . . The belief that single measurements can contradict the formulae of quantum physics seems logically untenable; just as untenable as the belief that a contradiction might one day be deduced between a formally singular probability statement . . . say 'the probability that the throw k will be five equals 1/6,' and one of the following two statements: . . . 'the throw is in fact a five,' or . . . 'the throw is in fact not a five.' "[75]

This is of course completely correct reasoning *provided* the elements of the collectives with which we are dealing in the quantum theory are all in a state that is well defined from the classical point of view, i.e., provided we already know what kinds of entities are to be counted as the elements of the collectives. Only if it is assumed that these elements are systems which are in classically well-defined states, is it possible to derive from the statistical character of the quantum theory the interpretation which Popper wants to defend. However it is also evident that the statistical character of the theory *taken by itself* is never sufficient for deriving such an assumption. For from the fact that a theory is statistical we can only infer that it works with *collectives* of objects, events, processes, rather than with these objects, events, processes themselves. We cannot draw any inference about the *individual properties* of these objects, events, processes. Any such information would have to be given *in addition* to the laws characterizing the relation between the frequencies in the collectives considered. Does Born's interpretation which, after all, establishes a connection between the formalism and results of measurement provide such information? It does not, or at least it should not if proper care is taken. For Born's rules, properly interpreted, do not make any assertion about the character of the elements of the quantum mechanical collectives. They only make assertions concerning the expectation values which these elements *exhibit on measurement*. That is, they leave still open at least two alternatives: (1) the elements possess their values before the measurement takes place and retain them throughout the measurement; (2) the elements do not possess their values before the measurement but are transformed, by the measurement, into a state containing these values in a well-defined manner. However great the empirical success of the statistical interpretation, it does not provide any means for deciding between (1) and (2). And this is a well-known characteristic of all statistical theories: even death statistics do not allow us to draw any conclusion concerning the manner in which death occurred, nor do they allow us to infer that human beings are entities whose traits are independent of observation, i.e., which can be assumed to be either alive or dead *independently* of the occasions on which they were *found* to be either alive or dead. In the case of human beings we possess of course independent evidence about their permanence, in a well-defined state between the moments of observation. The point is that this information is independent of the fact that in death statistics we are dealing with a statistical theory.

The same is true for the quantum theory: Popper's idea that an elementary particle always possesses a well-defined value of all the magnitudes that can be measured in it does not follow from Born's interpretation. It is an additional idea that must be justified, or at least discussed. It is precisely this idea that has been found to be inconsistent with the dual nature of light and matter and the individual validity of the conservation laws and that therefore had to be replaced, long ago, by the assumption of the indefiniteness of state descriptions.[76] To sum up: Popper's argument is invalid and its conclusion is false.

This being the case we must now look for a new interpretation of the elements of the quantum mechanical collectives. We must admit that what is being counted is not the number of systems *possessing* a certain well-defined property (for example a precise value of a classical magnitude): what is counted is rather the number of *transitions*, on measurement, from certain ill defined states into other ill defined states (viz. states in which the mentioned property possesses a well-defined value). And neither the frequency approach which deals with relations between collectives only and is neutral with respect to either the first or the second choice of elements; nor Born's rules which deal with results of measurement without allowing any inferences as regards the behavior that led to these results, can therefore be used as an argument against the customary (i.e., Bohr's) interpretation of formula (1).

It is worth pointing out, in this connection, that Born's rules cannot be used as an argument *for* this interpretation, either. More specifically, it is impossible to derive Bohr's hypothesis of indefinite state descriptions from the formalism of the wave mechanics plus the Born interpretation. Any such attempt would again involve an illegitimate transition from the properties of collectives of systems and their appearance at the end of measurements to the individual properties of these systems themselves and their behavior before and after the process of measurement. It is for this reason that von Neumann's famous "proof"[77] cannot succeed. A brief look at this proof shows at once where it fails.[78] The essence of the proof consists in the derivation of two theorems, the first of which asserts that no ensemble of quantum mechanical systems is dispersion free, whereas the second points out that the ensembles of minimum dispersion, the so-called homogeneous, or pure ensembles, are such that any one of its (finite) subensembles possesses the same statistical properties as it itself. Now it must be realized that the subensembles considered are restricted to those that can be described with the help of a statistical operator and which therefore, in the case of a pure state, have been prepared in exactly the same manner as the ensemble of which they all form a part. Applied to pure ensembles the second theorem therefore asserts no more than the principle of the excluded gambling system which by itself does not allow any inference as to the individual events that constitute the game. Conclusion: it is neither possible, as is attempted by von Neumann, to *replace* the qualitative considerations of section 2 by arguments drawn from the formalism of wave mechanics plus the Born interpretation; nor is it possible, as is attempted by Popper, to *reject* them on the basis of such arguments.[79] Indeed these qualitative considerations are needed in addition to Born's interpretations if a full understanding of the theory is to be achieved.

Now at this stage the adherents of the second suggestion will point out that there exist further reasons for the correctness of their interpretation. They will refer to an argument by Einstein, Podolski, and Rosen[80] (EPR for short) according to which the formalism of wave mechanics is such that it demands the existence of exact simultaneous values of non-commuting variables. Clearly, if this should be the case, then Bohr's interpretation of formula (1) would have to be dropped and it would have to be replaced by the interpretation of Einstein and Popper. At the same time all those difficulties which prompted Bohr to invent the hypothesis of the indefiniteness of state descriptions would reappear. Even worse—it would seem that an inconsistency has been discovered in the very foundations of the quantum theory. For if it should indeed be the case that the only way of combining duality, the quantum postulate, and the conservation laws consists in assuming indefiniteness of state descriptions, then the case of Einstein, Podolski, and Rosen would show that wave mechanics is intrinsically unable to allow for a coherent account embracing these three experimental facts. We now turn to a closer analysis of the argument of Einstein, Podolski, and Rosen.

(4) The Argument of Einstein, Podolski, and Rosen.

Assume that a system S (coordinates $q, q', q'' \ldots, q^n; r, r', r'', \ldots, r^m$; or (qr) for short) which is in the state Φ (qr) has been (either mentally, or by physical separation) divided into two subsystems, S'(q) and S''(r). It can be shown[81] that it is always possible to select a pair of observables $\alpha(q)$, and $\beta(r)$ (corresponding to sets of mutually orthogonal situations in S' and S'' respectively) with sets of eigenstates $[|\alpha_i (q)>]$; $[|\beta_i (r)>]$ such that

$$|\Phi (qr) > = \Sigma_i c_i |\alpha_i > |\beta_i > \qquad (2)$$

A pair of observables with the property just mentioned will be called *correlative* with respect to Φ, S' and S".

The special case discussed by Einstein, Podolski, and Rosen is characterized by the following three conditions:

[i]: there exists more than one pair of observables which are correlative with respect to Φ, S' and S".

[ii]: assume that $(\alpha\beta)$; $(\gamma\delta)$; $(\epsilon\xi)$; . . . are pairs of observables which are correlative with respect to Φ, S' and S"; then there is at least one pair of pairs, say $(\alpha\beta)$, and $(\gamma\delta)$, such that

$$\alpha\gamma \neq \gamma\alpha \quad \beta\delta \neq \delta\beta \tag{3}$$

[i] and *[ii]* are satisfied if and only if the constants c_i in (2) satisfy the conditions $|c_i|^2 = $ const. (4)

[iii]: the systems S'(q) and S"(r), i.e., the spatial regions defined by the (q) and (r), are separated such that no physical interaction is possible between them.[83]

From *[i]* it follows that, if $|\gamma_i >$ and $|\delta_i >$ are the eigenfunctions of γ and δ in S' and S" respectively, then Φ may also be represented in the form.

$$|\Phi(qr) > \,= \Sigma_i c'_i \,|\gamma_i > |\delta_i > \tag{5}$$

Now assume that the magnitude corresponding to α is measured in S' with the result α_k. From (2) as well as from the assumption

> that any measurement leaves the system in an eigenstate of the variable measured. (6)

it follows that the state of S" after the measurement will be the state $|\beta_k >$, i.e., it will be an eigenstate of β.

Assume, on the other hand, that γ is measured in S' with the result $|\gamma_i >$. It then follows from (5) and (6) that the state of S" after the measurement will be $|\delta_i >$, i.e., it will be an eigenstate of S.

Adding *[iii]* we may now derive the following result. First step: if S' and S" are separated in space such that no physical interaction is possible, then it is impossible that a physical change of S' will influence the state of S". More especially, it is impossible that a measurement in S' (which leads to a physical change of S') will influence the state of S". More especially still: if there is a measurement in S' whose result allows us to infer that S" is in a particular physical state, then, as no interaction can have taken place, we have to assume that S" was in the inferred state already *before* the performance of the measurement, and would have been in this state even if the measurement had never been carried out. Second step: applying the above result to the measurement of α and γ we may reason as follows: immediately after the measurement of α which yields the result α_k, S" is in the state $|\beta_k>$, and this is, according to what has been said above, also the state of S" immediately before the measurement. Hence, S" must be in some eigenstate of β whether or not a measurement of α has been performed (we assume, of course, that all observables are complete commuting sets). By the same argument it must also be in some eigenstate of δ, whether or not a measurement of γ has been performed. In short, it must always be in a classically well-defined state. From (3) and Bohr's hypothesis it follows that this is impossible. This contradiction between Bohr's assumption of the indefiniteness of state descriptions and the above argument has been called the paradox of Einstein, Podolski, and Rosen. It is preferable, however, not to talk of a paradox, but rather of an argument.[84]

For Einstein (and Popper) this argument refutes Bohr's hypothesis. Having presented it, Einstein therefore feels justified to regard the quantum theory "as an incomplete and indirect description of reality" such that "the ψ- function . . . relates . . . to an 'ensemble of systems' in the sense of statistical mechanics."[85] I shall soon deal with the merits of this argument. But before doing so I wish to discuss some of the objections which have been raised against it and all of which to me seem to be unsatisfactory.

Thus A. D. Alexandrow[86] and J. L. R. Cooper[87] have argued that the paradox cannot arise; for as long as [S'S"] is described by a wave function which cannot be broken up into a product, [iii] does not hold. To this it must be replied that within [iii] "separated," and "interaction" refer to *classical fields*, or at least to fields which contribute to the energy present in a certain space-time domain. Alexandrow and Cooper seem to assume that the ψ-field can be interpreted as such a field which is not borne out by the facts.

A much more typical counter argument is contained in a paper by Furry.[88] This paper has the advantage of being clear and straightforward and it also seems to reflect the attitude of a good many physicists. The physical process (interaction between S' and S") which terminates in the paradoxical combined state is construed by Furry in two ways, A and B. According to assumption A this process leads to transitions in the quantum mechanical states of S' and S". The transitions occur according to the laws of probability, but they terminate in well-defined states for both S' and S", which are related to each other in such a way that a measurement in S' will indeed lead to *certain* information about the state of S" (and vice versa). The correlation is between *states which are al-*

ready there or, to put it formally, it is due to the fact that the state of $S' + S''$ after the interaction is given by the mixture.

$$P_{\phi'} = \Sigma_i |c_i|^2 |\alpha_i><\alpha_i|\beta_i><\beta_i| \qquad (7)$$

We see that in this mixture the pair $(\alpha\beta)$ is such that if α is measured in S' with the result α_k, then β will be certain to exhibit, on measurement, the value β_k.

[Proof: $\text{Tr}\{P_{|\alpha_K>} P_{\phi'} P_{|\alpha_K>} P_{|\beta_1>}\}$ $|\text{Tr}\{P_{|\alpha_K>} P_{\phi'}\} = \delta_{K1}]$

Another feature of this case is that it leads to the violation of some conservation laws.[89] Furry alleges that A is the assumption made by Einstein.

Method B which, he says, is the method adopted by the quantum theory and which also preserves the conservation laws, implies that an interaction between two systems, S' and S'', will in general lead to a pure state

$$|\phi> = \Sigma_{ik} c_i k |\alpha_i> |\beta_k> \qquad (8)$$

and that correlations between the values of α and β will occur if and only if $c_{ik} = c_i \delta_{ik}$, or if Φ has form (2). The difference between method A and method B, therefore, consists in the fact that method A represents a state with the above properties by (7) whereas method B represents it by (2). It can easily be shown that the two methods of representation do not lead to the same observational results.

$$\left[\begin{array}{c} \text{Proof: for } [\alpha\gamma]; \; [\beta\delta] \neq 0 \text{ in general} \\ \text{Tr}\{P_{|\gamma_1>} P\Phi \; P_{|\gamma_1>}\delta\} \neq \text{Tr}\{P_{|\gamma_1>} P\Phi'_{|\gamma_1>}\delta\} \end{array} \right]$$

Method A is therefore inconsistent with the method adopted by the quantum theory, which latter is a direct consequence of the superposition principle. This many physicists regard as a refutation of Einstein's idea (which was silently applied in the first step of the derivation of the paradox) that "if without in any way disturbing a system we can predict with certainty the value of a physical quantity, then there exists an *element of physical reality* corresponding to this physical quantity,"[90] i.e., then this value belongs to the system independently of whether or not a measurement has been, or can be, carried out.

Now, concerning this argument we must consider two points. To start with, the fact that A differs from the method which is adopted by the quantum theory can be regarded as detrimental only if it has first been shown that in the special case dealt with by EPR the predictions of the quantum theory are empirically successful whereas the predictions implied by method A are not. The fact that the quantum theory has been confirmed by a good many experimental results is of no avail in this case, for we are now asking for the behavior of systems under conditions which have not yet been tested. And it was indeed Einstein's guess that the current formulation of the many-body problem in quantum mechanics might break down when particles are far enough apart.[92] The second point is that even if B were to give the correct statistical predictions, even then Einstein's argument would stand unassailed. For it is not an argument for a particular description, *in terms of statistical operators*, of the state of systems which are far apart. It is rather an argument against the assumption that any such description in terms of statistical operators can be regarded as complete, or against the assumption that "the ψ-function is . . . unambiguously coordinated to the physical state,"[93] or against the assumption that under all circumstances a physical system will be completely and exhaustively described by its statistical operator.

In the literature this last assumption has become known as the *completeness assumption*. As has been indicated in the preceding paragraph the completeness assumption implies Bohr's hypothesis. One may therefore interpret the argument of EPR both as an argument against the completeness assumption and as an argument against Bohr's hypothesis. In what follows both these interpretations will be used.

As regards the first point we may additionally remark that it has been attempted to decide experimentally between assumption A and assumption B. The experiment was carried out by C. S. Wu,[94] and it consisted in studying the polarization properties of correlated photons. Such photons are produced in the annihilation radiation of positron-electron pairs. In this case each photon is always emitted in a state of polarization orthogonal to that of the other which is similar to Bohm's example of EPR.[95] The result of the experiment was a definite refutation of the prediction made on the basis of method A and a confirmation of B, the method that is in accordance with the general validity of the superposition principle. However, as we have shown above, this result cannot be used for refuting the contention, which is the core of Einstein's argument, that what is realized in *both* cases is an ensemble of classically well-defined systems rather than a single case.[96]

Similar remarks apply to the analysis given by Blochinzev.[97] It is true, Blochinzev emphasizes that "within quantum theory we do not describe the 'state in itself' of the particle, but rather its relation to the one, or the other (mixed or pure) collective."[98] He points out that this relation is of a completely objective character and that any measurement is to be regarded as a process which separates certain subcollectives from the collective in which they were originally embedded. Now, the assertion that the quantum theory describes the elementary particles only insofar as they are elements of a collective would seem to make Blochinzev's interpretation coincide with the interpretation of Einstein, Slater, and Popper which also asserts that the present quantum theory is a theory of collectives. However, the important difference is that for Blochinzev the individual particle does not possess any state-property over and above its membership in a particular collective. "Our experiments," he writes,[99] "are precise enough to show us that the pair (p,q) of a single particle does not exist in nature." This means, of course, that Blochinzev, too, accepts the completeness assumption which is just the point at issue. Again, he has not shown that Einstein's argument contradicts the quantum theory; or that it contradicts "experience"; he has only shown that it contradicts the completeness assumption, i.e., he has shown that it serves the purpose for which it was constructed.

We see that all the arguments against EPR which we have discussed so far fail to refute it.[100] Apart from those suggestions which consist in introducing a sub-quantum mechanical level, and which thereby deny the *correctness* and not only the completeness of the present theory, the only argument left seems to be the one that led to Bohr's hypothesis in the first place and which is not dependent on the more detailed formal features of either the elementary quantum theory, or of any one of its improved alternatives (Dirac's theory of the electron; field theories). However with respect to these qualitative considerations many writers seem to be of the opinion that they count little when compared with the impressive utilization, by EPR, of the powerful apparatus of wave mechanics. In order to dispel this impression (which seems to reflect an overconfident and uncritical attitude with respect to mathematical formalisms) I shall now discuss the difficulties which arise when the *conclusion* of EPR is assumed to be correct, i.e., when it is assumed both that the elementary theory is correct and that a more detailed description of state can be given than is admitted by the completeness assumption. A state referred to by such a more detailed description will be called a *superstate*.[101]

(5) SUPERSTATES.

Given the laws of the quantum theory,[102] are superstates possible? In the present section I shall develop some arguments (i.e., additional to the qualitative arguments of section 2) against the possibility of superstates. The *first argument* will show that, dependent on the way in which they have been introduced, superstates either contain redundant elements, or are empirically inaccessible. To show that they contain redundant parts a few explanations must be given concerning the role of a state in physical theory.

What is the role of a dynamical state in a physical theory? The reply is that it contains part of the initial conditions which, if taken together with other initial conditions such as mass and charge, with boundary conditions (properties of the acting fields), as well as with some theories, will serve for the explanation, or the prediction, of the behavior of the systems which it is supposed to describe.[103] According to this definition an element of state will be superfluous, if it does not play any role in any prediction and explanation. It will be even more superfluous if this applies not only to the *future* properties and behavior of the system, but also to the properties and the behavior it possesses at the very moment at which the occurrence of this element is being asserted. In this case there exists no possibility whatever to test the assertion that the element has occurred and this element may properly be called *descriptively redundant*. To show that a superstate will contain descriptively redundant elements let us consider the case of a particle with total spin σ. Assume that σ and σ_x have been measured and the values σ' and σ_x' obtained. Then, according to the theory an immediate repetition of the measurement will again give these values. On the other hand, assume that σ_y is measured when the measurement of σ and σ_x has been completed. Then the formalism of the theory will inform us that *any* value of σ_y may be obtained which shows quite clearly that adding a specific value of σ_y (and, for that matter of σ_z) to the set $[\sigma' \ \sigma'_x]$ does not in the least change the informative content of our assertion. By generalization we obtain the following result: a set of magnitudes specifying the outcome of the measurement of a complete set of commuting observables has maximum informative content. Any addition to this set is descriptively redundant, *whatever the method* (EPR or other) by means of which it has been obtained, provided, of course, that this method did not involve a disturbance of the state already realized.

The superstates we have been discussing so far had the property that only part of them could be used for deriving information about the actual state of the physical system: i.e., assuming **P** and **Q** to be two different complete commuting sets pertaining to the same system, the superstate $[PQ]$ was chosen in such a manner that Prob. $(P/ \ [PQ] = 1$ and Prob. $(Q/ \ [PQ] = \text{const} \neq 1$, or the other way round. We may now want to define pair $[PQ]$ of new variables in the following manner.

$$\text{Prob } (P/ \ [PQ]) = \text{Prob } (Q/ \ [PQ]) = \text{Prob } (P/ \ [QP]) = \text{Prob } (Q/ \ [QP]) = 1 \tag{9}$$

Let us now investigate what is the consequence of such a definition (which has been adopted, implicitly, by D. Bohm[104]).

To start with it should be noted that the first and the last equation (9) are part of the *definition* of a superstate of this new kind, whereas in the case of the P, Q these equations follow from the quantum theory. Note further that we are here dealing with a minimum condition which is trivially satisfied in the classical case; the condition is that a series of statements describing a superstate of the kind discussed here should be such that it allows for the derivation of the value of any one of the elements of the superstate. We have not yet considered any dynamical law, such as perhaps a law governing the temporal development of the superstates or of functions of the superstate. Nor has the existence of dynamical laws (and of this specific case of dynamical laws, the conservation laws) been postulated. But it is clear that if (9) is not satisfied, then deterministic laws will not be possible. Thus the conditions (9) are a necessary presupposition of determinism in the quantum theory (and in any other theory). Let us now see where these conditions are going to lead us.

From (9) we can at once derive that

Prob $(P/[QP])$ = Prob $(P.[QP])/$Prob$([QP])$ = Prob $([QP]/P)$ / Prob $([QP])$. Prob (P)

Prob $(P/[PQ])$ = Prob $(P.[PQ])/$Prob $([PQ])$ = Prob $([PQ]/P)$ / Prob $([PQ])$. Prob (P)

hence Prob $([QP]/P)/$ Prob $([PQ]/P)$ = Prob $([QP])/$Prob $([PQ])$.

If we now postulate that the absolute probabilities of the superstates be independent of the order of their elements (and we indicate adherence to this postulate by now writing 'PQ' instead of '[PQ]'), then we obtain Prob $(P/ [PQ])$ = Prob $(P/ [QP])$ = Prob (P/PQ) = 1 [from (9)] = Prob (P/P) for any pair PQ satisfying (9) above, i.e., *the elements of the newly introduced superstates are statistically independent.*

(10)

Now let us assume, in order to provide this abstract scheme with some empirical content, that

$$P \leftrightarrow p \qquad (11)$$

where p is a complete set of commuting observables in the sense of the quantum theory. We shall also assume that the systems discussed are fully described by the complementary sets p and q.

On the basis of Bayes' theorem we obtain,

Prob (q/PQ) = Prob (P/qQ). Prob $(q/Q)/$Prob (P/Q) which leads to the following value for Prob (q/Q)

Prob (q/Q) = Prob (P/Q). Prob (q/PQ)/Prob (P/q) which is, by virtue of (10) equal to = Prob (P). Prob (q/PQ)/Prob (P/q) = by virtue of (11) = Prob (P). Prob (q/pQ)/Prob (p/q)

Now we have from the quantum theory that

Prob (p/q) = Prob $(p/q\ldots)$ = $|<p|q>|^2$, therefore

Prob (q/Q) = Prob (P). $\hspace{2cm}$ (12)

In a completely analogous manner

Prob (p/PQ) = Prob (P/pQ). Prob (p/Q)/Prob (P/Q) leads to

Prob (p/Q) = Prob (P). $\hspace{2cm}$ (13)

Now Prob (qQ) = Prob (P). Prob (Q) = Prob (PQ)

$\hspace{1cm}$ Prob (pQ) = Prob (P). Prob (Q) = Prob (PQ), hence

$\hspace{1cm}$ Prob (p) = Prob (q) $\hspace{2cm}$ (14)

Finally Prob (p) = *[*by virtue of (11)*]* = Prob (P) = Prob (q/Q) = *[*using (14)*]* = Prob (q), i.e.

q and Q (and, as can be easily shown, also p and Q) *are statistically independent*. Result: if we assume that there exist superstates which satisfy conditions (9); and if we also assume that one of the elements of these superstates is accessible to experimental investigation as it is provided by quantum mechanical measurement, *then the rest of the superstate will be statistically independent of any physical magnitude that can be measured in the system under consideration and cannot therefore be said to possess any empirical or even any ontological content*. Again it emerges that the maximum of information producible about a quantum mechanical system is given by the assertion that one of its complete sets of commuting observables possesses a certain value. Any additional assertion is arbitrary and not accessible to independent experimental test. Adopting Bohr's hypothesis of indefinite state descriptions we can easily explain this fact by pointing out that this inaccessibility is not due to the intricacies of the measuring process which forbid us to obtain more detailed information about nature, but rather to the *absence of more detailed features of nature itself*. That this is so has been explained in detail in the second section and the third section.

Now at this stage one might still be inclined to say, in opposition to Bohr's hypothesis, that the use of superfluous information, although not very elegant, and certainly metaphysical, can at most be rejected on the basis of considerations of "taste."[105] That this is not so is shown by the *second argument* against the admissibility of superstates which I am now going to discuss. According to this second argument, which is but a more detailed repetition of the arguments used in section two of the present paper, the use of superstates is incompatible with the conservation laws and with the dynamical laws in general. In the case of the energy principle this becomes evident from the fact that for the single electron $E = p^2/2m$, so that after a measurement of position any value of the energy may emerge and, after a repetition of the measurement, any different value. One may try to escape this conclusion, as Popper apparently has been inclined to,[106] by declaring that the energy principle is only statistically valid. However, it is very difficult to reconcile this hypothesis with the many independent experiments (spectral lines; experiment of Franck and Hertz; experiment of Bothe and Geiger) which show that energy is conserved also in the quantum theory and this not only on the average, *but for any single process of interaction*. The difficulty of the point of view of Einstein and Popper, which works with superstates of the first kind, i.e., with superstates which do not satisfy (9) and whose elements are determined by successive observations, becomes very obvious if we apply it to the case which is known as the *penetration of the potential barrier*. In this case we may obtain rather drastic disagreement with the principle of the conservation of energy[107] if we assert it in the form that for any superstate /Eqp/ as determined by three successive measurements E will satisfy the equation $E = p^2/2m + V(q)$.[107] If we add these difficulties to the arguments leading up to Bohr's hypothesis of indefinite state description in the first place we obtain very powerful reasons indeed to the effect that the conclusion of EPR cannot possibly be correct.[109] This makes it imperative to show how the argument can be made compatible with that hypothesis. An attempt in this direction and, to my mind, a quite satisfactory attempt, has been made by Bohr.[110]

(6) THE RELATIONAL CHARACTER OF THE QUANTUM MECHANICAL STATES.

If I understand Bohr correctly,[111] he asserts that the logic of a quantum mechanical state is not as is supposed by EPR. EPR seems to assume that what we determine when all interference has been eliminated is a *property* of the system investigated. As opposed to this Bohr maintains that all state descriptions of quantum mechanical systems are *relations* between the systems and measuring devices in action and are therefore dependent upon the existence of other systems suitable for carrying out the measurement. It is easily seen how this second basic postulate of Bohr's point of view makes indefiniteness of state description compatible with EPR. For while a property cannot be changed except by *interference* with the system that possessed that property, a relation can be changed without such interference. Thus the state "being longer than b" of a rubber band may change when we compress the rubber band, i.e., when we physically interfere with it. But it may also change when we change *b* without at all interfering with the rubber band. Hence, lack of physical interference excludes changes of state only if it has already been established that positions and momenta and other magnitudes are properties of systems, rather than relations between them and suitable measuring devices. "Of course," writes Bohr, referring to Einstein's example[112] "there is in a case like the one . . . considered no question of a mechanical disturbance of the system under investigation . . . But even at this stage there is essentially the question of *an influence on the very conditions which define the possible types of prediction regarding the future behavior* of the system," and he compares this influence with "the dependence on the reference system, in relativity theory, of all readings of scales and clocks."[113] I would like to repeat, at this stage, that Bohr's argument is not supposed to *prove* that quantum mechanical states are relational and indeterminate; it is only supposed to show under what conditions the indefiniteness assumption *which is assumed to have been established by independent arguments* can be made compatible with the case of Einstein, Podolsky, and Rosen. If this is overlooked one may easily get the impression that the argument is either circular, or *ad hoc*. That the argument is circular has been asserted by Professor H. Putnam.[114] In the case of relativity, says Putnam, we may set up two different reference systems and obtain *simultaneously* two different readings for the *same* physical system. This is not possible in the quantum theory, for it would presuppose, what is denied by Bohr, that we can make simultaneous measurements of position and momentum in S' (see the discussion in section 4), or that we can even *imagine* that position and momentum both possess definite values in S'. However this appearance of circularity disappears as soon as we realize that the hypothesis of indefiniteness of state descriptions is *presupposed* and that a way is sought to make it compatible with EPR. A similar remark applies to Popper's criticism[115] that the argument is *ad hoc*. One must as it were approach the argument from the realization that superstates cannot be incorporated into wave mechanics without leading to inconsistencies. Once this is admitted there arises the need for a proper interpretation of the very surprising case discussed by EPR. It is in this connection that Bohr's suggestion proves so extremely helpful.[116] Finally, we ought to discuss briefly the assumption which is silently made by almost all opponents of the Copenhagen point of view, that EPR creates trouble for this point of view but not for the quantum theory (the elementary theory, that is) itself. This overlooks that there is no interpretation available that gives as satisfactory an account of all the facts united by the theory as does the idea of the indefiniteness of state descriptions. If we therefore interpret EPR as fatal for this idea, then we are forced to the conclusion *that the theory itself is in trouble*. (This conclusion has been drawn, a.o., by Bohm and by Schrödinger.[117])

It is very important to realize the far-reaching consequences of Bohr's hypothesis. Within classical physics the interaction between a measuring instrument and an investigated system can be described in terms of the appropriate theory. Such a description allows for an evaluation of the effect, upon the system investigated, of the measurement, and it thereby allows us to select the best possible instrument for the purpose at hand. Hence, within classical physics, the classification of the measuring instruments is achieved, at least partly, by the theory that is being investigated. Now according to Bohr a quantum mechanical state is a relation between (microscopic) systems and (macroscopic) devices. Also a system does not possess any properties over and above those that are derivable from its state description (this is the completeness assumption). This being the case it is not possible, even conceptually, to speak of an *interaction* between the measuring instrument and the system investigated. The logical error committed by such a manner of speaking would be similar to the error committed by a person who wanted to explain changes of velocity of an object created by the transition to a different reference system as the result of an interaction between the object and the reference system. This has been made very clear by Bohr ever since the publication of EPR which refutes the earlier picture[118] where a measurement glues together, with the help of an indivisible quantum of action, *two different* entities, *viz.* the apparatus on the one hand and the investigated object on the other.[119] But if we cannot separate the microsystem from its relation to a classical apparatus, then the evaluation of a measuring instrument will have to be very different from the way in which such evaluation took place in classical physics; that is, it will no longer be possible to refer to the type of *interaction* occurring as a means of classifying measurements.[120] This has led to the assertion[121] that the classification of measuring instruments that is used by the quantum theory can at most consist in giving a list without being able to justify the presence of any member in the list. Such an assertion does not seem to be correct. First of all a proper application of the correspondence principle will at once provide means of measurement for position and momentum. Speaking more abstractly we may also say that now a measurement in a system whose ψ-function is element of a Hilbert space H leads to a destruction of coherence between certain subspaces H', H'', H'''—of H and can be character-ized by operators P', P'', P''', effecting projection into exactly these sub-spaces. It is, of course, required to give an interpretation of the P's—but this problem is identical with the corresponding problem in classical physics which is the interpretation of the primitive descriptive terms of the theory.[122]

We may sum up the results of the foregoing investigation in the follow-ing manner. We first presented a physical hypothesis which was intro-duced by Bohr in order to explain certain features of microscopic systems (for example, their wave properties). It was pointed out that this physical hypothesis is of a purely objective character and that it is also needed, *in addition to Born's rules*, for a satisfactory interpretation of the formal-ism of wave mechanics.[123] The argument of EPR then showed that a further assumption must be introduced in order to make Bohr's hypothe-sis compatible with this formalism. According to this further assump-tion, the state of a physical system is a relation rather than a property and it presupposes that an adequate measurement is being performed, or has been performed immediately before the statement that the state ob-tains. By a "measurement" is meant, in this connection, a certain type of macroscopic process—a terminological peculiarity which is rather un-fortunate and which must be blamed for the many subjectivistic conclu-sions that have been drawn from Bohr's ideas.

Now it would be incorrect to say that the presentation of the point of view of Bohr and of his followers is completed with the presentation of the two ideas we have just explained. For as is well known it has been attempted, both by Bohr, and by some other members of the Copenhagen circle, to give greater credibility to these ideas by incorporating them into a whole philosophical (ontological) system that comprises physics, biol-ogy, psychology, sociology, and perhaps even ethics. Now the attempt to relate physical ideas to a more general background and the correlated attempt to make them intuitively plausible is by no means to be under-estimated. Quite on the contrary, it is to be welcomed that these physi-cists undertook the arduous task to adapt also the more general notions of philosophy to two physical ideas which, as has been pointed out in section 2, possess some very radical implications. However this philo-sophical backing has led to a situation that is by no means desirable. Above all, this philosophical "backing," like so many philosophical argu-ments before, has led to the belief in the uniqueness and the absolute validity of both of Bohr's assumptions. It will, of course, be admitted that the quantum theory will have to undergo some very decisive changes in order to be able to cope with new phenomena (the first step of these changes is indicated by the transition from the elementary theory to Dirac's theory of the electron; the second step by the transition to the field theories). But it will also be pointed out that, however large these changes may be, they will always leave untouched the two elements mentioned, *viz.* the indefiniteness of state descriptions and the relational character of the quantum mechanical states, which, so it will be added, cannot be replaced by different ideas without leading either into formal inconsistencies, or into inconsistencies with experiment.[124] "The new conceptions" asserts L. Rosenfeld[125] "which we need" in order to cope with new phenomena "will be obtained . . . by a rational extension of the quantum theory"[126] which *preserves* the indeterminacies; and the new theories of the microcosm will therefore be increasingly indeterministic. Today this dogmatic *philosophical* attitude with respect to fundamentals seems to be fairly widespread.[127] In the remaining sections of the present paper I shall try to give my reasons why I believe it to be completely unfounded and why I moreover regard it as a very unfortunate feature of part of contemporary science.[128]

However, before going into details, the following remarks seem to be in order: the particular interpretation of the microscopic theories (and especially of the quantum theory of Schrödinger and Heisenberg) which results from the combination of these theories with Bohr's two hypotheses and with the more general philosophical background referred to above, this interpretation has been called the *Copenhagen Interpretation*. A close look at this interpretation at once shows that it is not *one* interpretation, but a variety of them. True, the indefiniteness assumption and, to a lesser extent, the assumption of the relational character of the quantum mechanical states always play an important role, and so do the uncertainty relations. Yet the exact interpretation of these assumptions and of Heisenberg's formulae is neither *clear*, nor is there a *single* such interpretation. Quite the contrary—what we find is that all philosophical creeds, from extreme idealism (positivism, subjectivism) to dialectical materialism, have been imposed upon these physical elements. Heisenberg[129] and von Weizsaecker[130] present a more Kantian version; Rosenfeld[131] has injected dialectics into his account of the matter; whereas Bohr himself is reported[132] to have criticized all these versions as not being in agreement with his own point of view. Quite obviously the fictitious unity conveyed by the term "Copenhagen Interpretation" must be given up. Instead we shall try to discuss only those philosophical ideas which Bohr himself has provided, and we shall refer to other authors only if their contributions can be regarded as an elaboration of such ideas. The outline of the general background will be started with a discussion of the idea of complementarity.

(7) COMPLEMENTARITY.

Bohr's hypothesis of indefinite state descriptions referred to description in terms of *classical concepts*, i.e., it referred to description in terms of either Newtonian mechanics (including the different formulations which were provided later by Lagrange and Hamilton), or of theories which employ contact action, or field theories. The hypothesis amounted to the assertion that description in terms of *these* concepts must be made "more

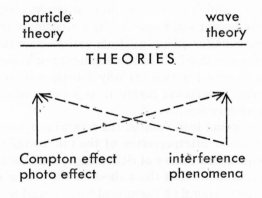

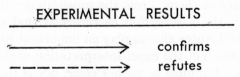

liberal"[133] if agreement with experiment is to be obtained. The principle of complementarity expresses in more general terms this peculiar restriction, forced upon us by experiment, in the handling of the classical concepts. In the form in which this principle is applied it is based mainly upon two empirical premises as well as upon some further premises which are neither empirical, nor mathematical, and which may therefore be properly called "metaphysical."[134] The *empirical premises* are (apart from the conservation laws) (1) the dual character of light and matter; and (2) the existence of the quantum of action as expressed in the laws

$$p = h/\lambda \qquad E = h\nu \qquad (15)[135]$$

I do not intend in this paper to discuss all the difficult considerations which finally led to the announcement of the dual character of light and matter. Although these considerations have sometimes been criticized as being inconclusive, they yet seem to me to be essentially sound. It is also beyond the scope of the present paper to explain how duality can be used for providing a coherent account of the numerous experimental results which form the confirmation basis of the contemporary quantum theory.[136] I shall merely state the principle of duality and make a few comments upon it. Duality means (cf. the diagram) that all the experimental results about light and matter divide into two classes. The facts of the first class, while contradicting any wave theory, can be completely and exhaustively explained in terms of the assumption that light (or matter) consists of particles. The facts of the second class, while contradicting any particle theory, can be completely and exhaustively explained in terms of the assumption that light (or matter) consists of waves. There exists, at least at the present moment, no system of physical concepts which can provide us with an explanation that covers and is compatible with *all* the facts about light and matter.

The following comments should be made. First: by a particle theory we understand, in the present context, any theory that works with entities of the following kind: they exert influence upon and are influenced by small regions of space only;[137] and they obey the principle of the conservation of momentum. No further assumptions are made about the nature of these particles and about the laws they obey. By a wave theory we understand, on the other hand, a theory that works with entities of the following kind: they are extended, their states at different places are correlated by a phase, and this phase obeys a (linear) superposition principle. It is the superposition principle that forms the core of all wave theories. What is refuted by either the Compton effect or by the photoelectric effect is not a *particular* wave theory (which may be characterized by a particular equation of motion for the waves), but the much more general assumption that light consists of extended and superimposable entities. Secondly it should be pointed out that the cross-relation between experimental evidence and theories, as indicated in the diagram, is essential for duality as well as for the idea of complementarity that is based upon it. I doubt whether anything like this exists in those domains in which complementarity has now become a kind of savior from trouble, such as in biology, psychology, sociology, and theology. Thirdly, it must be emphasized—and this remark will prove to be of great importance later on—that the wave theories (in the general sense explained above) and the particle theories do not only serve as devices which allow us to *summarize*, and to unify, a host of experimental results in an economical way. Without the key terms of either theory these results *could neither be obtained, nor could they be stated*. To take an example: interference experiments work with coherent or partly coherent light only. Hence, in preparing them proper attention must be paid to the relative phases of the incoming wave train which means that we have to apply the wave theory already in the preparation of the experiment. On the other hand such facts as the localizability of interaction between light and matter and the conservation of momentum in these interactions cannot be properly described without the use of concepts which belong to some particle theory. Using the term "classical" for concepts of either a wave theory or a particle theory, we may therefore say that "only with the help of classical ideas is it possible to ascribe an unambiguous meaning to the results of observation."[138]

Duality is regarded by Bohr and by his followers as an experimental fact which must not be tampered with and upon which all future reasoning about microphysical events is to be based. As a physical theory is acceptable only if it is compatible with the relevant facts, and as "to object to a lesson of experience by appealing to metaphysical preconceptions is unscientific,"[139] it follows that a microphysical theory will be adequate and acceptable only if it is compatible with the fact of duality, and that it must be discarded if it is not so compatible. This demand leads to a set of very general conditions to be satisfied by any microscopic theory. We are now going to state these conditions.

First of all the wave concepts and the particle concepts are the only concepts available for the description of the character of light and matter. Duality shows that these concepts cannot any more be applied generally, but can serve only for the description of what happens under certain experimental conditions. Using familiar terms of epistemology this means that the description of the *nature* of light and matter has now to be replaced by a description of the way in which light and matter *appear* under certain experimental conditions. Secondly, a change from conditions allowing for the application of, say, the wave picture to conditions allowing for the application of the particle picture will, in the absence of more general and more abstract concepts which apply under all conditions, have to be regarded as an *unpredictable jump*. The statistical laws connecting events in the first picture with events in the second picture will therefore not allow for a deterministic substratum, they will be *irreducible*. Thirdly, the combination of duality with the second set of empirical premises introduced above (the Einstein-de Broglie relations) shows that the duality between the wave properties and the particle properties of matter may also be interpreted as a duality between two sets of variables (e.g., position and momentum), which in the classical theory are both necessary for the complete description of the state of a physical system. We are forced to say that a system can never be in a state in which all its classical variables possess sharp values. If we have determined with precision the position of a particle, then its momentum is not only undetermined, it is even meaningless to say that the particle possesses a well-defined momentum. Clearly, the *uncertainty relations* now indicate the domain of meaningful applicability of classical functors (such as the functor "position"), rather than the mean deviations of their otherwise well-defined values in large ensembles. This is nothing but Bohr's hypothesis of the indefiniteness of state descriptions. The relational character of state descriptions results from the need to restrict the application of any set of concepts to a certain experimental domain. This is how the more general point of view explained here is related to the two specific hypotheses which we discussed in the preceding sections.

Now it is important to realize that the above argument is quite generally valid. It follows, and this is Bohr's contention, that it will hold for any theory into which Planck's h enters in an essential way. Hence, any future microscopic theory will have to be descriptive of appearances only, it will contain irreducible probabilities, and it will have to work with commutation relations between variables which are only partly well defined and meaningful. The development of microphysics can only lead to greater indeterminacy. It will never again return to a state of affairs where we are able to give a complete, objective, and deterministic description of the nature of physical systems and physical events. In the interest of economy of thought and effort theories of this kind should therefore be forever excluded from consideration.

I must repeat that in the above two paragraphs only a very sketchy outline has been given of the argument of Bohr and his followers and that it has not at all been shown what great variety of experimental facts is covered, and explained, by the two hypotheses which follow from this argument. This bare outline is not at all sufficient for making understandable the influence Bohr's ideas have had upon physicists and philosophers. But I think that it contains all the essential elements of the Copenhagen point of view, and that it will serve well as a starting point of criticism.

The argument proceeds from what seems to be a mere truism; it proceeds from the assertion that, duality being an experimental fact, it must not be tampered with, but must be regarded as an unalterable basis for any further theoretical consideration. After all, facts are the building stones out of which a theory may be constructed and therefore they themselves neither can nor should be modified. To proceed in this way seems to be the truly scientific attitude, whereas any interference with the facts shows what can only be called the first step towards wild and unwarranted speculation. It is not surprising that this starting point of the argument is frequently taken for granted, as it seems to be the natural procedure to adopt for a scientist. Did not Galileo start modern science by eliminating speculation and by directly putting questions to nature? And do we not owe the existence of modern science to the fact that problems were finally dealt with in an empirical manner rather than on the basis of groundless speculation?

It is here, at the very beginning, that the position of the orthodox must be criticized. For what is regarded by them as a truism is neither correct nor reasonable; and their account of history, too, is at variance with the actual development. Things were just the other way round. It was the Aristotelian theory of motion which was defended by reference to experimental results and it was Galileo who was not prepared to take these results at their face value but who insisted that they be analyzed and be shown to be due to the interplay of various and as yet unknown factors. "... if we are seeking to understand /the/ birth of modern science we must not imagine that everything is explained by the resort to an experimental mode of procedure, or even that experiments were any great novelty. It was commonly argued, even by the enemies of the Aristotelian system, that that system itself could never have been founded except on the footing of observation and experiment ... We may /also/ be surprised to note that in one of the dialogues of Galileo it is Simplicius, the spokesman of the Aristotelians—the butt of the whole piece—who defends the experimental method of Aristotle against what is described as the mathematical method of Galileo."[140] Indeed the whole tradition of science from Galileo (or even from Thales) up to Einstein and Bohm[141] is incompatible with the principle that "facts" should be regarded as the unalterable basis of any theorizing. In this tradition the results of experiment are not regarded as the unalterable and unanalyzable building stones of knowledge. They are regarded as capable of analysis, of improvement (after all, no observer, and no theoretician collecting observations is ever perfect), and it is assumed that such analysis and improvement is absolutely necessary. What would be a more obvious observational fact than the difference between celestial motions (regularity) and terrestrial motions (irregularity)? Yet from the earliest times the attempt was made to explain both on the basis of the same laws. Again, what would be a more obvious observational fact than the great variety of substances and phenomena met on the surface of the earth? Yet from the very beginning of rational thinking it was attempted to explain this variety on the basis of the assumption that it was due to the working of a few simple laws and a few simple substances, or perhaps even a single substance. Also the new theory of motion which was developed by Galileo and Newton cannot possibly be understood as a device for establishing relations between our experiences or between laws which are directly founded upon our experiences, and this for the simple reason that the laws expressing these observable motions (such as the law of free fall, or Kepler's laws) were asserted to be incorrect by this theory.[141] And this is quite in order. Our senses are not less fallible than our thoughts and not less capable of giving rise to deception. The Galilean tradition, as we may call it, therefore proceeds from the very reasonable point of view that our ideas *as well as* our experiences (complicated experimental results included) may be erroneous, and that the latter give us at most an *approximate* account of what is going on in reality. Hence, within this tradition the condition to be satisfied by a future theory of the microcosm is not that it be simply *compatible* with duality and the other laws used in the above argument, but that it be compatible with duality *to a certain degree of approximation* which will have to depend on the precision of the experiments used for establishing the "fact" of duality.[142]

A completely analogous remark holds for the assertion that Planck's constant will have to enter *every* microscopic theory in an essential way. After all, it is quite possible[143] that this constant has meaning only under certain well-defined conditions (just as the density of a fluid, or its viscosity, or its diffusion constant can be meaningfully defined only for not too small a volume) and that all the experiments we have made so far explore only part of these conditions. Quite obviously the invariance of h in all *these* experiments cannot be used as an argument against such a possibility. But if neither the constancy of h nor duality can be guaranteed to hold in new domains of research, then the whole argument is bound to break down: it does not guarantee the persistence of the familiar features of complementarity, of probabilistic laws, of quantum jumps, of the commutation relations in future investigations.

It ought to be pointed out, by the way, that the above two paragraphs cannot be regarded as a *refutation* of the principle that our theories must never contradict what at a certain time counts as an experimental fact. After all, it may well be possible (and it has been possible) to construct theories which satisfy this demand of maximal empirical adequacy with respect to a set of observations which are then removed from all analysis and criticism. Part of Aristotle's theory of motion was of this kind. However, it is very doubtful whether this restriction of research would ever allow for theories of the universality, the precision, and the formal accomplishment of Newton's celestial mechanics, or of Einstein's general theory of relativity, both of which lead to a correction of previously existing experimental laws.

Let us now assume, for the sake of argument, that a radically empiricistic point of view has been adopted, i.e., let us regard duality and the constancy of h as holding with absolute precision. Would then perhaps the argument be valid? This at once introduces the second "metaphysical" assumption that is used by Bohr and his followers. According to this second assumption the classical concepts are the only concepts which we possess. As we cannot construct a theory or a description of fact out of concepts which we do not possess; and as the classical concepts cannot any more be applied in an unrestricted way; for these two reasons it follows that we are stuck with the complementary mode of description. Against this argument which has been elaborated in some detail by Heisenberg[144] and by von Weizsaecker[145] it is sufficient to point out that introducing a set of concepts is not something that occurs independently of and prior to the construction of theories. Concepts are introduced as part of a theoretical framework, they are not introduced by themselves. However with respect to theories it must be asserted that man is not only capable of *using* them and the concepts which they embody for the construction of descriptions, experimental and otherwise, but that he is also capable of *inventing* them. How else could it have been possible, to mention only one example, to replace the Aristotelian physics and the Aristotelian cosmology by the new physics of Galileo and Newton? The only conceptual apparatus then available was the Aristotelian theory of change with its opposition of actual and potential properties, form and matter, the four causes, and the like. This conceptual apparatus was much more general and universal than the physical theories of today as it contained a general theory of change, spatio—temporal and otherwise. It also seems to be closer to everyday thinking and was therefore more firmly entrenched than any succeeding physical theory, classical physics included. Within this tremendously involved conceptual scheme Galileo's (or rather Descartes') law of inertia does not make sense. Should, then, Galileo have tried to get on with the Aristotelian concepts as well as possible because these concepts were the only ones in actual use and as "there is no use discussing what could be done if we were other [i.e., more ingenious] beings than we are?"[146] By no means! What was needed was not improvement, or delimitation of the Aristotelian concepts in order to "make room for new physical laws";[147] what was needed was an *entirely new theory*. Now at the time of Galileo human beings were apparently able to do this extraordinary thing and become beings different from what they were before (and one should again realize that the conceptual change that was implied was a much more radical one than the conceptual change necessitated by the appearance of the quantum of action). Are there (apart from pessimism with respect to the abilities of contemporary physicists) any reasons to assume that what was possible in the 16th and 17th centuries will be impossible in the 20th century? As far as I can understand it is Bohr's contention that such reasons do indeed exist, that they are of a logical rather than of a sociological character,[148] and that they are connected with the peculiar nature of classical physics.

Bohr's first argument in favor of this contention proceeds from the situation, outlined above, that we need the classical concepts not only if we want to give a *summary* of facts, but that without these concepts the facts to be summarized could not be *stated* either. As already Kant before him he observes that even our experimental statements are always formulated with the help of theoretical terms and that the elimination of these terms must lead, not to the "foundations of knowledge" as the positivists would have it, but to complete chaos. "Any experience," he asserts,[149] "makes its appearance within the frame of our customary points of view and forms of perception" and at the present moment the forms of perception are those of classical physics.

But does it follow, as is asserted by Bohr, that we can never go beyond the classical framework and that all our future microscopic theories must have duality built into them?

It is easily seen that the use of classical concepts for the description of experiments in contemporary physics can never justify such an assumption. For a theory may be found whose conceptual apparatus, when applied to the domain of validity of classical physics, would be just as comprehensive and useful as the classical apparatus without yet coinciding with it. Such a situation is by no means uncommon. The behavior of the planets, of the sun, and of the satellites can be described both by the Newtonian concepts and by the concepts of general relativity. The order introduced into our experiences by Newton's theory is retained *and improved upon* by relativity. This means that the concepts of relativity are sufficiently rich for the formulation even of all the *facts* which were stated before with the help of Newtonian physics. Yet the two sets of concepts are completely different and bear no logical relation to each other.

An even more striking example is provided by the phenomena known as the "appearances of the devil." These phenomena are accounted for both by the assumption that the devil exists, and by some more recent psychological (and psychosociological) theories.[150] The concepts used by these two schemes of explanation are in no way related to each other. Nevertheless the abandonment of the idea that the devil exists does not lead to experiential chaos, as the psychological scheme is rich enough to account for the order already introduced.

To sum up: although in reporting our experiences we make use, and must make use, of certain theoretical terms, it does not follow that different terms will not do the job equally well, or perhaps even better, because more coherently. And as our argument was quite general, it seems to apply to the classical concepts as well.

This is where Bohr's second argument comes in. According to this second argument, which is quite ingenious, we shall have to stay with the classical concepts, as the human mind will never be able to invent a new and different conceptual scheme. As far as I can make out, the argument for this peculiar inability of the human mind rests upon the following *premises*: (a) we invent (or should use) only such ideas, concepts, theories, as are suggested by observation; "only by observation itself," writes Bohr,[151] "do we come to recognize those laws which grant us a comprehensive view of the diversity of phenomena." (b) because of the formation of appropriate habits any conceptual scheme employed for the explanation and prediction of facts will imprint itself upon our language, our experimental procedures, our expectations, as well as our experiences. (c) classical physics is a universal conceptual scheme, i.e., it is so general that no conceivable fact falls outside the domain of its application. (d) classical physics has been used long enough for the formation of habits, referred to under (b), to become operative. The *argument* itself runs as follows: if classical physics is a universal theory (premise c) and has been used long enough (premise d), then all our experiences will be classical (premise b) and we shall therefore be unable to conceive any concepts which fall outside the classical scheme (premise a). Hence the invention of a new conceptual scheme which might enable us to circumvent duality is impossible.

That there must be something amiss with the argument is seen from the fact that all the premises except perhaps the first one apply also to the Aristotelian theory of motion. As a matter of fact the very generality of this theory would seem to make it a much stronger candidate for the argument than the classical physics could ever be. However the Aristotelian theory *has been* superseded by a very different conceptual apparatus. Clearly, this new conceptual apparatus was then not suggested by experience *as interpreted in the Aristotelian manner* and it was therefore a "free mental creation."[152] This refutes (a). That (b) needs modifying becomes clear when we consider that a scientist should always keep an open mind and that he should therefore always consider possible alternatives along with the theory he is favoring at a certain moment.[153] If this demand is satisfied, then the habits cannot form, or at least they will not any longer completely determine the actions of the scientist. Furthermore, it cannot be admitted that the classical scheme is universally valid. It is not applicable to such phenomena as the behavior of living organisms (which the Aristotelian scheme did cover), to personal consciousness, to the formation and the behavior of social groups, and to many other phenomena. We have to conclude, then, that Bohr's arguments against the possibility of alternatives to the point of view of complementarity are all inconclusive.

And this result is exactly as it should be. Any restrictive demand with respect to the form and the properties of future theories, any such demand can be justified only if an assertion is made to the effect that certain parts of the knowledge we possess are absolute and irrevocable. Dogmatism, however, should be alien to the spirit of scientific research, and this quite irrespective of whether it is now grounded upon "experience" or upon a different and more "aprioristic" kind of argument.

What has been refuted so far is the contention that complementarity is the *only possible point of view* in matters microphysical and that the only successful theories will be those which work with inbuilt uncertainties that are interpreted in accordance with Bohr's two hypotheses. Still, it has not been shown that complementarity is not *a possible point of view.* Quite on the contrary, we have tried to exhibit the advantages of Bohr's point of view and we have also defended this point of view against irrelevant attacks. It is now time to turn to the *difficulties* which beset the idea of complementarity even if it is not interpreted in the dogmatic manner which we have just criticized. These difficulties will be discussed in sections 10ff of the present paper. However, at first a few comments should be made on the results so far obtained.

(8) THE ROLL OF SPECULATION IN PHYSICS.

There are many physicists who, when presented with our above results will point out, rather impatiently, that a general discussion of possibilities is of no use whatever as long as a well-developed and successful alternative to the present quantum theory is missing. These physicists will refer to the fact that, after all, *there exists* a very successful body of theory which is in agreement with the idea of complementarity whereas the other side, despite all the talk about possibilities, has not yet produced anything that would only vaguely resemble this theory in formal accomplishment and empirical accuracy. "What is the message," exclaims Professor Hanson, expressing the view of many of his physicist colleagues,[154] "Bohm . . . wish/es/ to carry to Copenhagen?" And he implies that there is no message as there is "no algebraically detailed, experimentally acceptable" *theory* to the present quantum theory.[155] In an earlier paper[156] Professor Hanson allows for general speculations which are different from those contained in the Copenhagen picture. But he demands that a distinction be made between "those speculations which have proven themselves to *work* in theory and practice from those which have not yet been put to any test,"[157] i.e., which have not yet led to the construction of detailed physical theories. And he again implies that for this reason the ideas of Bohm and Vigier should be regarded with scepticism. It is this pragmatic criticism of unpopular and fairly general speculations which I want to examine in the present section.

It is clear that such criticism will be well liked by the great majority of physicists, as it enables them to enjoy the riches (or apparent riches) they possess without forcing them to think of means either to enlarge their capital, or to improve upon the quality of their currency. However, it becomes a dangerous tool when it is elevated from an instrument giving security to those who think that their everyday life as practicing scientists is sufficiently troublesome to excuse them from additional metaphysical worries, when it is elevated from such a psychological crutch into a philosophical principle. First of all it is somewhat doubtful whether even the quantum theory of today is adequately represented by the idea of complementarity. It is quite true that this idea gives a correct account of some general characteristics of the elementary theory; however, difficulties arise as soon as we either consider details, or leave the elementary theory and proceed to an analysis of the more recent field theories. This point will be elaborated later on. Secondly, the argument which praises the idea of complementarity for having given rise to a very valuable physical theory overlooks the fact that the full Copenhagen Interpretation was only completed *after* the introduction of wave mechanics. And wave mechanics, or the elementary theory, was completed by Schrödinger whose general philosophy was very different from the ideas which originated in Copenhagen.[158] However, quite apart from more detailed criticisms of this kind, it must be asserted that the discussion of possibilities and of alternatives to a current theory plays a most important role in the development of our physical knowledge. After all, a physicist who has been convinced by Bohr's arguments (which, as we have shown, are invalid) will exclude from consideration any theory that does not work with inbuilt uncertainties. He will thereby severely restrict his domain of research and he will do so because he thinks that what lies outside this domain is of no empirical value whatever. He will support his belief by arguments of the kind we have outlined above. Now it is very important to realize that it is always possible first to restrict oneself to theories which satisfy certain requirements and then to "save the phenomena" in one way or another. The impetus theory was such an attempt to save the Aristotelian theory of motion from refutation by new theories concerning the motion of projectiles.[159] It often turns out that such a procedure is possible only at the expense of simplicity, comprehensiveness, and intuitive appeal. As long as the belief in the uniqueness of the point of view adopted continues to influence the scientists, these complications will be felt to be unavoidable features of nature rather than avoidable features of their theories and they will be suffered with a patient shrug. At such a stage of complication and confusion a hint to the effect that this uniqueness is neither justifiable nor desired may be of paramount importance. It may give rise to the hope that there is a more direct way of attacking the difficulties created by the increasing complications of the theory and it may also encourage new ways of thinking. Think what would have happened if the idea that the sun alone possesses the power to influence the planets had been proposed, and then dogmatically retained. The mutual disturbances of the planets would soon have been discovered—but one would have tried to account for them by further complicating the arrangement of epicycles that Copernicus still used. The idea that any object may attract any other object opened up a completely new way of accounting of these irregularities. There are of course many physicists who will point out that their theories have been derived from experiment and do therefore not admit of alternatives. They overlook that experimental results only possess approximate validity and therefore admit of different, and even mutually inconsistent interpretations. *There is no way of singling out one and only one theory on the basis of observation.*[160]

However, if general principles such as those underlying the Copenhagen point of view are liable unduly and unjustifiably to restrict future research, is it then not better to omit them altogether and to be content with one's physics alone? The reply is that a complicated physical theory cannot be invented in its full formal splendor without some preparation. Consider for example the astronomical system of Ptolemy with its elaborate and delicate machinery of deferents, epicycles, excenters, and the like. Is it likely that the transition from "experience" to this theory can be made without intermediate steps? After all, what "experience" tells us is that the behavior of the planets is very complicated and quite different from the behavior of the fixed stars. The idea that both may be subjected to the same laws of circular motion could therefore not possibly have been suggested by what we see with our eyes; quite the contrary, this idea is to a certain extent even *contradicted* by the crude experience which was available to the ancient astronomers. Still it had to be used if a coherent treatment of both planets and fixed stars was to be possible. And as it was in disagreement with prior *prima facie* observations it had to be introduced as a metaphysical hypothesis, i.e., as a hypothesis about features of the world that are not accessible to direct observation. This metaphysical hypothesis was then the guiding principle of the planetary astronomy from Anaximander to Copernicus, and even Galileo. Without this idea it would perhaps have been possible to accumulate numerous useful empirical regularities about the planets, but it would have been quite impossible to devise a theory of the formal accomplishment and the empirical accuracy of the Ptolemaean astronomy. This shows very clearly that the pragmatic criticism which we presented at the beginning of the present chapter altogether puts the cart before the horse when demanding that the consideration of fully fledged scientific theories should come first and that the discussion of possibilities was only of secondary importance and should be carried out later, or perhaps not at all. As a second example of a metaphysical idea, take the idea that celestial and terrestrial events are guided by the same laws. Again, at the time when it was conceived this idea could not be called empirical as it was so obviously contradicted by the observable difference between the regularity and apparent purity of the celestial matter (astronomy), and the irregularity and sluggishness of the terrestrial matter (meteorology). Yet, how could the new mechanics of the heavens have been developed without a firm belief, not in one's senses, but in this extraordinary hypothesis? The best example, however, seems to me to be the atomic theory itself. For here it is shown more clearly than in other cases that a theory largely metaphysical need not on that account be irrational and arbitrary. As we know, the atomic theory was developed with the purpose of solving the following difficulty: according to the ideas about matter of Thales, Anaximander, and the other early Ionian monists the things in the universe consisted basically of a single kind of substance. From this premise Parmenides derived that change, being a transition from one thing to a thing of a different kind, could not exist in such a monistic universe. This derivation taken together with the fact that there *is* change was regarded by the atomists as a refutation of monism. They therefore replaced monism by their pluralistic atomic theories.[161] Now the arguments leading up to this replacement, although dealing with matters which are not all directly observable, are clear and easy to comprehend. This example and our above examination of the point of view of complementarity should be sufficient to dispel the notion that metaphysical considerations may perhaps play an important role in the development of scientific theories, but that they must be classified together with such other important, but irrational, factors of theory-construction as intelligence and absence of fatigue. The difference between a metaphysical point of view and a scientific theory does not consist in the fact that the former is utterly irrational and arbitrary whereas only the latter can be reasonably discussed. It rather consists in the fact that experience plays a smaller role in the discussion of the former, and that apparently adverse experiences are sometimes disregarded pending a more detailed development of the point of view: it took about 2,000 years until the atomic theory was sufficiently developed to lead to predictions that could be tested and compared with predictions made by alternative theories (Brownian motion). During this time the theory was frequently attacked on the basis of "experience." It was so attacked by the Aristotelians (whose theory of motion was more developed and more sophisticated than the theory of motion connected with the atomic theory), and it was so attacked, more recently, when it was shown to be inconsistent with a highly confirmed and formally highly developed physical theory, *viz.* thermodynamics (reversibility objection; recurrence objection). One can easily imagine what would have happened had the pragmatists and the radical empiricists had their way. The former could have pointed out, already in the time of Aristotle, that the atomic theory had not yet led to any ". . . detailed, experimentally acceptable" dynamics,[162] that the speculations of the atomists had not "proven themselves to *work* in theory and practice"[163] and that they should therefore not be taken too seriously. And the latter, pointing to the strong empirical backing of thermodynamics, could have altogether dismissed the atomic theory as being in disagreement with experiment.[164] What would our present situation be under these circumstances? We would now be working with a host of empirical generalizations such as Balmer's formulae, the rules of Ritz, rules concerning the fine structure of spectra, and we would not possess a coherent account of spectra, the motion of small particles, electric conductivity and the like. I conclude, then, that the development of comprehensive scientific theories essentially depends upon the development, through argument and discussion, of metaphysical points of view together with the attempt to make these points of view more and more specific until their truth can finally be decided by experiment. Also results should not be expected too quickly. It took about 2,000 years before the metaphysical idea of atomism had been transformed into an independently testable scientific theory. During these 2,000 years the atomists were frequently attacked by opponents who contrasted their own detailed physics (e.g., thermodynamics) with the "idle speculations" of the atomists and who thought that such a remark was a good argument against the further pursuit of atomism. The final success of the atomic philosophy shows how little such pragmatic arguments count and how important it is to pursue a reasonable idea, even if practical results in the form of mathematical formalisms or empirical predictions are not immediately forthcoming.

(9) VON NEUMANN'S INVESTIGATIONS.

We have not yet dealt with all the arguments against the possibility of alternatives to the point of view of complementarity There are many physicists who would readily admit that Bohr's *reasoning* is not very convincing and that it may even be invalid. But they will point out that there exists a much better way of arriving at its *result,* viz. von Neumann's proof to the effect that the elementary quantum theory is incompatible with hidden variables. This proof has not only been utilized by those who found the metaphysical elements in Bohr's philosophy not to their taste, it has also been used by members of the Copenhagen school in order to show that what Bohr had derived on the basis of qualitative arguments could be proved in a rigorous way. However, one ought to keep in mind that the relation between the point of view of Bohr and the point of view of von Neumann is by no means very close. For example

Bohr has repeatedly emphasized that the measuring device must be described in *classical* terms[165] whereas it is essential for von Neumann's theory of measurement that both the system investigated and the measuring device be described with the help of a ψ-function. The latter procedure leads to difficulties which do not arise in Bohr's treatment. Hence, when dealing with von Neumann's investigations, we are not dealing with a refinement, as it were, of the arguments of Bohr—we are dealing with a completely different approach.

In section 3 we described the proof itself and we had then occasion to point out that it involves an illegitimate transition from the properties of ensembles to the properties of the elements of these ensembles. In the present section we shall assume the proof to be correct and we shall point out that even then it cannot be used as an argument to the effect that the atomic theory will forever have to work with inbuilt uncertainties.

The proof consists in the derivation of a certain result from the quantum theory (the elementary theory) in its present form and interpretation. It follows at once that even if the result were the one claimed by von Neumann it could not be used for excluding a theory according to which the present theory is only approximately correct, i.e., agrees with experiments in some respects but not in others. However simple this argument—the fact that the present theory is confirmed at all has created such a bias in its favor that a little more explanation seems to be required.[166] Assume for that purpose that somebody tries to utilize von Neumann's proof in order to show that *any* future theory of the microcosm will have to work with irreducible probabilities. If he wants to do this then he must quite obviously assume that the principles upon which von Neumann bases his result are valid under *all* circumstances future research might uncover. Now the assertion of the absolute validity of a physical principle implies the denial of any theory that contains its negation. For example, the assertion of the absolute validity of von Neumann's premises implies the denial of any theory that ascribes to these premises a limited validity in a restricted domain only. But how could such a denial be justified by *experience* if the denied theory is constructed in such a way that it gives the same predictions as the defended one wherever the latter has been found to be in agreement with experiment? And that theories of the kind described can indeed be constructed has been shown, most clearly, by Professor D. Bohm.[167]

Apart from his error with respect to the result of his proof von Neumann himself was completely aware of the limitations of this alleged result. "It would be an exaggeration," writes he,[168] "to maintain that causality has thereby *[*i.e., by the proof of the two theorems referred to in section 3*]* been done away with: quantum mechanics has, in its present form, several serious lacunae and it may even be that it is false." Not all physicists have shared this detached attitude. Thus having outlined the proof, Max Born[169] makes the following comment: "Hence, if any future theory should be deterministic, it cannot be a modification of the present one, but must be essentially different. How this should be possible without sacrificing a whole treasure of well-established results I leave the determinist to worry about." Does he not realize that precisely that same argument could be used for the retention of absolute space in mechanics, or against the introduction of the statistical version of the second law? And has the fact that very different theories, such as the Newtonian mechanics on the one side and general realitivity on the other, can be used for describing the same facts (for example, the path of Jupiter) not already made it clear that theories can be "essentially different" without a "sacrifice of a whole treasure of well-established results" being involved? This being the case there is no reason whatever why a future atomic theory should not return to a more classical outlook without contradicting actual experiment, or without leaving out facts already known and accounted for by wave mechanics. It follows that von Neumann's imaginary results cannot in any way be used as an argument against the application at the microlevel of theories of a certain type (for example, deterministic theories).

Professor Hanson's attitude is still less comprehensible. He, too, tries to defend indeterminism and the absence of hidden parameters by a combined reference to von Neumann's proof and "nature."[170] But he also realizes, as did von Neumann, that the elementary theory on which the proof is based is "but a programmatic sketch of something more comprehensive"[171] and that it is empirically unsatisfactory. He even admits that a more comprehensive and really satisfactory theory "simply does not exist."[172] Now if all that is granted—how then can he still try to make use of von Neumann's argument whose result will be correct and satisfactory only if the premises are correct, satisfactory, and complete, i.e., only if the elementary theory is correct, satisfactory and complete? After all, who can now say that the observational and other difficulties of the elementary theory are *not* due to the fact that hidden parameters *do* exist and have been omitted from consideration?

What we have shown so far is that all the arguments which have been used in the literature against alternatives to complementarity are invalid.

There does not exist the slightest reason why we should assume that the proper road to future progress will consist in devising theories which are even more indeterministic than wave mechanics, and that the appropriate formalism will forever have to be one with inbuilt commutation relations. All the way through the question has been left undecided as to whether the more general ideas of the point of view of complementarity give an adequate account of the *existing theories*, i.e., whether these ideas give an adequate account of the elementary theory and of the field theories. The answer to this question which will exhibit various difficulties will be given in the remaining sections of the paper, where we shall also have an opportunity to consider some of the more formal alternatives to the ideas of Bohr.

(10) Observational Completeness.

It was the intention of Bohr and Heisenberg, but notably of the latter, to develop a theory which was thoroughly observational in the sense that a sentence expressing an unobservable state of affairs could not be formulated in it. According to the point of view of complementarity, the mathematics of the theory is to be regarded only as a means for transforming statements about observable events into statements about other observable events, and it has no meaning over and above that function. This is not the case with either our everyday language, or with classical physics. Both allow for the existence of physical situations which cannot be discovered by any observation whatever. As an example,[173] we consider the case of two banknotes, both printed with the help of the same printing press, the one under legal circumstances, the other by a gang of counterfeiters who used the same press at night, and illegally. If we assume that the banknotes have been printed within a very short interval of time and that they show the same numbers, and if we further assume that they somehow got mixed up, then we shall have to say that by virtue of their different history they possess certain properties, different for both, which we shall never be able to distinguish. Another example frequently referred to is the intensity of an electromagnetic field at a certain point.[174] The usual methods of measuring this field use bodies of finite extension and finite charge and they can therefore inform us only about average values, but not about the exact values of the field components. As there exist laws of nature according to which there is a lower limit to the size of test bodies, it is even physically impossible to perform a measurement which would result in such information. A third example which should be even more instructive is the disappearance of historical evidence in the course of time. That Caesar sneezed twice on the morning of April 5, 67 B.C. should either be true or false. However as it is very unlikely that this event was recorded by any contemporary writer, and as the physical traces it left in the surroundings as well as the memory traces it left in the brains of the bystanders have long since disappeared (in accordance, among other things, with the second law of thermodynamics) we now possess no evidence whatsoever. Again we are presented with a physical situation which exists (existed), and yet cannot be discovered by any observational means.

A physicist or a philosopher who is biased in favor of a radical empiricism will quite naturally regard such a situation as unsatisfactory. He will be inclined to reject statements such as those contained in our examples by pointing out that they are observationally insignificant, and in doing so he will be guided by the demand that one should not allow talk about situations which can be shown to be inaccessible to observation. Classical physics does not satisfy this demand automatically. It allows for the consistent formulation of sentences with no observational consequences, *together with* the assertion that such consequences do not exist. An attempt to enforce the radical empiricist's demand will therefore have to consist in an *interpretation* of classical physics according to which some of its statements are cognitively meaningful, whereas others are not. This means that the exclusion of the undesirable sentences will have to be achieved by a philosophical maneuver which is superimposed upon physics. Classical physics itself does not provide means for excluding them.[175]

There exist, however, *philosophical* theories which possess exactly this character. An example is Berkeley's theory of matter (if we omit the *ad hoc* hypothesis that objects unperceived by human beings are still being perceived by God). According to this theory material objects are bundles of sensations and their existence consists in their being perceived or observed. If this theory is developed in a formally satisfactory manner then it does not allow for the consistent formulation of any statement about material objects in which it is asserted that there is a situation which is not accessible to perception. One may call such a theory *observationally complete*. When formulating matrix mechanics, Heisenberg had the intention of constructing a *physical* theory that was observationally complete in exactly this sense, observation with the help of classically well-defined apparatus replacing the more direct form of observation with the help of one's senses. It is assumed in the more general ideas held by the members of the Copenhagen school, and notably by Bohr, that the elementary quantum theory in its present form and interpretation corresponds with this intention. It will turn out that this assumption is not justified or, at least, nobody has as yet shown it to be correct. However, let us first examine an apparently very strong argument in its favor.

Consider a state $|\Phi>$ which is such that it cannot be characterized by the values of any complete set of commuting observables. Such a state would be truly unobservable. For first of all there is no measurement (in the sophisticated sense of the quantum theory) which can bring it about; and secondly there is no measurement which on immediate repetition would lead to the result characteristic for this state as we have assumed that there is no such result. If we still want to assert the existence of such a state then we must regard it as an element of Hilbert space (we adopt von Neumann's formalism) and it must be possible to represent it in the form

$$|\Phi> = \Sigma_i \, c_i \, |\alpha_i>$$

where the $|\alpha_i>$ form a complete orthonormal set which is connected with the complete commuting set of observables α. Now incorporate $|\Phi>$ into an orthonormal set $\{|\Phi_i>\}$ in such a manner that the set $\{|\Phi>\}$ + $\Sigma_i\{|\Phi_i>\}$ is complete. Then for any $|\alpha_k>$

$$|\alpha_k> = \Sigma_i \, |\Phi_i><\Phi_i|\alpha_k> + |\Phi><\Phi|\alpha_k>$$

which on measurement of the observable corresponding to the set $\{|\Phi>\}$ + $\Sigma_i\{|\Phi_i>\}$ would yield $|\Phi>$ unless $<\Phi|\alpha_k> = <\alpha_k|\Phi>^* = c_k^* = 0$. Now as $<\alpha_k|$ may be any eigenstate of α it follows that $|\Phi> = 0$: *states which are not accessible to observation do not exist.*

Now if this argument is supposed to prove observational completeness with respect to *classical states of affairs* then the formal scheme of it must be filled with empirical content. More especially, we must make the following assumptions. First, it must be assumed that there exist changes of states which can transform any state into a mixture of the eigenstates of any observable α, or into an α-mixture as we shall call it. This demand is a purely theoretical demand which must be satisfied by the *formalism* of the theory and which is independent of the interpretation of this formalism. Secondly, it must be assumed that states or observables can be characterized in a purely classical manner. Thirdly, we must demand that for any observable thus interpreted there exists a classical device capable of transforming *any* state into an α-mixture (again classically interpreted). Finally it must also be the case that the methods of measurement in actual use today produce α-mixtures with respect to the observables they are supposed to measure, or else the numbers obtained are of no relevance whatever.

Now, as regards the first assumption, it must be pointed out that it can be discussed only if a definite meaning has been given to the phrase "any state," i.e., if the class of all states has been well defined. As is well known, there is no unanimity on this point. The usual attitude is altogether to neglect the question and to decide it differently in different concrete cases. The trouble with this procedure is, of course, that it must lead to a breakdown of the universal applicability of the Born-interpretation in the sense that no theoretical justification will be available for the comparison of probabilities that have been obtained in different cases, or even in different treatments of one and the same case.[176] On the other hand, the only presentation of the theory which gives a definite account of the manifold of states to be used, von Neumann's presentation, has sometimes been regarded as too narrow as it excludes as illegitimate procedures for which it provides no equivalent whatever, and which yet seem to be necessary for the calculation of some of the most important experimental applications of the theory (problem of scattering).[177] We see that one of the basic presuppositions of assumption one is still far from clear. However, suppose that a satisfactory way has been found of delimiting the totality of allowed states. Is it then possible to justify in a theoretical way the assumption that there exist changes from pure states into mixtures?

There exist two attempts at such a justification. The first attempt is based upon the Born interpretation. This interpretation associates a certain probability to each transition from originally given states into one of the eigenstates of the observable measured (let us assume that α is this observable). These probabilities will have to be obtained on the basis of counting all those systems which after measurement possess identical eigenvalues α', α'', α''' etc. From these two assumptions it follows at once that immediately after a measurement of a state that is not an eigenstate of α, the state of the system has turned into an α-mixture (this consequence has sometimes been called the *projection postulate*). Now it must be realized that this "transcendental deduction" of what was above called the second assumption works only on condition that Born's statistical interpretation is universally applicable, and this is exactly what we want to find out. For it is the universal applicability of Born's rules which guarantees the observational completeness of the theory. What we have shown is that this universal applicability can be guaranteed only if we add the projection postulate to the theory: the projection postulate is a necessary condition of the observational completeness of the theory. However, is it possible to justify this postulate in an independent way?

An attempt at an empirical justification of the postulate which also brings in the empirical considerations demanded by assumption three is due to von Neumann.[178] Von Neumann interprets the Compton effect as a quantum mechanical measurement. The quantity to be measured is any coordinate of the place of collision P. One way of measuring P (method 1) consists in determining the path of the light quantum after the collision. Another way of measuring P (method 2) consists in determining the path of the electron after the collision. Now assume that M_1 has been performed. Before we could only make statistical assumptions about its outcome (e.g., about ϑ or about P). But as $tg\alpha = \dfrac{\lambda}{\lambda + \lambda_c} \, tg \, \dfrac{\vartheta}{2}$ (λ the wave length of the incident photon which is assumed to be known, λ_c the

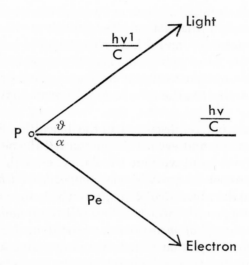

Compton wave length, α and ϑ as indicated) the outcome of M_2 is certain once M_1 has been performed and the result used: M_2 leads to exactly the same result as M_1. It follows that a state in which the value of P was not well defined is transformed by M_1, i.e., by a measurement of this very quantity, into a state in which its value is well defined. Or, by generalization: a general state is transformed into an eigenstate of the quantity measured.

The simplicity of this argument and the force derived from it is only apparent. It is due to the fact that a rather simple way has been used of describing what happens before and after the interaction of the electron and the photon. The application of wave mechanics[179] to the problem shows that the interpretation of the result in terms of quantum jumps is only a first approximation unless one has already introduced this hypothesis from the very beginning and used it during the calculation. Also the detailed account is much too complicated to allow for a simple argument such as the one just presented. We know too little about processes of interaction to be able to make any experimental result the basis for an argument with regard to certain features of the theory. Another, completely different argument against the validity of von Neumann's empirical derivation of quantum jumps is the following: the state of the system /electron+photon/ after the interaction is a state of type (2) (section 4) with α and ϑ being correlated in a manner similar to the manner in which α and β are correlated in (2). Now an observation of a specific value of α can lead to the prediction of the correlated value of ϑ (or of β in the example of section 4) only if immediately after the observation the state of the system /electron+photon/ has been reduced to a state in which both α and ϑ have sharp values, i.e., only if the projection postulate has already been applied. Which shows that even if von Neumann's rather simple assumptions about the interaction process were acceptable, that even then the argument would have to be rejected as being circular.

However we have not yet discussed all the difficulties. Even if the argument were admissible, and even if it represented the situation in a sufficiently detailed way, and without circularity, even then it would only show that the projection postulate is *compatible with experience;* it would not remove the *theoretical difficulties* which are connected with it. These theoretical difficulties which I shall call the *fundamental problem of the quantum theory of measurement* consist in the following fact: (1) the Schrödinger equation transforms pure states into pure states; (2) in general the situation described by a mixture cannot be described by a single wave function; hence, (3) the projection postulate cannot be explained on the basis of Schrödinger's equation alone, and it is even inconsistent with it if we assume that this equation is a process equation which governs all physical processes at the microlevel. The discussion of this fundamental problem leads straight into the quantum theory of measurement.

(11) MEASUREMENT.

A measurement is a physical process which has been arranged either for the purpose of testing a theory or for the purpose of determining some as yet unknown constants of a theory. A complete account of measurement will give rise to at least three sets of problems. First of all, there is the problem of whether the statements obtained with the help of the experiment are relevant, i.e., whether they indeed concern the theory or the constants in question, and under what conditions. Problems of this kind may be called *problems of confirmation*. In the present paper they will not be dealt with in a systematic manner. Another set of problems concerns the question whether the observable elements of the process (or of the equilibrium state in which it usually terminates) stand in a one-to-one relationship to the (not necessarily directly observable) elements whose properties we are investigating when performing the measurement. This set of problems may be split into two parts *viz.* (1) the question under what circumstances a situation may be called observable; and (2) the question whether it is possible *by physical means* to bring about a situation in which observable states are correlated with nonobservable states in such a manner that an inference is possible from the structure of the first to the structure of the second. Question (1) is a question of psychology. It is the question whether and how human beings, assisted or not assisted by instruments, react towards situations of a certain kind. Problems connected with question (1) will be called *observer problems*. Question (2) is a question of physics. It is the question whether the physical conditions which must be satisfied by a well-designed measurement are compatible with the laws of physics. Problems connected with question (2) will be called *physical problems of measurement*. Quite obviously the physical problems admit of a solution only if first a physical characterization, in terms of some theory, is available of those states of affairs which are observable.

In the present section we shall be mainly concerned with the physical problems of measurement in the quantum theory, although we may occasionally also deal with observer problems and problems of confirmation. More especially, we shall be dealing with the question whether and how the physical conditions which must be satisfied by any well-designed measurement of a quantum mechanical observable can be made compatible with the dynamical laws, and especially with Schrödinger's equation. This essentially is our problem: the theory is observationally complete only if the projection postulate is added to its basic postulates. The projection postulate is incompatible with the unrestricted validity of Schrödinger's equation. How can this apparent inconsistency be resolved?

According to Popper this problem is only an apparent one and it "arises in all probability contexts."[180] For example "assume that we have tossed [a] penny and that we are shortsighted and have to bend down before we can observe which side is upmost. The probability formalism tells us then that each of the possible states has a probability of ½. So we can say that the penny is half in one state and half in the other. And when we bend down to observe it the Copenhagen spirit will inspire the penny to make a quantum jump into one of its two eigenstates. For nowadays a quantum jump is said . . . to be the same as a reduction of the wave packet. And by 'observing' the penny we induce exactly what in Copenhagen is called a 'reduction of the wave packet.' "[181]

This is a very seductive proposal indeed, for there is no uneasiness combined with the classical case. But this is due to the fact that *in the classical case we are not dealing with wave packets*. What we are dealing with are mutually exclusive alternatives only one of which, *and this we know*, will be realized in the end. The classical description allows for this possibility for it is constructed in such a manner that the statement "the probability that the outcome is a head is ½" is compatible with "the outcome is actually a head." We may therefore interpret the transition from the first statement to the second statement as the transition from a less definite description to a more definite one, as a transition that is due to a change in our knowledge but that has no implications whatever as regards the actual physical state of the system which we are describing. The second statement does not assert the occurrence of a process that is denied by the first statement. Hence, the "jump" that occurs is a purely subjective phenomenon and a rather harmless phenomenon at that.

This is not so in the quantum mechanical case. Consider for this purpose a measurement whose possible outcomes are represented by the states Φ' and Φ'' and which occurs when the system is in a state $\Phi = \Phi' + \Phi''$. In this case Φ cannot be regarded as an assertion to the effect that one or two mutually exclusive alternative, Φ' or Φ'' occur, for when Φ is realized physical processes may occur which do not occur, neither when Φ' is realized, nor when Φ'' is realized. This, after all, is what interference amounts to. The transition, on measurement, from Φ to, say, Φ'', is therefore accompanied by a change in physical conditions which does not take place in the classical case. Even worse: what the Schrödinger equation yields when applied to the system $\Phi +$ a suitable measuring apparatus is, strictly speaking, another pure state $\Psi = A\Phi' + B\Phi''$ so that now *a mere look* at the apparatus (after which we assert that we have found Φ'') seems to lead to a physical change, namely to the destruction of interference between $A\Phi'$ and $B\Phi''$. It is this characteristic of the quantum mechanical case that is completely overlooked in Popper's analysis.[182]

Another fairly simple suggestion is due to Landé. Landé tries to solve what we have above called the fundamental problem of measurement by denying that Schrödinger's equation is correctly interpreted as a process equation. In order to show this,[183] he proceeds from the usual interpretation of $<\phi|\alpha_i>$ and $<\phi|\beta_k>$ (α and β two complete sets of commuting observables) as different expectation functions belonging to *one and the same state*, and he suggests that this interpretation be also used in the case of the temporal development of states, i.e., he suggests that also $\Phi(t')$ and $\Phi(t'')$ be interpreted as two different expectation functions belonging to the same state rather than as two different states. If this interpretation is adopted[184] then Schrödinger's equation no longer plays the role of a process equation which transforms states into other ("later") states, but it then plays the role of an equation which transforms expectation functions of one state into other expectation functions *of the very same state*. In this interpretation, states never change unless we perform a measurement in which latter case there occurs a sudden transition from a state into one of the eigenstates of the observable measured. This procedure only apparently removes the temporal changes. Strictly speaking it is nothing but a verbal manoeuver. By pushing the temporal changes into the representatives it now makes the dynamical variables time-dependent, whereas in the usual presentation, which is criticized by Landé, the variables do not change in time. However a representation of the quantum theory in terms of stable states and moving variables is well known: it is the Heisenberg representation.[185] And as this latter representation can be shown to be equivalent to the one Landé wants to abandon (the Schrödinger representation) it follows that his criticism, and his alternative suggestion completely lose their point.

We now turn to a very brief examination of von Neumann's theory of measurement.[186] In von Neumann's investigations the projection postulate and Schrödinger's equation are given equal importance. The process of measurement itself is regarded as an *interaction* between a macrosystem (represented by some wave function) and a microsystem (represented by another wave function). The main result is that the projection postulate is compatible with the formalism of wave mechanics and Born's interpretation. This theory has been attacked for epistemological, physical, and mathematical reasons, and it seems now definitely established that it cannot be regarded as a satisfactory account of the process of measurement in the quantum theory. The *epistemological* difficulty of von Neumann's theory[187] consists in this: the theory allows for the application of the projection postulate even on the macrolevel, and it then leads to the paradoxical result that by simply taking notice of a macroscopic trace the observer may destroy interferences and thus influence the physical course of events.[188] The source of this difficulty is easily seen: it lies in the fact that a *microaccount* is given both of the measuring apparatus and of the system investigated although only the latter can be said to have microscopic dimensions and although only the latter is investigated in such a detailed manner that its microscopic features and their dual nature become apparent. Clearly such a procedure will not reflect properly the behavior of macroobjects *as seen by a macro-observer* as it does not contain the approximations which are necessary for a return to the classical level. One of the most obvious *physical* consequences is that the entropy of the total system *[micro + macrosystem]* remains unchanged as long as the projection postulate is not applied. This is very different from the corresponding result in the classical case, a difference which cannot be ascribed to the appearance on the microlevel of the quantum of action.[189] It seems therefore advisable to employ a greater latency of description when discussing the process of measurement. A very similar suggestion emerges from some considerations which are due to Elsasser:[190] The observation of the trace, or of the macroscopic movement which terminates the process of measurement, will usually take some time interval Δt of macroscopic dimensions. During this time the measuring apparatus is supposed to retain its main *classical* properties, or, to express it differently, it is supposed to remain an element of a statistical ensemble which is defined in a way which depends on the imprecision of macroscopic operations. Now if we assume that the measuring apparatus is in a pure state in which variables complementary to variables on which the main apparatus variables depend in a decisive manner possess sharp values, then such constancy of classical properties over a classically reasonable time interval cannot any more be guaranteed. Suppose, for example, the pure state in which the apparatus allegedly dwells is one in which all the elementary constituents of the apparatus possess a well-defined position. Then formula (1) will predict that the corresponding momenta will range over all possible values, i.e., the system will disintegrate in a very short time.[191] Hence, "if systems of many degrees of freedom are involved the possibility of giving a unique quantum mechanical representation of a system by a pure state, and the possibility of leaving it in approximately the conditions under which it appears as sample of a given collective, will in general exclude each other."[192] Finally I would like to draw attention to the *mathematical* fact, first pointed out by Wigner,[193] that only an approximate measurement is possible of operators which do not commute with a conserved quantity.[194] All these results taken together make it very clear that the problem of measurement demands application of the methods of statistical mechanics *in addition to* the laws of the elementary theory. A similar suggestion seems to emerge from the analysis of P. Jordan[195] and of H. Margenau.[196] In a very suggestive paper, Jordan has pointed out that the application of statistical considerations may lead to the elimination, on the macroscopic level, of the very troublesome interference terms which in von Neumann's account were removed with the help of the projection postulate. Margenau, on the other hand, has drawn attention to the fact that no stage of a real measurement is correctly described by the projection postulate. The postulate does not correctly describe the state of the system investigated *after* the result of the measurement has been recorded (in the form of, e.g., a macroscopic trace on a photographic plate). The reason is that the process of recording very often destroys the system.[197] Nor does the postulate describe the state of the system *before* the recording. The reason is that at this moment the beams corresponding to the various eigen-functions of the observable measured are still capable of interfering so that the system cannot be said to dwell in any one of them to the complete exclusion of dwelling in a different one.[198] Taking all this into account, Margenau drops the projection postulate and assumes that state functions are objectively real probabilities which are *tested* by a measurement without being *transformed* by it into a different state function. What is important in such a test is not the fact that the state of a system has become an eigenstate of the observable measured; what is important is the emergence of a set of numbers which is the one and only result of the measurement and its only point of interest.

It seems to me that none of the objections I have reported in the last paragraph can be raised against a theory that has been developed by G. Ludwig of the University of Berlin.[199] Ludwig's account is based upon the Schrödinger equation and certain assumptions concerning the formal features (in terms of the elementary theory) of the macroscopic level. The following result is obtained: measurements are complicated thermodynamic processes which terminate in a state in which the macroobservables of the measuring instrument M which are correlated with the microproperties of the system S under investigation possess fixed values, i.e., values that are independent of the nature of the macroprocedure which has led to their determination. The projection postulate is not used anywhere in the calculation of the expected changes of either S or of M. Yet the theory results in something very close to this postulate; for in the equilibrium state that terminates the measurement the expectation values of obtaining certain macroscopic results are identical with the expected values for the correlated microscopic properties. It is for this reason that Ludwig regards the projection postulate as an "abbreviated account of a very complicated process."[200] It would seem that a very careful interpretation is needed of this result. It cannot mean that the measurement transforms the state of the system S into a state that is very close to, though not identical with, the state predicted by the projection postulate. This interpretation is excluded by virtue of the fact that the measurement leads in many cases to a destruction of the system investigated. All we can say in *these* cases is that the final macroscopic situation adequately mirrors the number of the eigenstates of the observable measured and their relative weights in the state of S *before* the measurement commenced. Such an interpretation which is also defended by Margenau would be very close to Bohr's where "the 'properties' of a microscopic object are nothing but possible changes in various macroscopic systems."[201] Indeed, I must confess that I cannot see a very great difference between Margenau's suggestions and the theory of Bohr where the microsystem and the macrosystem are supposed to form an indivisible block the only changes of which are those that can be described in classical terms. As the above quotations shows Ludwig himself regards his own theory as an attempt at a more formal presentation of Bohr's point of view. And this it is but only to a certain extent.[201a] For whereas in Ludwig's account the properties of the macroscopic level agree with the properties required by the classical physics only to a certain degree of approximation, such a theoretical (and practically negligible) difference is not admitted by Bohr: according to Bohr the measuring instrument is *fully classical* and restrictions occur only if we try to understand the microsystems, per analogy, in classical terms. Also Bohr's account is not beset by the mathematical[202] and philosophical[203] difficulties that are still present in Ludwig's theory. Altogether his semiqualitative ideas still seem to be preferable to all those very sophisticated mathematical accounts (including Ludwig's) where measurement is regarded as an *interaction* between systems that can be described, either exactly, or to a certain degree of approximation, by the formalism of the elementary theory. Let us briefly recall the main features of Bohr's theory: we are concerned with macrosystems which are described in classical terms, and with the calculation of expectation values *in these systems only*.[204] The properties of a microobject are nothing but possible changes in these macroscopic systems. This interpretation of measurement removes most of the unsatisfactory features of theories of interaction. However for this interpretation of the process of measurement—and with this remark we resume our discussion of the observational completeness of the quantum theory—the truth of what we called above the second and the third assumption now becomes of paramount importance: if all statements of the theory are to be about macroscopic situations then it is decisive indeed to show (a) that for every observable α there exists a classical device capable of transforming any state into an α-mixture; and (b) that the elements of the resulting mixture can again be observed as macroscopic modifications of measuring instruments. And it is equally important to show that all the magnitudes that are customarily used for the description of quantum mechanical systems are observables in the sense of the theory (or hypermaximal operators, if von Neumann's approach is adopted). Needless to say, this problem is far from being solved. But the situation is even worse. The difficulties of the problem of observation in the quantum theory seem to be much greater than the difficulties of the analogous problem within say, classical point mechanics and this despite the fact that a great deal of the former theory was constructed with the explicit purpose of not admitting anything unobservable. The reason can be easily seen. Fundamentally any property of a classical system of point particles can be calculated from the positions and momenta of the elements. In the quantum theory, the existence of the commutation relations necessitates the use of a new instrument for any function of non-commuting variables. This greatly increases the number of measuring instruments required for giving meaning to the main terms of the theory. It can be shown that this number must be Aleph One. If we now realize that so far measuring instruments have been found only for the simplest magnitudes, and that there does not seem to exist any way of finding instruments for the measurement of more complicated magnitudes such as, for example, the angle between two mutually inclined surfaces of a crystal,[205] then we must admit that the idea of the observational completeness of the quantum theory is not far from being a myth. Also the empirical content of a theory usually contains the preceding theories as approximations. Despite the many assertions to the contrary and despite the fact that the idea of a "rational generalization" is built in such a manner that a transition to the classical level seems to be an almost trivial affair,[206] no proof is as yet available to the effect that the *existing* theories contain the classical point mechanics as a special case. This further reduces their empirical content.

Taking all this into account we seem to arrive at the following paradoxical result: more than any other theory in the history of physics (the

Aristotelian physics perhaps, excluded) the quantum theory has been connected with a radically empiricistic outlook. It has been asserted that we have here finally arrived at a theory which directly deals with observations (observations of the classical kind, that is). It now turns out that this theory is much further removed from what it regards as its own empirical basis, *viz.* classical observational results, than was any of the theories which preceded it. "Quantum mechanics" writes Schrödinger,[207] "claims that it deals ultimately, and directly, with nothing but actual observations since they are the only real things, the only source of information, which is only about *them*. The theory of measurement is carefully phrased so as to make it epistemologically unassailable. But what is all this epistemological fuss about if we have not to do with actual, real findings 'in the flesh,' but only with imagined findings?" A similar sentiment is expressed by Bridgman.[208] According to him, a first glance at the quantum theory seems to show that it is a "thoroughly operational theory" which impression "is achieved by labelling some of the mathematical symbols 'operators,' 'observables,' etc. But in spite of the existence of a mathematical symbolism of that sort, the exact corresponding physical manipulations are . . . obscure, at least in the sense that it is not obvious how one would construct an idealized laboratory apparatus for making any desired sort of measurement."

It is therefore not only incorrect, and dogmatic, to say that complementarity is the *only possible* point of view in matters microphysical, there also exist grave doubts as to whether it is even a *possible* point of view, i.e., there exists grave doubt as to whether it accurately represents the one fully developed quantum theory of today, *viz.* the elementary quantum theory of Schrödinger and Heisenberg. And we may also say that the empiricistic and positivistic objections which some of the followers of the Copenhagen point of view have raised against alternative interpretations apply with full force to the elementary theory which, they claim, is correctly represented by complementarity. This does not diminish the great merits of this interpretation as regards our understanding of the microscopic level. It only shows that like so many other things it has its faults and should therefore not be regarded as the last, the final, and the only possible word in matters microphysical.

(12) RELATIVITY AND QUANTUM MECHANICS; THE FIELD THEORIES.

In the present section I want to deal, in a very sketchy manner, with the question as to whether the actual development of the field theories has confirmed Bohr's predictions. It is difficult to see this question in its proper light. After all, the great influence of Bohr's ideas which has been transmitted in various forms to what one might call the "younger generation" has led to the tendency to stick to theories of a certain kind, come what may. However, I think there are decisive arguments to the effect that this will not do. Also the field theories have started moving away from the correspondence principle and to develop formalisms which start in a fairly independent manner. It is quite clear why this must be so: the methods of quantization which have led to such tremendous successes in the quantum theory of particles and fields will continue to succeed only as long as there exist classical theories which after proper reformulation can be subject to quantization. As soon as the reservoir of classical theories is exhausted, the development of the quantum theory will either have to stop, or it will have to free itself from the correspondence principle which has been the physical rationale behind the point of view of complementarity. Such a development would also seem to be desirable in order to guarantee the symmetry between space and time coordinates which is demanded by relativity.[209] A further reason for trying to develop the quantum theory independently of the principle of correspondence which has been explained by Hill[210] seems to be this: "The classification of atomic and nuclear energy states depends heavily on the . . . vector coupling model. The physical meaning of this model is that it expresses the conservation of angular momentum. In a mathematical sense it represents the Lie algebra of the 3 dimensional continuous rotation group of ordinary Euclidean space. The usual classification scheme of atomic spectra therefore becomes direct evidence for the Euclidean character of space, at least on the level of atomic dimensions. If we adjoin the continuous rotation group and the crystalline groups, we can generate the full continuous group of translations and rotations as the characteristic symmetry group of 3-dimensional Euclidean space *in the large.*" This means that the synthesis of the quantum theory and of general relativity will necessitate a complete recasting of the structure of either general relativity, or of the quantum theory. The results we have obtained so far imply that such attempts will have to be judged by their fruits, i.e., by the predictions they may produce at some future time rather than by a point of view which, despite its obvious merits, is neither infallible, nor the only possible microphilosophy.

NOTES

The passage from Huyghens' at the beginning of the paper appears in his annotations on Baillet's *Life of Descartes* (a book which was published in 1691) and is printed in V. Cousin's *Fragments Philosophiques* tome ii, p. 155. Quoted from E. Whittaker, *A History of the Theories of Aether and Electricity,* Vol. I. London, 1951.

1. "The Development of the Interpretation of the Quantum Theory," in *Niels Bohr and the Development of Physics,* London, 1955, p. 13.

2. Some very important elements of this interpretation were developed in connection with the older quantum theory and the correspondence principle. This is true of the assumption of the indefiniteness of state descriptions. However, it would be somewhat rash to assert, as has been done by Heisenberg and others [cf. the reference in the last footnote] that his interpretation was a natural outcome of the "Korrespondenzdenken" and that its growth was not at all influenced by considerations of an entirely different character. For this cf. fn. 4, 5, as well as section 4.

3. An example is L. de Broglie. Cf. *Une tentative d'interprètation causal et non-linéaire de la mechanique ondulatoire,* Paris, 1956, Introduction.

4. To be more precise, the decisive date was the Fifth Solvay Conference which took place in Brussels in October, 1927 and which led to a complete victory for the point of view of Bohr and his collaborators. For this evaluation cf. Heisenberg *loc. cit.,* p. 16; de Broglie *La Méchanique quantique, restera-t-elle indeterministe?* Paris, 1953, Introduction; and Niels Bohr, "Discussions with Einstein of Epistemological Problems in Atomic Physics," originally published in *Albert Einstein, Philosopher-Scientist,* The Library of Living Philosophers, Inc. 1949, pp. 199ff, reprinted in *Atomic Physics and Human Knowledge,* New York, 1958, esp. pp. 41ff. The Proceedings of this very decisive Conference have been published; Institut International de Physique Solvay, *Rapport et discussions du 5e Conseil,* Paris, 1928. Cf. however the next footnote.

5. For *it was not before 1935 that the idea of the relational character of the quantum mechanical states was added to the Copenhagen Interpretation.* Despite later assertions to the contrary this meant a tremendous change of point of view. For a more detailed discussion cf. section 6 and footnote 116.

6. Schrödinger's attitude was not consistent. He has published papers which contain vigorous attacks upon the philosophical attitude of Bohr and his followers. However in private discussions he seemed to be much more impressed by the soundness of Bohr's point of view and of the positivistic theory of knowledge in general (by which I do not mean to imply that Bohr's ideas are positivistic).

7. An example is Jordan's *Komplementaritaet und Verdraengung* where occult phaenomena are also treated.

8. An example of P. Jordan *Die Physik und das Geheimnis des organischen Lebens,* Braunschweig 1943. For Bohr's own speculations cf. the relevant articles in *Atomic Physics and Human Knowledge.*

9. In a talk in Askov (Denmark) in the year 1949 which I attended, Bohr pointed out that there may exist a complementary relationship between love and justice. References to this talk and to the assertion just mentioned may be found in one of the August numbers of *Berlingske Tidende.*

10. In a draft of a paper "Complementarity in Quantum Mechanics: A Logical Analysis" (Draft, October, 1960) Messrs Hugo Bedau and Paul Oppenheim state their interest to investigate the possibility of applying Bohr's concept of complementarity to the relation between science and religion. For a discussion of already existing attempts in this direction and a criticism cf. P. Alexander, "Complementary Descriptions," *Mind,* Vol. LXV (1956), pp. 145-165. Cf. also MacKay, D. M., "Complementarity," *Aristotelian Society,* Suppl. Vol. XXXII (1958), pp. 105-122. Assertions involving gods are also found in W. Heisenberg, *Syllabus of the Gifford Lectures,* 1956, esp. p. 16: "It has certainly been the pride of natural science since the beginning of rationalism to describe and to understand nature without using the concept of God, and we do not want to give up any of the achievements of this period. But in modern atomic physics we have learned how cautious we should be in omitting essential concepts just because they lead to inconsistencies."

11. It is necessary to point out that most of these successes have only been *partial* successes. The elementary quantum theory, Dirac's theory of the electron, the earlier field theories—all these theories have been found to be unsatisfactory in one way or another. That is they were successful in certain domains, completely unsuccessful in others. And the more recent theories are characterized by a much less close adherence to the principle of correspondence and the philosophy of complementarity connected with it. Cf. J. Schwinger, *Quantum Electrodynamics,* Dover, 1958, pp. xivff as well as Bogoliubov-Shirkov, *Introduction to the Theory of Quantized Fields,* New York, 1958, p. 16.

12. Thus Hanson [*Am. Journal of Physics,* Vol. 27 (1959), pp. 4ff, reprinted in Danto-Morgenbesser, *Philosophy of Science,* New York, 1961, pp. 450ff; cf. esp. p. 454] points out that the development of the field theories and of Dirac's theory of the electron was strongly influenced by the point of view of complementarity. Despite Hanson's explicit assertion to the effect that Dirac himself has felt that way, I am somewhat doubtful as far as the second case is concerned: the paper where the theory is first developed uses some purely formal considerations (properties of the Hamiltonian) which seem in no way connected with the idea of complementarity; and the interpretation which this theory finally received (hole-theory) even runs counter to the assumption of

the relational character of quantum mechanical states. Still, it is quite possible that in the *preparation* of this paper Dirac has made use of some ideas which are essential to Bohr's point of view. Which is only one more argument in support of my demand which I have voiced since 1954 that the history of the quantum theory be based upon *live interviews* (to be carried out as speedily as possible) and *not* on papers only. It should be realized that very little of the thought that has led to the invention of the Copenhagen Interpretation has found *immediate* expression in papers. And it should also be realized that a history of the quantum theory will therefore be of value only if it is based upon what is to be found in print *as well as* upon carefully prepared interviews of its main participants.

13. "L'évidence de la complémentarité" in *Louis de Broglie, Physicien et Penseur,* Paris, 1953, p. 44.

14. Cf. fn. 11.

15. This point has been made by D. Bohm; cf. his "Quantum Theory in Terms of 'Hidden Variables,' " *Phys. Rev.,* Vol. 85 (1951), pp. 166ff.

16. As I have shown in "Explanation, Reduction, and Empiricism," *Minnesota Studies in the Philosophy of Science,* Vol. III, the empirical content of a theory of the generality of the present quantum theory depends to a decisive degree on the number of alternative theories which, although in agreement with all the relevant facts, are yet inconsistent with the theory in question. The smaller this number, the smaller the empirical content of the theory. The invention of alternatives which are inconsistent with the present quantum theory is therefore a necessary demand of empiricism.

17. For a more detailed description of this undesirable state of affairs cf. section 7 of my paper referred to in footnote 16.

18. von Weizsaecker *[*"Komplementaritaet und Logik" in *Die Naturwissenschaften,* Vol. 17 (1955), pp. 521ff*]* and Groenewold *[*private communication*]* have asserted that the fruitfulness of the Copenhagen interpretation was to a large extent due to the vague and indefinite manner in which it has been formulated, and discussed. I completely agree that precision may (and often does) go hand in hand with sterility (which is one of the reasons why I cannot embrace a great deal of contemporary philosphy of science). However, it cannot be allowed that vagueness is made the handmaid of dogmatism. That is, it cannot be allowed that a theory is made vague in such a manner that it cannot any more be reached by criticism.

19. Cf. section 4 and footnote 116.

20. Cf. the reference in footnote 15.

21. Cf. the quotation from Rosenfeld in text to footnote 13.

22. *Die Physik und das Geheimnis des organischen Lebens,* Braunschweig, 1943, p. 114.

23. "Discussions with Einstein," in *Albert Einstein, Philosopher-Scientist,* Evanston, 1948, p. 229.

24. *Dialectica,* Vol. 2 (1948), p. 309 (editorial of a special issue on the interpretation of the quantum theory).

25. *Mathematical Foundations of Quantum Mechanics,* Princeton, 1955, p. 326.

26. "The Development of the Interpretation of the Quantum Theory," *op. cit.,* p. 19.

27. *Op. cit.,* p. 18.

28. W. Pauli, "Remarques sur le problème des paramètres cachés dans la mécanique quantique et sur la théorie de l'onde pilote," in *Louis de Broglie,* etc., p. 40.

29. Pauli, *op. cit.,* p. 41.

30. Cf. the above quotation from Jordan. The irrelevance of all these replies to Bohm's investigations has been stated very clearly by J. Agassi *[British Journal for the Philosophy of Science,* Vol. IX (1958), p. 63]: "That Bohm's theory is *factually* false, or at least, very much *ad hoc* is, of course, entirely irrelevant, since the question is whether von Neumann's argument consists of a proof that a theory like Bohm's must be *logically* false."

    That the idea of complementarity asserts the *logical* impossibility of a model like Bohm's has been asserted by P. Jordan. According to him *[Anschauliche Quantentheorie* Leipzig, 1936, p. 116; my italics*]* a model like Bohm's which works with well-defined trajectories "would be inconsistent, not only with the (changeable) notions of classical physics, *it would even be inconsistent with the laws of logic."* Similar sentiments have been expressed, in a less definite form, by Bohr and Heisenberg. Cf. the latter's *Physics and Philosophy,* New York, 1958, p. 132 as well as *Niels Bohr and the Development of Physics,* p. 18.

31. There are also other, and more technical objections against Bohm's model. Thus Pauli has pointed out in 1927 that the theory of the pilot wave requires an electron in an s-state to be at rest whereas electrons are always found in a well-defined state of motion. This objection which has been repeated, more recently, by Einstein *[cf.* his paper in *Scientific Papers Presented to Max Born,* Edinbourgh, 1953*]* can however be answered by the Bohm-model *[cf.* Bohm's comments in the same volume*]*.

32. An excellent example is the discussion of the quantum theory in Chs. VIII and IX of M. Bunge's *Metascientific Queries,* Springfield, 1959. *[Cf.* my review of that book in *Phil. Rev.,* Vol. LXX (1961)*]*. Similar remarks apply to some of Popper's criticisms of the quantum theory. For details cf. fn. 123.

33. L. Rosenfeld in *Observation and Interpretation,* London, 1957, p. 45.

34. I am here referring to what is known as Planck's *First Theory* in which both absorption and emission were regarded as discontinuous processes [Verh. d. phys. *Gesellschaft,* Vol. II (1900), p. 237], and which also implies discontinuities in space [Cf. Whittaker, *History of the Theories of Aether and Electricity,* Vol. II, Edinbourgh, 1953, p. 103].

35. *Journal de Physique,* V. II (1912), p. 1.

36. N. Bohr, *Atomic Theory and the Description of Nature,* Cambridge, 1932, p. 65.

37. I shall not contend that this is the only possible way of getting around the difficulty, but it is a very reasonable physical hypothesis which has not yet been refuted by any of the arguments aimed against it.

38. By the expression "dynamical state" we refer to "quantities which are characteristic of the motion" of the system concerned (such as the positions and the momenta of its components) rather than those quantities which, like mass and charge, serve as a characteristic of what kind of system it is. For this explanation cf. Landau-Lifshitz *Quantum Mechanics,* London, 1958, p. 2 as well as N. Bohr, *Atomic Physics and Human Knowledge,* p. 90; cf. also H. A. Kramers, *Quantum Mechanics,* New York, 1957, p. 62.

39. It is to be admitted, however, that most derivations of the uncertainties, and especially those based upon Heisenberg's famous thought-experiments *do* make use of philosophical theories of meaning. Usually these arguments (and other arguments which proceed from the commutation relations of the elementary theory) only establish that inside a certain interval *measurements cannot be carried out,* or that the products of the mean deviations of certain magnitudes *cannot be ascertained* below Planck's constant h. The transition from this stage of the argument to the assertion that it would be *meaningless* to ascribe definite values to the magnitudes in this interval is then achieved on the basis of the principle that what cannot be ascertained by measurement cannot be meaningfully asserted to exist. This premature use of untenable philosophical theories of meaning has led to a very curious situation. It has led to a situation where physical principles, such as the principle of the indefiniteness of state descriptions are attacked, *and defended* for the wrong reasons. The principle "that it is impossible, in the description of the state of a mechanical system, to attach definite values to both of two canonically conjugate variables" (N. Bohr in *Phys. Rev.,* Vol. 48 (1935), p. 696) has been *attacked* because it was believed to be the result of positivistic considerations. And it has also been *defended* by such considerations [cf. M. Schlick, *Naturwissenschaften,* Vol. 19 (1931), pp. 159ff as well as Heisenberg, *The Physical Principles of the Quantum Theory,* University of Chicago Press, 1930, esp. p. 15. In the case of Heisenberg the result obtained is not even the *universal* indefi-

niteness of state descriptions as it is admitted that "the uncertainty relation does not refer to the past"—p. 20. It is also interesting to note the difference between the terminology of the German and the English version. In the German version assertions concerning the situation inside the domain of indefiniteness are called "inhaltsleer" (cf. p. 11 of the German edition, *Die Physikalischen Prinzipien der Quantenmechanik,* Leipzig, 1930)—"devoid of content," whereas the English version used the term "meaningless."] The positivistic defense of the principle seems to have been adopted even by some physicists, and this from the very beginning. And yet this principle can—and, so we should add, *must*—be interpreted as a physical hypothesis according to which a relaxation is necessary in the classical description which, being an "idealization" [Bohr, *Atomic Description,* etc., p. 5; cf. also p. 63], goes beyond the evidence available at the time when it was first introduced and has now been found in need of modification. It seems that this was also Bohr's own point of view. Despite occasional lapses into positivistic jargon and argumentation, he has always claimed to be a realist and he has therefore been somewhat critical of Heisenberg's positivism [Bohm and Groenewold, private communication]. The actual historical development is still far from clear however and this because of the fact that little has been published of the early discussions which later on led to the development of the Copenhagen point of view. Here is a challenging task for contemporary historians of science. Get the information, by letter, on tape, in discussions, before the main actors of this fascinating intellectual drama have died!

40. *Atomic Theory,* etc., p. 16.

41. Cf. E. Heitler, *Quantum Theory of Radiation,* Oxford, 1957, p. 65; D. Bohm, *Quantum Theory,* Princeton, 1951, pp. 97f.

42. Cf. for example A Landé, "The Logic of Quanta," *British Journal for the Philosophy of Science,* Vol. VI (1956), p. 300 as well as "From Duality to Unity in Quantum Mechanics," *Current Issues in the Philosophy of Science,* New York, 1961, pp. 350ff.

43. With respect to light this was shown by Janossi. Cf. the booklet edited by the *Hungarian Academy of Sciences,* 1957, where also previous experiments are reported, as well as Janossi, *Acta Physica Hungarica,* Vol. IV (1955) and *Nuovo Cimento,* Vol. VI (1957).

44. The idea of action at a distance has been discussed, and regarded as a possible explanation by Hans Reichenbach. Cf. his *Philosophic Foundations of Quantum Mechanics,* Berkeley and Los Angeles, 1945, sec. 7. Action at a distance is not the solution which Reichenbach himself adopts. For an evaluation of Reichenbach's analysis and of his own solution (three-valued logic) cf. my paper "Reichenbach's Interpretation of the Quantum Theory," *Philosophical*

Studies, Vol. IX (1958), pp. 47ff.

45. *Observation and Interpretation,* ed Körner, London, 1957, pp. 65ff. Landé's suggestions are in many respects similar to those of Popper. I should like to point out that the arguments in the text can be repeated in a slightly different fashion even if the minimum should not be an absolute minimum. (An attempt to invalidate the argument by reference to the fact that the minima may not be absolute is due to Professor A. Landé.)

46. A. Landé, *Quantum Theory, A Study of Continuity and Symmetry,* New Haven, 1955.

47. Professor K. R. Popper, private communication.

48. I am referring here to the experiments of Bothe and Geiger, *Zs. Physik,* Vol. 35 (1926) pp. 639ff as well as to the results of Compton and Simon, *Phys. Rev.,* Vol. 25 (1925) pp. 306ff.

49. For this point cf. p. 89 of my "Complementarity," *Proceedings of The Aristotelian Society,* Suppl. Vol. XXXII (1958). If I am correct in this, then all those philosophers who try to solve the quantum riddle by trying to provide an alternative interpretation of the *current theory* which leaves all the laws of this theory unchanged are wasting their time. Those who are not satisfied with the Copenhagen point of view must realize that only a new theory will be capable of satisfying their demands. Of course, they may try in advance to consider the effects which the success of such a new theory might have upon the interpretation of the current theory. However, an essential part of any such interpretation will have to be the admission that the current theory and the empirical laws upon which it is based *are not entirely correct.*

It is interesting to note the similarity between the present situation in the quantum theory and the problems which confronted the followers of Copernicus. As is well known, the issue was then not the predictive correctness of the Copernican theory (which was admitted by the opponents) but the extent to which the Copernican hypothesis could be regarded to mirror the actual structure of the universe. That is the church did not contest the *predictive value* of the Copernican hypothesis. What it objected to was the realistic interpretation of this hypothesis, i.e., the assumption that the hypothesis could be regarded as a description of the world. Now it is most important to realize that this move, on the part of the church, was neither wholly due to a philosophical conservatism, nor was it wholly due to the fear that a realistic interpretation of Copernicus' hypothesis might do considerable damage to theological dogma. There were weighty *physical* arguments against the assumption of a real motion of the earth. These physical arguments were an immediate consequence of the then popular Aristotelian physics. In short the situation was as follows: the conjunction of Aristotelian physics and a realistically interpreted Copernican theory was inconsistent with some widely known empirical results. Aristotelian physics was highly confirmed by experiment. On the other hand the Copernican theory led to the correct celestial predictions and had therefore to be regarded as empirically adequate. Was it not natural, in these circumstances, to assume that no realistic importance should be ascribed to Copernicus and that the merit of this theory consisted merely in having found a coordinate system in which the problem of the planets assumed an especially simple form? This move could not be countered by a purely philosophical criticism and the demand that every theory be interpreted in a realistic fashion. A *philosophical* criticism of the instrumentalistic interpretation of the Copernican theory quite obviously could not remove the inconsistency between a Copernican universe and the Aristotelian dynamics. *Nothing less than a new theory of motion would do,* a new theory of motion, moreover, which would not be as strictly empirical and commonsensical as the Aristotelian theory and which could therefore count on strong opposition. This was clearly realized by Galileo. "Against the physical principles of conventional cosmology, which were always brought out against him, he needed an equally solid set of principles—indeed, more solid—because he did not appeal to ordinary experience and common sense as his opponents did." [G. di Santillana, *The Crime of Galileo,* Chicago, 1955, p. 31; cf. also the pages following the quotation as well as my article on the philosophy of nature in *Fischer Lexikon, Band Philosophie,* Frankfurt/Main, 1958.] It seems to me that this feature of the situation has not always been realized by philosophers (as an example we may take K. R. Popper's "Three Views Concerning Human Knowledge"; *Contemporary British Philosophy,* Vol. III (1956), pp. 2ff). Nor has it been realized that the present situation in the quantum theory is very similar. "The view of physical science founded by Cardinal Bellarmino and Bishop Berkeley has won the battle without a further shot being fired" writes Popper (*loc. cit.,* p. 8). This is simply not true. First of all there is a tremendous difference between the instrumentalism of Bellarmino and the instrumentalism of Berkeley. The instrumentalism of Bellarmino *could* have been supported by physical arguments drawn from contemporary physical theory. The instrumentalism of Berkeley could not have been so supported and was of a purely philosophical nature. Secondly the arguments in the text above should have shown that there exist weighty *physical* reasons why at the present moment a realistic interpretation of the wave mechanics does not seem to be feasible (see also the arguments in the next section). A philosophical crusade for realism alone will not be able to eliminate these arguments. At best, it can ignore them. What is needed is a new theory. Nothing less will do.

I have to admit, however, in view of a criticism of the above passage by J. W. N. Watkins, that philosophical arguments for realism, though not sufficient, are therefore not unnecessary. It has been shown that given the laws of wave mechanics, it is impossible to construct a realistic interpretation of this very same theory. That is, it has been shown that the usual philosophical arguments in favor of a realistic interpretation of theoretical terms do not work in the case of wave mechanics (for such arguments cf. my paper "Das Problem der Existenz Theoretischer Entitäten" in *Probleme der Erkenntnis Theorie, Festschrift für Viktor Kraft,* Vienna, 1960). However, there still remains the fact that theories which *do* admit of a realistic interpretation are definitely preferable to theories which do not. It was this belief which has inspired Einstein, Schrödinger, Bohm, Vigier and others to look for a modification of the present theory that makes realism again possible. The main aim of the present article is to show that there are no valid reasons to assume that this valiant attempt is bound to be unsuccessful. For some reasons why realistic theories are preferable to instrumentalistic ones, cf. section 4 of my paper "Professor Bohm's Philosophy of Nature," *British Journal for the Philosophy of Science,* Vol. X (1960), pp. 326ff.

50. Cf. e.g., Max Born, *Atomic Physics,* London, 1957, p. 76.

51. For the mathematics cf. Heisenberg, *The Physical Principles of the Quantum Theory,* Chapter II, section 1, or L. Schiff, *Quantum Mechanics,* New York, 1955, pp. 54-56. For a more careful discussion cf. E. L. Hill, *Lecture Notes on Quantum Mechanics 1958-1959,* University of Minnesota, sections 4.9 and 4.10.

52. There is a difference in the constants, but otherwise the formula is the same.

53. In his essay *Zur Metatheorie der Quantenmechanik,* Helsinki, 1950 E. Kaila has asserted that this manner of derivation exhibits a limitation in the validity of the uncertainty relations. Every case of motion is regarded as a case of diffraction and therefore assumes that certain boundary conditions are first satisfied. According to Kaila this shows that the uncertainties are a result of the fact that boundary conditions have been imposed. A particle whose motion is not restricted by any boundaries may therefore possess a well-defined position and a well-defined momentum. This assumption can of course be made. But it is not very much more reasonable than the assumption that a glass-pane alone in the universe is as hard as iron but ceases to be that hard immediately after the creation of the first stone.

54. *Zs. Physik,* Vol. 43 (1927) as well as Chapter II of the *Physical Principles of the Quantum Theory.*

55. I.e., it can lead to a *physical* interpretation of (1) rather than to a situation where physical principles and a rather doubtful epistemology are superimposed upon each other. For this cf. also fn. (39).

The fact that the customary interpretation of the uncertainty relations cannot be derived from wave mechanics in connection with Born's rules alone and that some further assumptions must be added, this has been felt by many thinkers. *[*An example is K. R. Popper, *Logic of Scientific Discovery,* New York, 1959, Ch. IX.*]* However, they were mistaken when assuming that the missing link would necessarily have to be a positivistic theory of knowledge. It is quite correct that "Heisenberg's rejection of the concept of path, and his talk of 'non-observable magnitudes' clearly show the influence of philosophical and especially of positivistic ideas" (Popper, *op. cit.,* p. 232). But this is not the only possible way to arrive at the assumption of the indefiniteness of state descriptions, nor is it the best one. And an attack upon Heisenberg's procedure will therefore at most reveal *his* arguments as unsatisfactory. It does not amount to a refutation of indefiniteness. Nor does it remove the difficulties which led to the assumption of indefiniteness in the first place.

56. Cf. e.g., W. Heitler in *Albert Einstein, Philosopher-Scientist,* ed. Schillpp, Evanston, 1949, pp. 181-198.

57. Thus Heisenberg writes in *The Physicist's Conception of Nature,* London, 1958, p. 25: ". . . the new mathematical formulae no longer describe nature itself, but *our knowledge* of nature." The similar position of Eddington, Jeans and of others is too well known to be repeated here. All this sounds, of course, very pleasant in the ears of obscurantists as is confirmed by numerous so called "philosophical" articles: In physics as in real life the principle is valid that when the cat's away, the mice will play.

58. For an analysis of the more general confusions in the philosophy of quantum mechanics, cf. B. Fogarasi, *Kritik des Physikalischen Idealismus,* Budapest, 1953. For a comparative evaluation of the various interpretations of (1) (and there exists quite a lot of them!) cf. M. Bunge, *Metascientific Queries,* Springfield, Illinois, 1959, Ch. IX/4 as well as the literature quoted therein. A most valuable and detailed attempt to separate physical and philosophical assumptions in the interpretation of the quantum theory has been made by Prof. A. Grünbaum in his paper "Complementarity in Quantum Physics and its Philosophical Generalizations," *The Journal of Philosophy,* Vol. LIV (1957), pp. 713-727.

59. For this cf. also the introduction.

60. In order to get an idea about the amount of these facts the reader should consult an early edition (for example the third edition) of Vol. I of Sommerfeld's *Atombau und Spektrallinien.* Cf. also Geiger-Scheel, *Handbuch der Physik,* first edition, Vols. 4 (1929), 20 (1928), 21 (1929), 23 (1926), as well as Wien-Harms, *Handbuch de Physik,* Vols. 21 (1927), 22 (1929).

61. Some physicists felt, with some justification, that the theory was close to being *ad hoc*. ". . . it was so direct a transcription of the Balmer formulae that there could be little credit in such a performance as it stood." B. Hoffmann, *The Strange Story of the Quantum,* Dover, 1959, p. 58. The reader should not stop, however, after this quotation but he should go on reading and learn in this manner to what extent the theory was more than just a transcription of Balmer's formulae.

62. For a very clear presentation of this idea behind the correspondence principle cf. G. Ludwig, *Die Grundlagen der Quantenmechanik,* Berlin, 1954, Ch. I. As Aage Petersen has pointed out to me, Bohr's ideas may be compared with Hankel's principle of the permanence of rules of calculation in new domains [For this principle cf. Chapter 4 of F. Waismann's *Einfuehrung in das Mathematische Denken,* Vienna, 1947]. According to Hankel's principle the transition from a domain of mathematical entities to a more embracing domain should be carried out in such a manner that as many rules of calculation as possible are taken over from the old domain to the new one. For example, the transition from natural numbers to rational numbers should be carried out in such a manner as to leave unchanged as many rules of calculation as possible. In the case of mathematics, this principle has very fruitful applications. Its application to microphysics is suggested by the fact that some important classical laws remain *strictly valid* in the quantum domain. A *complete* replacement of the classical formalism seems therefore to be unnecessary. All that is needed is a modification of that formalism which retains the laws that have found to be valid and makes room for those new laws which express the specific behavior of the quantum mechanical entities. According to Bohr the modification must be based upon a more "liberal attitude towards" the classical concepts (*Atomic Description,* etc., p. 3). We must realize that these concepts are *"idealizations"* (p. 5; italics in the original), or "abstractions" (p. 63) whose suitability for description or explanation depends upon the relative smallness of the quantum of action and which must therefore be "handled with caution" (p. 66) in new experimental domains. "Analysis of the elementary concepts" (66) has to reveal their limitations in these new fields (4, 5, 8, 13, 15, 53, 108) and new rules for their use have to be devised "in order to evade the quantum of action" (18). These rules must satisfy the following demands: (a) they must allow for the description of any conceivable experiment in classical terms— for it is in classical terms that results of measurement and experimentation are expressed; (b) they must "provide room for new laws" ("Can Quantum Mechanical Description of Physical Reality Be Considered Complete?" *Phys. Rev.,* Vol. 48 (1935), p. 701; *Atomic Theory,* etc. pp. 3, 8, 19, 53), and especially for the quantum of action (18); (c) they must always lead to correct predic-

tions. (a) is needed if we want to retain the idea, to be discussed later on in section 7, that experience must be described in classical terms; (b) is needed if we want to avoid any clash with the quantum of action; (c) is needed if this set of rules is to be as powerful as a physical theory in the usual sense. Any set of rules satisfying (a), (b), and (c) is called by Bohr a "natural generalization of the classical mode of description" (4, 56, 70, 92, 110; "Causality and Complementarity" in *Dialectica* 7/8 (1948), p. 316; "Discussions with Einstein" in *Albert Einstein, Philosopher-Scientist*, pp. 210, 239), or a "reinterpretation . . . of the classical electron theory" (*Atomic Theory*, etc., p. 14). "The aim of regarding the quantum theory as a rational generalization of the classical theories" writes Bohr (*Atomic Theory*, etc., pp. 70; 37; 110) "has led to the formulation of the . . . correspondence principle." The correspondence principle is the tool by means of which the generalizations may be, and have been obtained.

Now it is very important to realize that a "rational generalization" in the sense just explained does not admit of a realistic interpretation of any one of its terms. The classical terms cannot be interpreted in a realistic manner as their application is restricted to a description of experimental results. The remaining terms cannot be interpreted realistically either as they have been introduced for the explicit purpose of enabling the physicist to handle the classical terms properly. The instrumentalism of the quantum theory is therefore *not a philosophical manoeuvre that has been willfully superimposed upon a theory which would have looked much better when interpreted in a realistic fashion. It is a demand for theory construction that was imposed from the very beginning and in accordance with which, part of the quantum theory was actually obtained.* Now at this point the historical situation becomes complicated for the following reason: the *full* quantum theory (and by this we mean the full elementary theory) was created by Schrödinger who was a realist and who hoped to have found a theory that was more than a "rational generalization of classical mechanics" in the sense just explained. That is, the full quantum theory we owe historically to a metaphysics that was diametrically opposed to the philosophical point of view of Niels Bohr and his disciples. This is quite an important historical fact as the adherents of the Copenhagen picture very often criticize the metaphysics of Bohm and Vigier by pointing out that no *physical theory* has as yet been developed on that basis. [For such a criticism cf. N. R. Hanson, "Five Cautions for the Copenhagen Critics," *Philosophy of Science*, Vol. XXVI (1959), pp. 325-337, esp. pp. 334-337.] They forget that the Copenhagen way of thinking *has not produced a theory either*. What it *has* produced is the proper interpretation of Schrödinger's wave mechanics *after* this theory had been invented. For it turned out that Schrödinger's wave mechanics was just that complete rational generalization of the classical theory that Bohr, Heisenberg and their collaborators had been looking for and parts of which they had already succeeded in developing.

63. E. C. Kemble, *The Fundamental Principles of Quantum Mechanics,* New York, 1937, p. 55.

64. ". . . the paradoxical aspect of the quantum theory" writes Niels Bohr ("Discussions with Einstein," quoted from *Atomic Physics and Human Knowledge,* p. 37) "were in no way ameliorated, but even emphasized, by the apparent contradiction between the exigencies of the general superposition principle of the wave description and the feature of individuality in the elementary atomic processes."

65. Cf. *Scientific Autobiography and Other Papers,* New York, 1949, pp. 135f. Similar sentiments have been expressed, much later, by F. C. S. Northrop (*Logic of the Sciences and Humanities,* New Haven, 1948, p. 27) and by E. Nagel ("The Causal Character of Modern Physical Theory," *Readings in the Philosophy of Science,* ed. Feigl-Brodbeck, New York, 1953, pp. 419-437).

66. Planck is, of course, aware of this fact, and he therefore distinguishes between the "world picture" of physics on the one hand, and "the sensory world" on the other, and he ascribes to the former a merely symbolic content (*op. cit.,* p. 129). However, this cannot be reconciled with the claim that "determinism is . . . strictly valid in the world picture of quantum mechanics" (136) as it is clear that the causal relation can hold between real events only.

67. von Neumann, *Mathematical Foundations of Quantum Mechanics,* Princeton, 1955, VI/2.

68. For an excellent and intuitive presentation of this fact cf. E. Schrödinger, "Die gegenwaertige Lage in der Quantenmechanik," *Naturwissenschaften,* Vol. 23 (1935).

69. For details cf. section 11.

70. The reason is as follows: the development, according to the Schrödinger equation, of the combined state of the system plus the measuring apparatus results in a state that contains the possible outcomes of measurement as interfering parts. If we now assume that states of quantum mechanical systems exist in reality and that therefore any change of state corresponds to a real change, then we shall have to admit that a look at a macroscopic object leads to an immediate elimination of interference terms at distant places.

71. A. Einstein, "Physics and Reality," reprinted in *Ideas and Opinions,* London, 1954, p. 35. The point of view expressed by Einstein and Popper (see the next footnote) is held also by J. Slater (*J. Frankl. Inst.,* Vol. 207 (1929), p. 449; cf. also Van Vleck on pp. 475ff of the same volume), and by E. C. Kemble (*op. cit.*) who says (p. 55) that "we are . . . led to conceive of quantum mechan-

ics as primarily a variety of statistical mechanics similar to the classical statistical mechanics of Gibbs." However, Kemble is aware of the fact, to be explained later on in the present paper, that the elements of the collectives are no longer systems which are existing in a well-defined classical state (note on page 55). It ought to be pointed out that despite appearances the point of view of Blochinzew is not identical with that of Einstein either. It will be discussed later in the present paper.

72. *Logic of Scientific Discovery,* New York, 1959, p. 227. The book is a translation of the *Logik der Forschung* of 1935.

73. *Op. cit.,* p. 224.

74. von Neumann, *op. cit.,* p. 300.

75. Popper, *op. cit.,* pp. 228f.

76. Cf. our argument in the last section and footnote 55. Popper quite correctly observes that the Copenhagen Interpretation goes beyond the assertion of the validity of Born's rules. He is also correct when pointing out that physicists like Heisenberg attempted to base their stronger assertion upon a positivistic theory of meaning that was far from satisfactory. However, he seems to have overlooked the fact that the stronger interpretation of the uncertainty relations, stronger, that is, than the interpretation he would have been prepared to accept, can be defended by purely physical arguments.

77. von Neumann, *op. cit.,* IV/2.

78. Cf. also my paper "Eine Bemerkung zum Neumannschen Beweis," *Zeitschrift fuer Physik,* Vol. 145 (1956), pp. 421-423, where I used suggestions first made by Popper and Agassi.

79. It ought to be pointed out that our discussion so far was based upon the general part of wave mechanics only, i.e., upon those laws which describe the properties of the space of the ψ-functions. It is this general theory (which alone is presupposed in Born's interpretation) with which we were concerned when discussing the views of Popper and von Neumann. However, if we add the dynamical laws (the Schrödinger equation; the conservation laws) to the general theory, then we obtain very strong arguments for the necessity of an interpretation as it was outlined in section 2. This formal feature of the theory mirrors the fact to which we have repeatedly pointed that the indefiniteness of state descriptions is necessary in order to account for the individual conservation of energy and momentum. Von Neumann's arguments are not completely useless, though. They may be regarded as proof to the effect that the general theory is *consistent* with Bohr's interpretation (this has been pointed out to me by H. J. Groenewold).

80. "Can quantum mechanical description of Physical Reality be Considered Complete?", *Phys. Review,* Vol. 47 (1935), pp. 777ff. In the next section the

argument will be presented in a generalized form.

81. von Neumann, *op. cit.*, pp. 429ff.

82. For proof cf. Schrödinger, *Proc. Camb. Soc.*, Vol. 31 (1935), pp. 555ff; Vol. 32 (1936), pp. 446ff as well as H. J. Groenewold, *Physica*, Vol. 12 (1948).

83. This condition suggests choosing the α, β, γ, δ in such a manner that they all commute both with the (q) and with the (r). An example which possesses this property has been described by D. Bohm in his *Quantum Theory*, Princeton, 1951, Ch. 22. If such a choice is not made then it is always possible to assail the argument with reasons that have to do only with the specific form in which it is presented. For such an unintentionally irrelevant attack cf. de Broglie, *Une Tentative d'Interprétation Causale et non Linéaire de la Mécanique Ondulatoire*, Paris, 1956, pp. 76ff. de Broglie discusses Bohr's example *[Phys. Rev.*, Vol. 48 (1935), pp. 696ff*]* of a pair of particles with known $q_1 - q_2$ and $p_1 + p_2$ respectively. Now the state just described (which satisfies *[i]* and *[ii]* above, q_1 and p_1 being the relevant variables) is realized only as long as the pair dwells near the two-slit-screen whose slit-distance defines $q_1 - q_2$. However, in this case *[iii]* will be violated. The argument is of course irrelevant as Einstein's point is independent of the way in which the state satisfying *[i]* and *[ii]* has been created. It can also be shown *[cf.* Schrödinger, "Die gegenwaertige Lage in der Quantenmechanik," *Naturwissenschaften*, 1935*]* that t seconds after the pair has left the slit Einstein's argument can be raised with respect to the variables p_1 and $q_1 - (P_1/m)t$. Still, it is an advantage to possess an example that cannot be criticized for the reasons just mentioned. Also Bohm's example is not beset by the difficulties of the continuous case (for these difficulties cf. Bohm and Aharonov, *Phys. Rev.*, Vol. 108 (1957), pp. 1070ff, Appendix).

84. The paradoxical aspect arises as soon as the argument is combined with the completeness assumption. In this case we obtain the result that changes of state may occur which are (1) well predictable (although their exact outcome is not predictable); and which (2) occur in places which are very far from the reach of physical forces. It is this feature of the argument that among other things has led to the assumption of a sub-quantum mechanical level involving laws different from the laws of the quantum theory which allow for the occurrence of coordinated fluctuations. Such an assumption would of course lead to predictions that in some respect are different from the predictions of the present theory. For example, it would imply a disturbance of the correlations if the measuring apparatus interacting with the first system is turned around very rapidly. Such a difference of predicted results is far from undesirable, however. It is a guide to new experiments which then will be able to decide as to which point of view should be adopted in the end. Cf. D. Bohm, *Causality*

and Chance in Modern Physics, Routlege and Kegan Paul, London, Chs. III, IV as well as *Observation and Interpretation,* ed. Körner, London, 1957, pp. 33-40, 86-87. For a more general discussion concerning the relation of theories cf. my essay "Explanation, Reduction, and Empiricism" in the *Minnesota Studies for the Philosophy of Science,* Vol. III, Minneapolis, 1962.

85. Cf. footnote 71 as well as *Albert Einstein, Philosopher-Scientist,* ed. Schillpp, Evanston, Illinois, 1948, pp. 666ff.

86. *Proc. Acad. UdSSR,* Vol. 84 (1952), p. 253.

87. *Proc. Cambr. Phil. Soc.,* Vol. 46 pt. 4 (1951), p. 620.

88. *Phys. Rev.,* Vol. 49 (1936), pp. 397ff; cf. also Groenewold *loc. cit.* M.H.L. Pryce, too, has used the argument in private discussions.

89. Thus in Bohm's example of footnote 83 angular momentum will not be conserved.

90. *Phys. Rev.,* Vol. 47 (1935), p. 777.

91. For a more detailed account of the problems of confirmation that arise in this case and for a criticism of the (implied) attitude of the orthodox cf. section 7 of my paper referred to in fn. 84.

92. Cf. Bohm-Aharonov, *loc. cit.,* p. 1071 as well as *Observation and Interpretation,* pp. 86ff.

93. Einstein, "Physics and Reality," *loc. cit.,* p. 317.

94. *Phys. Rev.,* Vol. 77 (1950), pp. 136ff. That the case is equivalent to the one discussed by EPR is shown in Heitler, *Quantum Theory of Radiation,* p. 269. Cf. also the analysis by Bohm-Aharonov, *loc. cit.*

95. For proof of equivalence with the case of EPR cf. the last footnote.

96. A similar position is held by D. R. Inglis, *Revs. of Modern Physics,* Vol. 33 (1961), pp. 1-7, especially the last section.

97. *Sowjetwissenschaft,* Naturwissenschaftliche Reihe, Vol. VI (1954), pp. 545ff. *Grundlagen der Quantenmechanik,* Berlin, 1953, pp. 497-505.

98. *Sowjetwissenschaft,* etc., p. 564.

99. *Grundlagen,* p. 50.

100. This is admitted, implicitly, by D. R. Inglis, *loc. cit.*

101. The first to use this expression seems to have been H. J. Groenewold, *loc. cit.*

102. I would like to repeat that in this section and in the following sections it will be assumed that the elementary theory is essentially correct. Interpretations which dispute the absolute correctness of the elementary theory will be discussed later.

103. Cf. Popper, *op. cit.,* sec. 12.

104. Cf. the reference in footnote 15.

105. This is Heisenberg's attitude. Cf. his *Physical Principles,* etc., p. 15.

106. I am here referring to discussions I had with Professor Popper. The responsibility for the presentation is, however, entirely mine.

107. In conversation, Landé has expressed the hope that further development of the point of view discussed here will lead to a satisfactory account of the case of the penetration of a potential barrier. This is quite possible. However what I am concerned with here is to show the strength of the Copenhagen Interpretation to those who are of the opinion that the transition to a different interpretation is more or less a matter of philosophical taste rather than of physical inquiry.

108. For a numerical evaluation cf. Blochinzev, *Grundlagen*, p. 505. Cf. also Heisenberg, op. cit., pp. 30ff.

109. It ought to be mentioned that Bohm *[loc. cit.,* in footnote 15*]* has shown how superstates which obey conditions (9) can be made compatible with the dynamical laws. However the unsatisfactory feature remains that these superstates violate the principle of independent testability and that their introduction must therefore be regarded as a purely verbal maneuver. Yet it is important to repeat that von Neumann (*op. cit.,* p. 326) thought that his "proof" would be strong enough to exclude even such verbal manoeuvres.

110. Einstein, too, regards Bohr's attempt as coming "nearest to doing justice to the problem." *Albert Einstein, Philosopher-Scientist,* p. 681.

111. *Phys. Rev.,* Vol. 48 (1936), pp. 696ff. Cf. also D. R. Inglis, *loc. cit.*

112. *Loc. cit.*

113. *Loc. cit.,* p. 704.

114. Private communication.

115. *Op. cit.,* pp. 445ff.

116. It ought to be pointed out, however, that there is one assumption in the earlier speculations about the nature of microscopic objects which has been definitely refuted by EPR. It is the assumption that "the most important difference between quantum theory and the classical theories consists in the fact that in the case of an observation we must carefully consider the disturbance, due to experiment, of the system investigated." (Heisenberg, *Naturwissenschaften* (1929), p. 495; cf. also Bohr, *Atomic Theory,* etc., pp. 5, 11, 15, 54, 68, 93, 115; also *Dialectica* 7/8 (1948), p. 315). And it is the corresponding assumption that the indeterminancy of the state of quantum mechanical systems is essentially due to *this* disturbance (cf. Bohm-Aharonov, *Phys. Rev.,* Vol. 108 (1957), pp. 1070ff as well as K. R. Popper, *op. cit.,* pp. 445ff). What is shown by EPR is that physical operations, such as measurements, may lead to sudden changes in the state of systems which are *in no physical connection whatever* with the domain in which the measurement is being performed. Unfortunately the attitude of the adherents of the Copenhagen point of view with respect to this

argument had very often been that the reply which was given by Bohr (and which cost him, as is reported, some headaches) was already implicit in the earlier ideas which would mean that these ideas were much more vague than one would at first have been inclined to believe.

117. For Bohm cf. footnote 84. According to Schrödinger the paradox is an indication of the fact that the elementary quantum theory is a non-relativistic theory. Cf. his essay "Die gegenwaertige Lage in der Quantentheorie," *Naturwissenschaften,* 1935, especially the last section.

118. Cf. footnote 116.

119. This is sometimes obscured by the fact that Bohr's account of measurement is not the only one. Very often physicists rely on a simplified version of von Neumann's theory where the relation between the measuring instrument and the system under investigation is indeed treated as an interaction (this theory will be discussed later in the present paper, especially in sections 10 and 11), or else they use a theory of measurement similar to the one explained by Bohm (*Quantum Theory,* Princeton, 1951, Ch. XXII) which is also a theory of interaction. Heisenberg himself had treated measurements as interactions from the very beginning and he had also pointed to the fact, which is proved in von Neumann's theory, that the "cut" ("Schnitt") between the object and the measuring device can be shifted in an arbitrary manner. Very often such more formal accounts have been regarded as elaborations of Bohr's own point of view. This is not the case. Bohr's theory of measurement and von Neumann's theory (or any other theory that treats measurement as an interaction) are *two entirely different theories.* As will be shown later von Neumann's theory encounters difficulties which do not appear in Bohr's account. Bohr himself does not agree with von Neumann's account (private communication, Ascov 1949). A *formal* theory which is very close to Bohr's own point of view has been developed by Groenewold. Cf. his essay in *Observation and Interpretation,* pp. 196-203.

120. Cf. fn. 84 as well as section 4 of my paper "Complementarity," *Proc. Arist. Soc.,* Suppl. Vol. XXXII (1958).

121. This assertion has been made by Hilary Putnam.

122. For the specific difficulties of the quantum mechanical case, cf. section 11 of the present paper.

123. This means, of course, that formula (1) can be derived in two entirely different manners. The first derivation is of a fairly qualitative character. It makes use of the considerations which we put forth in section 2 and introduces the quantum of action with the help of de Broglie's formula $p = h/\lambda$. This derivation makes it very clear to what extent the existence of duality and the quantum of action forces us to restrict the application of such classical terms as

position, momentum, time, energy, and so on, and it thereby transfers some intuitive content to formula (1). The second derivation which is completely formal in character makes use of the commutation relations of the elementary theory (cf. for example H. Weyl, *Gruppentheorie und Quantermechanik,* Berlin, 1931, pp. 68 and 345; English translation pp. 77 and 393ff). Now it is very important to realize that the result of the first and intuitive derivation *may be regarded as a test of the adequacy of the wave mechanics* and indeed of any future quantum theory. For assume that the wave mechanics would give an uncertainty that is much smaller than the one derived with the help of duality (which is a highly confirmed empirical fact), de Broglie's relation (which is also a highly confirmed empirical fact) and Bohr's assumption of the indefiniteness of state descriptions (which is the only reasonable hypothesis that allows for the incorporation of the quantum postulate and the conservation laws). This would amount *to a refutation of wave mechanics,* i.e., it would amount to the proof that the wave mechanics is not capable of giving an adequate account of duality, the quantum postulate, and the conservation laws. On the other hand, the agreement between the qualitative result and the quantitative result now transfers an intuitive content to the formalism.

The fact that formula (1) can be derived in two entirely different manners and that the quantum theory combines both derivations has been realized by various thinkers. Thus Popper (*op. cit.,* p. 224) points out "that Heisenberg's formulae . . . result as logical conclusions from the theory; but the *interpretation* of these formulae as rules limiting attainable precision of measurement, in Heisenberg's sense, does not follow from the theory." And Kaila (*Zur Metatheorie der Quantenmechanik,* Helsinki 1950) has made the existence of various interpretations of (1) the basis of an attack against the quantum theory. Now as against Popper it must be pointed out that the interpretation in question *does* follow from the theory provided the theory has been interpreted in accordance with the intentions of Bohr and Heisenberg. For in this case the interpretation uses, in addition to Born's rules, also the hypothesis of the indefiniteness of state descriptions. Popper regards such an addition to Born's rules as illegitimate and as a result of positivistic inclinations. We have already shown (footnote 76) that this is incorrect and that there are physical reasons which demand indefiniteness. Unfortunately these physical reasons are almost always presented in positivistic language which creates the impression that the peculiarity of the quantum theory, i.e., the features which are ascribed to it over and above the Born interpretation are indeed due to an epistemological manoeuver.

124. For this sentiment cf. W. Pauli, *Dialectica,* Vol. VIII (1954), p. 124; L. Rosenfeld, *Louis de Broglie, Physicien et Penseur,* Paris, 1953, pp. 41, 57; P. Jordan,

Anschauliche Quantentheorie, Berlin, 1936, pp. 1, 114f, 276; G. Ludwig, *Die Grundlagen der Quantenmechanik,* Berlin, 1954, pp. 165ff.

In the last footnote we have shown how the adequacy of the formal uncertainties, i.e., of the uncertainties that follow from the commutation relation can be tested by qualitative considerations concerning the dual character of *elementary particles.* As has been shown by Bohr and Rosenfeld (*Dan. Mat.-Phys. Medd.,* Vol. XII (1933) Nr. 8 as well as Bohr-Rosenfeld, *Phys. Rev.,* Vol. 78 (1950), pp. 794ff) the adequacy of the *field theories* and their consistency with the required restriction of the applicability of the classical terms can be shown in a similar manner. Cf. also L. Rosenfeld, "On Quantum Electrodynamics" in *Niels Bohr and the Development of Physics,* London, 1955, pp. 70-95 as well as Heitler, *Quantum Theory of Radiation,* Oxford, 1957, pp. 79ff.

125. *Observation and Interpretation,* p. 45. For the idea of a "rational extension," or a "rational generalization" cf. footnote 62. A "rational extension" of the quantum theory would be any formalism that is consistent with the qualitatively derived uncertainties.

126. Cf. also my paper "Complementarity."

127. It is interesting to note that we are here presented with a dogmatic *empiricism.* Which shows that empiricism is no better antidote against dogmatism than is, say, Platonism. It is easily seen why this must be so: both empiricism and Platonism (to mention only one philosophical alternative) make use of the idea of *sources* of knowledge; and sources, be they now intuitive ideas, or experiences, are assumed to be infallible, or at least very nearly so. Only a little consideration will show, however, that neither can give us an undistorted picture of reality as neither our brains, nor our senses, can be regarded as faithful mirrors. For the similarities between empiricism and Platonism cf. my paper "Explanation, Reduction, and Empiricism," in *Minnesota Studies in the Philosophy of Science,* Vol. III. For the idea of sources of knowledge behind both these philosophies cf. K. R. Popper, "On the Sources of Knowledge and Ignorance," read to the *British Academy* on 20. January 1960.

128. For a more detailed account cf. my papers "Complementarity," *loc. cit.* Professor Bohm's Philosophy of Nature," *British Journal for the Philosophy of Science,* Feb. 1960; "Niels Bohr's Interpretation of the Quantum Theory," in *Current Issues in the Philosophy of Science,* New York, 1960, as well as "Explanation, Reduction, and Empiricism," *loc. cit.*

129. Cf. *Physics and Philosophy,* New York, 1958. In their physics, too, Heisenberg and Bohr went different ways. "Bohr tried to make the dualism between the wave picture and the particle picture the starting point of a physical interpretation" writes Heisenberg (*Theoretical Physics in the Twentieth Century, A Memorial Volume to Wolfgang Pauli,* ed. Fierz and Weisskopf, New York,

1960, p. 45) "whereas I attempted to continue on the way of the quantum theory and Dirac's transformation theory without trying to get any help from the wave mechanics." "Bohr" writes Heisenberg at a different place (*Niels Bohr and the Development of Physics,* p. 15) "intended to work the new simple pictures, obtained by wave mechanics, into the interpretation of the theory, while I for my part attempted to extend the physical significance of the transformation matrices in such a way that a complete interpretation was obtained which would take account of all possible experiments." On the whole Bohr's approach was more intuitive, whereas Heisenberg's approach was more formalistic, indeed so much so that Pauli felt called upon to demand that "it must be attempted to free . . . Heisenberg's mechanics a little more from the flood of formalism characteristic for the Göttinger savants [vom Göttinger formalen Gelehrsamkeitsschwall]"; (letter from Pauli to Kronig of October 9th, 1925; quoted from *Theoretical Physics in the Twentieth Century,* p. 26).

130. von Weizsaecker's point of view is most clearly explained in his book *Zum Weltbild der Physik,* Leipzig, 1954.

131. Cf. his article in *Louis de Broglie,* etc. As opposed to Rosenfeld P. Jordan (*op. cit.*) and Pauli seem to represent a purely positivistic position.

132. D. Bohm and H. J. Groenewold, private communication.

133. N. Bohr, *Atomic Theory,* etc., p. 3. Cf. also footnote 62.

134. I use here the word "metaphysical" in the same sense in which it is used by the adherents of the Copenhagen point of view, *viz.* in the sense of "neither mathematical nor empirical." That the Copenhagen Interpretation contains elements which are metaphysical in this sense has been asserted, in slightly different words, by Heisenberg who declared in 1930 (*Die Physikalischen Grundlagen der Quantentheorie,* p. 15) that its adoption was "a question of taste." This he repeated 1958 in the now more fashionable linguistic terminology (Cf. *Physics and Philosophy,* New York, 1958, pp. 29f.)

135. The assumption of the existence of the quantum of action is very often given an interpretation that goes beyond these two equations; however, I agree with Landé and Kaila (*Zur Metatheorie der Quantemechanik,* Helsinki, 1950, p. 48) who have both pointed out, though with somewhat different reasons, that a more "substantial" interpretation of the quantum of action than is contained in these two equations is neither justified, nor tenable. The original view according to which the quantum of action is an indivisible "link" between interacting systems which is responsible for their mutual changes has been refuted by Einstein, Podolski, and Rosen. For this cf. footnote 116.

136. For an account of these results cf. the literature in footnote 60. It is worth pointing out, by the way, that duality is only one of various ordering principles that are needed to give a rational account of the facts upon the atomic level,

and especially of the properties of atomic spectra. It took some time to separate the facts relevant for the enunciation of the principle of duality from numerous other facts which had to be explained in a different manner, *viz,* on the basis of Pauli's exclusion principle and the assumption of an electronic spin.

137. This explanation is given by Heisenberg, *op. cit.,* p. 7.

138. Niels Bohr, *op. cit.,* p. 16.

139. L. Rosenfeld in *Observation and Interpretation,* p. 42.

140. H. Butterfield, *The Origins of Modern Science,* London, 1957, p. 80. Butterfield's book contains a very valuable account of the role of the experimental method in the seventeenth century.

141. Cf. the latter's *Causality and Chance in Modern Physics,* London, 1957.

141a. For a more detailed account cf. K. R. Popper "The Aim of Science," in *Ratio,* Vol. I (1957), pp. 24ff as well as my paper referred to in fn. 84.

142. For a more detailed account cf. again my paper referred to in fn. 84.

143. Cf. Bohm, *op. cit.,* Ch. IV.

144. *Physics and Philosophy,* New York, 1958, esp. p. 56: "It has sometimes been suggested that one should depart from the classical concepts altogether and that a radical change of the concepts used for describing the experiments might possibly lead back to a . . . completely objective description of nature. This suggestion, however, rests upon a misunderstanding . . . Our actual situation in science is such that we *do* use the classical concepts for the description of the experiments. There is no use discussing what could be done if we were other beings than we are."

This is an astounding argument indeed! It asserts, in fact, that a language that is used for describing observational results and that is fairly general cannot possibly be replaced by a different language. How, then, did it happen that the Aristotelian physics (which was much closer to the everyday idiom and to observation than the physics of Galileo and Newton!) was replaced by the point of view of the classical science? And how could the theory of witchcraft be replaced by reasonable psychology, based as it was upon innumerable *direct* observations of daemons and daemonic influence? (Think of the phenomenon of split personality which lends very direct support to the idea of daemonic influence!) On the other hand why should we not try to improve our situation and thereby indeed become "other beings than we are"? Is it assumed that the physicist has to remain content with the state of human thought and perception as it is given at a certain time and that he cannot (or should not) attempt to change, and to improve upon that state? Only the inductivistic prejudice that all a physicist can do is to assemble facts and present them in a formally satisfactory way, only such a prejudice can explain the defeatist attitude which is expressed in the above quotation.

145. *Zum Weltbild,* etc., p. 110: "Every actual experiment we know *is* described with the help of classical terms and we do not know how to do it differently." The obvious reply is, of course: "Too bad; try again!"

146. Cf. footnote 144.

147. Cf. footnote 62.

148. As will be evident from the quotation in footnote 144 Heisenberg and von Weizaecker seem to base their argument upon the *sociological fact* that the majority of the contemporary physicists uses the language of classical physics as their observation language. Bohr seems to go further. He seems to assume that the attempt to use a different observation language *can never succeed.* His arguments in favor of this contention are very similar to the arguments by transcendental deduction used by Kant. The fact that Heisenberg and von Weizsaecker seem to represent a less dogmatic and more practical position has prompted Hanson to distinguish between two different wings, as it were, in the Copenhagen school; the extreme Right, represented by Bohr, which regards the attempt to introduce a new observation language as *logically* impossible; and the Center, represented by von Weizaecker and Heisenberg, where such an attempt is only regarded as being *practically* impossible. I deny that this distinction exists. First of all the difference between *logical* impossibility and *sociological* impossibility (or *practical* impossibility), although regarded with awe by a good many philosophers is too subtle to impress any physicist. Neither will the assertion of logical impossibility deter him from trying to achieve the impossible (for example, to achieve a relative theory of space and time); nor will he feel relieved when he is being offered practical impossibility instead of logical impossibility. But we find that the distinction which Hanson wants to draw between Heisenberg and Bohr is not really one which Heisenberg himself would recognize, or at least so it appears from his writings. For on p. 132 of *Physics and Philosophy* the possibility of an alternative to the Copenhagen point of view is equated with the possibility that 2 times 2 may equal five, that is, the issue is now made a matter of logic. For this point cf. also the discussion between Professor Hanson and myself in *Current Issues in the Philosophy of Science,* pp. 390-400. There *do,* of course, exist some very decisive differences between Bohr's approach and Heisenberg's approach, But these differences lie in an entirely different field. Cf. for this footnotes 129 and 119.

149. *Op. cit.,* p. 1.

150. Cf. Huxley's highly interesting discussion of the merits of the Cartesian psychology as a means for the explanation of demonic appearances as well as his account of what is and what is not unthinkable at a certain time and within a certain point of view in Ch. VII of his *Devils of Loudun,* New York,

1952. Cf. also my discussion of the self-petrifying influence of *single* theories in section 7 of my "Explanation, Reduction, and Empiricism."

151. *Loc. cit.*

152. Albert Einstein in *Ideas and Opinions,* London, 1954, p. 291 (reprint of an article that was first published in 1936); cf. also H. Butterfield, *op. cit.*

153. As J. Agassi has pointed out to me that this principle was consciously used by Faraday in his research work. Against the use of such a procedure it has been argued, by T. S. Kuhn (private communication) that the close fitting between the facts and the theory that is a necessary presupposition of the proper organization of the observational material can be achieved only by people who devote themselves to the investigation of one single theory to the exclusion of all alternatives. For this *psychological* reason he is prepared to defend the (dogmatic) rejection of novel ideas at a period when the theory which stands in the center of discussion is being built up. I cannot accept this argument. My first reason is that many great scientists seemed to be able to do better than just devote themselves to the development of one single theory. Einstein is the outstanding recent example. Faraday and Newton are notable examples in history. Kuhn seems to be thinking mainly of the average scientist who may well have difficulties when asked not only to work out the details of some fashionable theory but also to consider alternatives. However, even in this case I am not sure whether this inability is "innate," as it were, and incurable, or simply due to the fact that the *education* of the "average scientist" is in the hands of people who subscribe, implicitly, to Kuhn's doctrine of the necessity of concentration. My second reason for not being able to accept this argument is as follows: assume that it is indeed correct that human beings are not able at the same time to work out the details of one theory *and* to consider alternatives. Who says, then, that details are more important than alternatives which, after all, keep us from dogmatism and are a very concrete and lively warning of the limitations of all our knowledge? If I had to choose between a very detailed account of the fabric of the universe at the expense of not being able to see its limitations and between a less detailed account whose limitations however were very obvious, then I would at once choose the latter. The details I could gladly leave to those who are interested in practical application.

154. The following quotations are from Hanson's article "Five Cautions for the Copenhagen Critics," *Philosophy of Science,* Vol. 26 (1959), pp. 325-337. The present quotation is p. 337.

155. *Loc. cit.,* p. 334.

156. Reprinted in Danto-Morgenbesser (eds.) *Philosophy of Science,* New York, 1960, pp. 450-470. The present quotation is to be found on page 455. A few

lines above this quotation, Hanson asserts that "There is as yet no working alternative to the Copenhagen Interpretation." I do not quite understand this assertion. For quite obviously Bohm, Vigier and their collaborators have provided just this: an interpretation of the elementary theory, and of the field theories which does not any more work with irreducible probabilities and which is still compatible with the existing formalisms. Maybe Hanson still believes, as he did in 1958 (*Patterns of Discovery,* pp. 172ff) that von Neumann's proof can be used for eliminating any such interpretation. This belief can easily be shown to be incorrect. For this cf. my arguments in section 2 and section 9. Maybe Hanson is willing to accept an interpretation only if it is connected with a detailed and empirically satisfactory formalism. This is the pragmatic argument we are about to refute. Besides, Hanson himself regards the elementary theory as "an arbitrarily delimited sub-theory of the more general quantum theory of fields" (*Philosophy of Science,* Vol. 26, p. 329) which latter *"simply does not exist"* as a mathematically sound theory (*loc. cit.;* his italics). From which it would follow that also the point of view of complementarity has not yet been connected with an "algebraically detailed, experimentally" satisfactory theory (an opinion, by the way, which I myself cannot wholly agree with; but this is not the point). A third possibility is that Hanson means by the "Copenhagen Interpretation" not just Bohr's general point of view but this point of view *taken together with the elementary theory and the field theories* (Cf. for this *loc. cit.,* p. 336). This procedure has also been adopted by Heisenberg (cf. his contribution to *Niels Bohr and the Development of Physics,* pp. 18, 19); it is extremely misleading. For first of all, the *full* elementary theory was constructed not in Copenhagen, but by Schrödinger who held a philosophy that was completely different from the philosophy of Heisenberg, Weizsaecker, and others. And secondly the most satisfactory forms of the field theory do not any more agree with the principle of correspondence, but are developed on an independent basis. In no case it is possible to agree with Hanson's assertion, even if it should be supported by the "next synchotron operator" (Danto-Morgenbesser, *op. cit.,* p. 455). However, after all this has been said, it should be added that the point of view of Bohm and Vigier has already been developed in much greater detail than is commonly supposed by most of the opponents. Thus Vigier has been able to find a classical model the quantization of which gives at one stroke the four and only four possible interactions (gravitation, electromagnetic field, weak and strong interaction) and represents such abstract notions as isospin as the result of quantization in ordinary space-time. The Gell-Mann scheme also emerges and the calculation of the correct masses now only depends on the proper calculation of the interactions (a problem that also exists in the orthodox theories). The fact that only four interactions emerge from the model makes it a very strong one and much less *ad hoc* than the usual theories which can accommodate any kind of field in a simple additive manner.

157. Danto-Morgenbesser, *op. cit.*, p. 455.

158. Cf. also footnote 156.

159. For an excellent account and sources (in the original Latin with English translation) cf. M. Clagett, *The Science of Mechanics in the Middle Ages,* Madison, 1954.

160. Cr. again my "Explanation, Reduction, and Empiricism."

161. The atomic theory was not the only reply that was given to the Parmenidean argument. Aristotle's physics is another such reply and it was this theory that was adopted throughout the Middle Ages.

162. Cf. footnote 154.

163. Cf. footnote 156.

164. I am here thinking mainly of the reversibility objection that for some physicists constituted a serious objection against the kinetic theory.

165. Cf. footnote 119. Cf. also Bohr's definition of a "phenomenon" in *Dialectica* 7/8 (1948), p. 317 as well as in *Albert Einstein, Philosopher-Scientist,* pp. 237f.

166. For details cf. again my "Explanation, Reduction, and Empiricism."

167. Cf. the references in fn. 15 and in fn. 141.

168. *Op. cit.,* p. 327.

169. *Natural Philosophy of Cause and Chance,* Oxford, 1948, p. 109.

170. "Five Cautions," etc. *loc. cit.,* p. 332.

171. *Loc. cit.,* p. 329.

172. *Loc. cit.*

173. The example is due to K. R. Popper.

174. Cf. E. Kaila, *op. cit.,* p. 34.

175. It is worth while pointing out that the Aristotelian physics was much closer to the crude experiences of everyday life than is the classical physics.

176. Cf. E. L. Hill, *Phys. Rev.,* Vol. 104 (1956), pp. 1173ff.

177. J. M. Cook (*Journal Math. Phys.,* Vol. 36 (1957), pp. 82ff shows that within Hilbert space the scattering problem can be solved only if $\int\int\int |V(xyz)-|^2 dxdydz < \infty$ which excludes the Coulomb case. I owe this reference to Professor E. L. Hill. In a discussion of the above paper, Bolsterli (Univ. of Minnesota) has pointed out that this does not invalidate the applicability of von Neumann's approach to the problem of scattering. The solution lies in not working with the complete Coulomb field, but in using a suitable cutoff. This is, of course, a possible procedure; but it is very *ad hoc* and not at all satisfactory as long as a general procedure for determining the size of the cutoff is not available.

178. *Op. cit.*, p. 212.

179. Cf. e.g., Sommerfeld, *Atombau and Spektrallinien*, Braunschweig, 1939, Ch. VIII; W. Heitler, *Quantum Theory of Radiation*, 3rd edition, sec. 22ff.

180. *Observation and Interpretation*, p. 88.

181. *Op. cit.*, p. 69.

182. I discussed this difficulty with Professor Popper on a beautiful summer morning driving from London to Glyndebourne and he seemed then to agree with my arguments (1958).

183. *Am. Journal for Physics,* Vol. 27 (1959), Nr 6 as well as *Zeitschrift fuer Physik,* Vol. 153 (1959), pp. 389-393.

184. Cf. my critical note in *Am. Journal of Physics,* Vol. 28 (1960), Nr 5.

185. Landé's very valuable investigation (cf. especially *Foundations of Quantum Theory, A Study in Continuity and Symmetry,* New Haven, 1955) are much more adapted to the Heisenberg representation, and therefore much closer to the Copenhagen point of view than are the interpretations which proceed from the Schrödinger representation. They may be regarded as an attempt to derive the Born interpretation and the completeness assumption (which Landé uses in the above-mentioned book, pp. 24f, but which he unfortunately drops later on) as well as some other characteristic features of the quantum level (quantum jumps; superposition) from purely thermodynamical considerations and some very plausible philosophical assumptions. At this stage the result of Landé's investigations is much closer to the Copenhagen point of view than both Landé and the orthodox are prepared to admit (cf. a similar judgment by H. Mehlberg, *Current Issues in the Philosophy of Science,* p. 368.) This is only one of the many instances in the history of the quantum theory where people passionately attack each other when they are in fact doing the same thing.

186. *Op. cit.*, Ch. VI.

187. For a more detailed discussion cf. my papers "On the Quantum Theory of Measurement" in *Observation and Interpretation,* pp. 121-130 and the corresponding paper in *Zs. Physik,* Vol. 148 (1957), pp. 551ff.

188. It was E. Schrödinger who first drew attention to this paradoxical consequence of the theory. Cf. his article "Die gegenwaertige Lage in der Quantenmechanik," *Naturwissenschaften,* Vol. 23 (1935), p. 812. Cf. also the discussion by P. Jordan in *Philosophy of Science,* Vol. 16 (1949), pp. 269ff.

189. As a matter of fact, we at once obtain an H-theorem when we introduce the usual subdivision of phase space expressing the limitations of measurement on the macrolevel. For a first application of a procedure of this kind cf. J. von Neumann, *Zs. Physik,* Vol. 57 (1929), pp. 80ff.

190. *Phys. Rev.,* Vol. 52 (1937), pp. 987ff.

191. Cf. also Ludwig's considerations concerning the possibilities of measurement and of actually *creating* such a state in *Grundlagen der Quantemechanik,* pp. 171f.

192. *Loc. cit.,* p. 989.

193. *Zs. Physik,* Vol. 131 (1952), pp. 101ff.

194. For a more detailed account cf. the paper "On the measurement of Quantum Mechanical Operators" by H. Araki and M. M. Yanase which the latter author was kind enough to let me have prior to its publication.

195. *Loc. cit.*

196. Physics Today, Vol. 7 (1957); *Philosophy of Science,* Vol. 25 (1958), pp. 23-33. Cf. also John McKnight "The Quantum Theoretical Concept of Measurement," *Phil. of Science,* Vol. 24 (1957), pp. 321-330 and Loyal Durand III, Princeton 1958, *On the Theory and Interpretation of Measurement in Quantum Mechanical Systems* (available in stencilled form).

197. I have not been convinced that this difficulty which plays a central role in Margenau's considerations is a difficulty of principle rather than a technical difficulty that can be superseded by the construction of a more efficient measuring apparatus. Margenau himself has indicated that in the case of the position

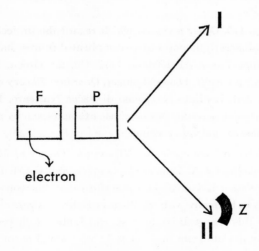

measurement of either a photon or an electron the Compton effect may be used in such a manner that the system investigated is not destroyed. We may also use, at least theoretically, the mutual scattering of photons or the correlations between polarization which exist in the radiation created by the annihilation of a positron-electron pair (cf. the literature in footnote 94). Concerning the use of a polariser the following procedure suggests itself: take the example of a photon and examine whether it left the polariser P (which we shall assume to be capable of transmitting photons of mutually perpendicular polarization in two different directions, I and II) in direction I. Assume furthermore that only such photons are counted whose passage through a filter F (and through P) can be ascertained by catching Compton recoil electrons that have been emitted by F. Of those photons we know with certainty that they have passed P and will therefore travel along I and II. Now if immediately after the capture of a recoil electron no reaction is observed in a photomultiplier Z that is located in II then we may be certain that the photon left in direction I with the opposite polarization—and this without any interference with the photon itself *after* its passage through P. *[This example is an elaboration of a suggestion made by E. Schrödinger in Naturwissenschaften, Vol. 22 (1934), p. 341].*

198. I would like to point out that this is an attempt, on my part, to reconstruct Margenau's argument which is not too clear on this second point.

199. *Die Grundlagen der Quantenmechanik,* Ch. V.

200. "Die Stellung des Subjekts in der Quantentheorie" in *Veritas, Iustitia, Libertas,* Festschrift zur 200 Jahresfeier der Columbia University; Berlin 1952, p. 266. This paper also contains a popular account of Ludwig's theory and a comparison of this theory with the customary point of view as expressed by von Weizsaecker.

201. *Grundlagen,* p. 170. Other accounts which regard the projection postulate as an approximate description of a more complicated process have been given by Bohm, *Quantum Theory,* Princeton, 1951, Ch. 22; Green, *Nuovo Cimento,* Vol. IX (1958), pp. 880ff; Daneri-Loinger, *Quantum Theory of Measurement,* Pubblicazioni dell' Instituto Nazionale di Fisica Nucleare, 1959, esp. sec. 9. All these alternative accounts however, use examples and by no means as general and detailed as Ludwig's account.

201a. In their most recent communication *(Quantum Theory of Measurement and Ergodicity Conditions)* A. Daneri, A. Loinger, and G. M. Prosperi quote a remark by Professor L. Rosenfeld to the effect that "the conception of Jordan and Ludwig is in harmony with the ideas of Bohr". As regards Jordan's intuitive approach this may well be the case. But Ludwig's ideas on measurement most definitely deviate from those of Bohr who would never dream of representing the state of a macrosystem by a statistical operator. Considering the difficulties of Ludwig's approach, such an identification would also seem to be unfair to Bohr.

202. One difficulty which has been pointed out by Ludwig himself (*Z. Naturforschung,* Vol. 12a (1957), pp. 662ff) and which is also discussed in Daneri-Loinger, *op. cit.,* is that no satisfactory definition has been given of macroobservables.

203. According to Hilary Putnam, Ludwig's theory leads to the following difficulty: the final stage, in Ludwig's theory, is interpreted as a purely classical mixture only one of whose elements may be assumed to really exist. The derivation, from the formalism of the quantum theory, does *not* give us such a mixture. It rather provides us with a mixture *all* of whose elements have an equal claim to existence. Thus the transition to the usual classical interpretation of the resulting mixture is completely unaccounted for.

204. For a detailed account along these lines cf. H. J. Groenewold's essay on measurement in *Observation and Interpretation.*

205. Cf. E. Schrödinger in *Nature,* Vol. 173 (1954), pp. 442.

206. Cf. footnote 62.

207. *Nuovo Cimento,* 1955, p. 3.

208. *The Nature of Physical Theory,* Dover, 1936, pp. 188f.

209. Cf. J. Schwinger, *Quantum Electrodynamics,* Dover, 1959, p. XIV.

210. "Quantum Physics and the Relativity Theory," in *Current Issues,* etc., pp. 429-441. Cf. also my comments on this paper, *op. cit.,* and Hill's reply.

Index of Names

Index of Topics

Anisotropy of time, 150-161, 165, 168, 172, 182
Aristotelian theory of motion and birth of modern science, 234, 235
Aristotle's conceptions in biology, 138, 142, 143

Balmer formulae, 236, 264
Bayes theorem, 215
Berkeley's theory of matter, 240
Biological sciences and man, 57, 60, 68, 70, 71, 72, 73, 74, 75, 79, 82, 105, 115, 117, 118, 131, 134, 143
Biology, characteristics of, 133
Biology and philosophy of science, 4
Black, M., critique of, 154-155, 184
Bothe and Geiger experiment, 217
Branch systems and analysis of entropy, 166, 167, 169, 170, 171, 186

Cartesian philosophy, 67, 221, 229, 276
Causality, 11-12, 50, 52-53, 114, 134, 137, 153, 172, 238, 265, 266
Chronometry, 149
Complementarity theory, 191, 192, 193, 222, 227, 232, 252, 255, 257, 260, 263
Compton effect, 222, 223, 243, 281
Conservation laws, 200, 201, 216, 222
Copenhagen school of quantum theory, 191, 192, 193, 200, 201, 218, 219, 221, 225, 232, 233, 240, 246, 252, 254, 256, 265, 267, 270, 274, 278
Correspondence principle, 219, 253, 254
Cosmology and human self-consciousness, 35

Deductive-nomological explanation, 9-34, 151, 166, 174
Determinism, 127, 215, 224, 225, 238, 266
Dialectical materialism, 221
Dirac electron theory, 221, 255
Doppler shift, 181, 182
Duality of light and matter, 195, 204, 207, 222, 223, 224, 226, 271, 273, 274

Eddington's analysis of time and entropy, 156-158
Einstein-De Broglie relations, 225
Einstein-Podolski-Rosen argument, 208-209, 210, 211, 213, 214, 217, 218, 219, 220, 274
Empiricism, modes of, 240, 242, 251, 252, 256, 273

Empathy, 109
Entelechy, 143
Entropy, 156, 157, 159, 161, 163, 165, 166, 167, 168, 173, 174, 175, 184
Epistemology, problems of, 66, 153, 202, 224, 229, 230, 247, 252, 262, 263, 272
ESP and animals, 104
ESP and drugs, 105
ESP and electromagnetic phenomena, 98, 105
Extrasensory perception, theories of, 84-105, 113

Fourier analysis, 202
Franck and Hertz experiment, 217
Free will, problem of, 111, 112, 127

Galileo and origins of modern science, 226, 261, 274
Genes, 116

Heisenberg uncertainty principle, 201, 205, 225, 259, 262
Heme, structure of, 140
Hemoglobin, function of, 140, 141
Hidden parameters and quantum theory, 193, 194, 236, 238, 257
Hilbert space, 219, 241, 279
Hill-Grünbaum analysis of irreversibility, 173-179
Historical explanation, genetic in form, 21-34
Historical explanation, nomological in form, 19-34
Historical explanation and probability theories, 27
Human behavior and predictability, 48-50, 110, 116, 118, 120-127
Human behavior, theories of, 59-60, 61, 62, 76, 89, 90, 107, 109, 114, 115, 118, 119, 126, 131, 152, 171
Hume's argument against miracles, 108

Ionian atomism, 235
Ionian monism, 235
Irreversibility, concepts of, 151-153, 173, 174, 175, 176, 177, 178, 180

Kantian philosophy, 77, 276
Kinetic theory of gases, 161, 162, 163

Law, scientific, 58, 100, 127, 134, 136, 186
Logic, symbolic, 3-4